JOB HUNTER'S SOURCEBOOK

ISSN 1053-1874

A   GALE   CAREER   INFORMATION   GUIDE

JOB HUNTER'S SOURCEBOOK

Where to find employment leads and other job search resources

TWELFTH EDITION
Volume 3

Sources of Essential Job Hunting Information

Entries 13362-15231

Joseph Palmisano, Project Editor

GALE
CENGAGE Learning

Detroit • New York • San Francisco • New Haven, Conn • Waterville, Maine • London

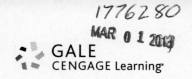

GALE
CENGAGE Learning·

Job Hunter's Sourcebook, 12th Edition

Product Management: Jerry Moore

Project Editor: Joseph Palmisano

Editorial Support Services: Scott Flaugher

Composition and Electronic Prepress: Gary Leach

Manufacturing: Rita Wimberley

Gale, Cengage Learning
27500 Drake Rd.
Farmington Hills, MI 48331-3535

ISBN-13: 978-1-4144-9026-7 (set)
ISBN-10: 1-4144-9026-7 (set)
ISBN-13: 978-1-4144-9027-4 (vol. 1)
ISBN-10: 1-4144-9027-5 (vol. 1)
ISBN-13: 978-1-4144-9028-1 (vol. 2)
ISBN-10: 1-4144-9028-3 (vol. 2)
ISBN-13: 978-1-4144-9029-8 (vol. 3)
ISBN-10: 1-4144-9029-1 (vol . 3)

ISSN 1053-1874

Printed in the United States of America
1 2 3 4 5   16 15 14 13 12

FD184

Contents

"The person who gets hired is not necessarily the one who can do that job best; but, the one who knows the most about how to get hired."

Richard Bolles
What Color Is Your Parachute?

Job hunting is often described as a campaign, a system, a strategic process. According to Joan Moore, principal of The Arbor Consulting Group, Inc. in Plymouth, Michigan, "Launching a thorough job search can be a full-time job in itself. It requires as much energy as you would put into any other major project—and it requires a creative mix of approaches to ensure its success."

Job Hunting Is Increasingly Complex

Today's competitive job market has become increasingly complex, requiring new and resourceful approaches to landing a position. The help-wanted ads are no longer the surest route to employment. In fact, most estimates indicate that only a small percentage of all jobs are found through the classified sections of local newspapers.

Although approaches vary among individual job seekers and the levels of jobs sought, a thorough job search today should involve the use of a wide variety of resources. Professional associations, library research, executive search firms, college placement offices, direct application to employers, professional journals, and networking with colleagues and friends are all approaches commonly in use. Job hotlines and resume referral services may be elements of the search as well. High-tech components might include the use of resume databases, and electronic bulletin boards that list job openings.

Job Hunters Are Changing

Just as the methods of job seeking have changed, so have the job hunters themselves. As Joyce Slayton Mitchell notes in College to Career, "Today, the average young person can look forward to six or seven different jobs, six or seven mini-careers, that will make up his or her lifetime of work." Lifelong commitment to one employer is no longer the norm; professionals seeking to change companies, workers re-entering the job market after a period of absence, and people exploring new career options are also represented in significant numbers in the job seeking pool. And in a time of significant corporate change, restructuring, divestiture, and downsizing, many job seekers are in the market unexpectedly. These include a growing number of white-collar workers who find themselves competing against other professionals in a shrinking market.

Help for Job Hunters

As the job market has become more competitive and complex, job seekers have increasingly looked for job search assistance. The rapid growth in the number of outplacement firms and employment agencies during the last 30 years reflects the perceived need for comprehensive help. Similarly, the library has become an increasingly important and valuable resource in the job hunt. In fact, some librarians report that their most frequently asked reference questions pertain to job seeking. In response to this need, many libraries have developed extensive collections of career and job-hunting publications, periodicals that list job openings, and directories of employers. Some libraries have developed centralized collections of career information, complemented by such offerings as resume preparation software, career planning databases, and interviewing skills videotapes.

Valuable Guide for Job Seekers

Job Hunter's Sourcebook (JHS) was designed to assist those planning job search strategies. Any job hunter—the student looking for an internship, the recent graduate, the executive hoping to relocate—will find *JHS* an important first step in the job search process because it identifies and organizes employment leads quickly and comprehensively. Best of all, *JHS* provides all the information a job hunter needs to turn a local public library into a customized employment agency, available free-of-charge. *Library Journal* and the New York Public Library concurred, and gave the first edition of this work their annual outstanding reference awards.

Job Hunter's Sourcebook (JHS) is a comprehensive guide to sources of information on employment leads and other job search resources. It streamlines the job-seeking process by identifying and organizing the wide array of publications, organizations, audio-visual and electronic resources, and other job hunting tools.

JHS completes much of the research needed to begin a job search, with in-depth coverage of information sources for more than 200 specific professional and vocational occupations. Listings of resources on more than 30 essential topics of interest to job hunters complement the profiles on specific occupations, providing the job seeker with leads to all the information needed to design a complete job search strategy.

Job Hunter's Sourcebook can be used to:

Find a job. *JHS* is designed for use by job seekers at all levels—from those seeking a first job, to executives on the move, to those in transition. Each individual may select from the wide range of resources presented to develop a customized job campaign.

Use career resources more effectively. As library research becomes an increasingly important component in the job hunting process, librarians are providing more information and support to job seekers. *JHS* helps users go directly to the most appropriate library material by providing comprehensive lists of job hunting resources on high-interest professional and vocational occupations.

Build a better career resources collection. Librarians, career counselors, outplacement firms, spouse relocation services, job referral agencies, and others who advise job seekers can use *JHS* to start or expand their collections of career and job hunting materials.

Comprehensive Coverage and Convenient Arrangement

The job search resources in *JHS* are conveniently arranged into three volumes, which are followed by a master index:

Volumes One and Two: Sources of Job-Hunting Information by Professions and Occupations—identifies information sources on employment opportunities for 249 specific types of jobs. A "List of Profiled Professions and Oc-

cupations" lists hundreds of alternate, popular, synonymous, and related job titles and links them to the jobs profiled in *JHS*, providing quick access to information sources on specific occupations or fields of interest by all their variant names—from accountant to aircraft mechanic and sports official to stockbroker. Each profile contains complete contact information and lists a variety of sources of job-opportunity information organized into eight easy-to-use categories:

1. Sources of Help-Wanted Ads
2. Placement and Job Referral Services
3. Employer Directories and Networking Lists
4. Handbooks and Manuals
5. Employment Agencies and Search Firms
6. Online Job Sources and Services
7. Tradeshows
8. Other Sources, including internships and resources such as job hotlines

Volume Three: Sources of Essential Job-Hunting Information—features such employment topics as:

- Interviewing Skills
- Employment Issues for Disabled Workers
- Electronic Job Search Information
- Working at Home
- Opportunities for Freelance Workers and Independent Contractors
- Opportunities for Temporary Workers

Each category includes:

- Reference Works
- Newspapers, Magazines, and Journals
- Audio/Visual Resources
- Online and Database Services
- Software
- Other Sources, such as special associations, job hunting kits, and organizers

The information sources listed under each topic are arranged by type of resource and include complete contact information.

Index to Information Sources—comprehensively lists all of the publications, organizations, electronic resources, and other sources of job hunting information contained in *JHS*.

Please consult the User's Guide for more information about the arrangement, content, and indexing of the information sources cited in *JHS*.

JHS Profiles High-Interest Professions and Occupations

JHS catalogs job hunting resources for more than 200 professional, technical, and trade occupations, carefully selected to provide a broad cross-section of occupations of interest to today's job seekers. The majority are profiled in the Department of Labor's *Occupational Outlook Handbook (OOH)*, a leading career resource containing detailed descriptions of professional and vocational occupations. Most of the professions cited in *OOH* are also included in *JHS*, as are representative vocational occupations selected from those listed in *OOH*. To round out this list, additional occupations were included on the basis of Bureau of Labor Statistics data projecting them as high-growth positions.

Coverage of Employment Alternatives and Trends

In addition to focusing on such "how-to" topics as resume writing and interviewing, the "Sources of Essential Job-Hunting Information" offers resources for non-traditional work options and diverse segments of the work force. Working part-time, at home, and in your own business are featured chapters, as are opportunities for minorities, older workers, women, disabled workers, and gay and lesbian job seekers. A chapter covering sources of electronic job search information is included, as well as a category titled, "Online Job Sources and Services." This category lists Internet websites related to specific job profiles.

New to this Edition

The twelfth edition is a complete revision of the previous *JHS*, incorporating thousands of updates to organization and publication data. This edition also features 5 new career profiles, including environmental scientists and specialists, instructional coordinators, and pharmacy technicians.

Method of Compilation

JHS contains citations compiled from direct contact with a wide range of associations and organizations, from dozens of publisher catalogs and other secondary sources, and from selected information from other Gale databases. While many resources cited in *JHS* contain career planning information, their usefulness in the job hunting process was the primary factor in their selection. Their annotations are tailored to support that function.

Comments and Suggestions Are Welcome

Libraries, associations, employment agencies, executive search firms, referral services, publishers, database producers, and other organizations involved in helping job seekers find opportunities or companies find candidates are encouraged to submit information about their activities and products for use in future editions of *JHS*. Comments and suggestions for improving this guide are also welcome. Please contact:

Project Editor
Job Hunter's Sourcebook
Gale, Cengage Learning
27500 Drake Rd.
Farmington Hills, MI 48331-3535
Phone: (248) 699-4253
Fax: (248) 699-8075
URL: gale.cengage.com

Job Hunter's Sourcebook (JHS) is divided into three volumes:

- Volumes One and Two: Sources of Job-Hunting Information by Professions and Occupations
- Volume Three: Sources of Essential Job-Hunting Information

Access to entries is facilitated by a "List of Profiled Professions and Occupations" and an "Index to Information Sources." Users should consult each section to benefit fully from the information in *JHS.*

Master List of Profiled Professions and Occupations

A "List of Profiled Professions and Occupations" alphabetically lists the job titles used to identify the professions and occupations appearing in Volumes One and Two of *JHS*, as well as alternate, popular, synonymous, and related job titles and names, and occupational specialties contained within job titles. Citations include "See" references to the appropriate occupational profiles and their beginning page numbers.

JHS is designed to meet the needs of job seekers at all levels of experience in a wide range of fields. Managers as well as entry-level job hunters will find information sources that will facilitate their career-specific searches. In addition, information on professions and occupations related to those profiled will be found.

All Career Levels. The title assigned to each profile identifies its occupational field or subject area; these titles are not meant to indicate the level of positions for which information is provided. Information systems managers, for example, will find highly useful information in the "Computer Programmers" and "Computer Systems Analysts" profiles, while financial analysts will benefit from information in the "Financial Managers" profile. The "General Managers and Top Executives" profile, on the other hand, is broad in nature and useful to any management-level search; it does not focus upon a specific profession or occupation.

Other Occupations. Job seekers not finding their specific career fields listed in this guide will discover that related profiles yield valuable sources of information. For example, legal secretaries will find relevant information about employment agencies serving the legal profession and about prospective employers in the "Legal Assistants" and "Law-

yers" profiles. An individual interested in finding a position in radio advertising sales might look to the entries in the broadcasting- and sales-related profiles to find appropriate resources. Career changers, too, can use *JHS* profiles to identify new professions to which their previously acquired skills would be transferable.

Volumes One and Two: Sources of Job-Hunting Information by Professions and Occupations

These volumes feature profiles of job-hunting information for 249 specific careers. Profiles are listed alphabetically by profession or occupation. Each profile contains up to eight categories of information sources, as described below. Within each category, entries are arranged in alphabetical order by name or title. Entries are numbered sequentially, beginning with the first entry in the first profile. All resources listed are included in each relevant profile (and in Volume Three chapters, as appropriate) providing a complete selection of information sources in each occupational profile.

Sources of Help-Wanted Ads. Includes professional journals, industry periodicals, association newsletters, placement bulletins, and online services. In most cases, periodicals that focus on a specific field are cited here; general periodical sources such as the *National Business Employment Weekly* are listed in Volume 3 under "Help-Wanted Ads." Publications specific to an industry will be found in all profiles related to that industry. Candidates in some occupational areas, such as word processing, are usually recruited from the local marketplace and therefore are not as likely to find openings through a professional publication. Profiles for these occupations may contain fewer ad sources as job hunters are better served by local newspapers and periodicals. Entries include: the source's title and the name, address, and phone number of its publisher or producer; publication frequency; subscription rate; description of contents; toll-free or additional phone numbers; and fax numbers, when applicable. Source titles appear in italics.

Placement and Job Referral Services. Various services designed to match job seekers with opportunities are included in this category. Primarily offered by professional associations, these services range from job banks to placement services to employment clearinghouses, operating on the national and local levels. Entries include: the association's or organization's name, address, and phone number; its membership, activities, and services; toll-free or additionall phone numbers; and fax numbers. E-mail and website addresses are provided, when available.

Employer Directories and Networking Lists. Covers directories and rankings of companies, membership rosters from professional associations, and other lists of organizations or groups that can be used to target prospective employers and identify potential contacts for networking purposes. In some cases, Who's Who titles are included where these can provide a source of contact information in a specialized field. General directories of companies such as Standard and Poor's Register of Corporations, Directors, and Executives are cited in Volume Three in the "Identifying Prospective Employers" profile. Entries include: the title and name, address, and phone number of the publisher or distributor; publication date or frequency; price; description of contents; arrangement; indexes; toll-free or additional phone numbers; and fax numbers, when available. Directory titles appear in italics.

Handbooks and Manuals. This category notes books, pamphlets, brochures, and other published materials that provide guidance and insight to the job-hunting process in a particular occupational field. Entries include: the title and name, address, and phone number of its publisher or distributor; editor's or author's name; publication date or frequency; price; number of pages; description of contents; toll-free or additional phone numbers; and fax numbers, when known. Publication titles appear in italics.

Employment Agencies and Search Firms. Features firms used by companies to recruit candidates for positions and, at times, by individuals to pursue openings. The following firms are covered:

1. Employment agencies, which are generally geared toward filling openings at entry- to mid-levels in the local job market. Candidates sometimes pay a fee for using their services. When possible, JHS lists agencies where the employer pays the fee.

2. Executive search firms, which are paid by the hiring organization to recruit professional and managerial candidates, usually for higher-level openings and from a regional or national market. Executive search firms are of two types: contingency, where the firm is paid only if it fills the position, and retainer, where the firm is compensated to undertake a recruiting assignment, regardless of whether or not that firm actually fills the opening. The majority of the search firms cited in JHS are contingency firms. Although executive search firms work for the hiring organization and contact candidates only when recruiting for a specific position, most will accept unsolicited resumes, and some may accept phone calls.

3. Temporary employment agencies, which also are included in some profiles because they can be a way to identify and obtain regular employment.

For the most part, each profile lists firms that typically service that career. Firms specializing in a particular industry are included in all profiles relevant to that industry. JHS covers a mix of large and small firms. Major national search firms, which are quite broad in scope, are listed only under the "General Managers and Top Executives" profile. Some occupations are not served by employment agencies or search firms (fire fighter, for example); therefore, there are no entries for this category in such profiles. Entries include: the firm's name, address, and phone number; whether it's an employment agency, executive search firm, or temporary agency; descriptive information, as appropriate; toll-free and additional phone numbers; and fax numbers, when applicable.

Online Job Sources and Services. Publicly available electronic databases, including websites that facilitate matching job hunters with openings are cited. Many are tailored to specific occupations. Entries include: the name of the product or service; the name, address, and phone number of the distributor or producer; price; special formats or arrangements; descriptive information; toll-free or additional phone numbers; and fax numbers, when applicable. For websites, URL is included along with descriptive information.

Tradeshows. Covers exhibitions and tradeshows held in the United States. Entries include: the name of the tradeshow; the name of the sponsoring organization; contact information for the sponsoring organization, including address, phone number, toll-free or additional phone numbers, fax number, email address, and URL; types of exhibits; and dates and location, when available.

Other Sources. This category comprises a variety of resources available to the job seeker in a specific field: job hotlines providing 24-hour recordings of openings; lists of internships, fellowships, and apprenticeships; bibliographies of job-hunting materials; video and audio cassettes; and salary surveys to be used as a guide when discussing compensation. Professional associations of significance or those that provide job hunting assistance (but not full placement services) are also included here. Because of the trend toward entrepreneurship, this section offers information sources on being one's own boss in a given field as well. Resources on job and career alternatives are provided for certain professions (such as educators), as is information on working abroad.

Entries for associations and organizations include: name, address, and phone number; the membership, activities, and services of associations; toll-free or additional phone numbers; and fax numbers. E-mail and website addresses are provided, when available. Entries for other resources include: title of the publication or name of the product or service; the name, address, and phone number of its publisher, distributor, or producer; editor's or author's name; pubication date or frequency; price; special formats or arrangements; descriptive information; hotline, toll-free, or additional phone phone numbers; and fax numbers, when available. Publication, videocassette, and audiocassette titles appear in italics.

Volume Three: Sources of Essential Job-Hunting Information

This volume presents 33 profiles on topics of interest to any job hunter, such as resume writing or interviewing, as well as those of specialized interest, such as working at home (see "List of Profiled Professions and Occupations" for the complete list). Profiles are arranged alphabetically by topic and contain up to six categories of information, as listed below. Within each category, citations are organized alphabetically by name or title. Entries are also numbered sequentially, continuing the number sequence from Volumes One and Two. The publications, periodicals, and other sources listed are fully cited in all relevant chapters (and in occupational profiles, as appropriate), providing the reader with a complete selection of resources in single, convenient location.

Reference Works. Includes handbooks and manuals, directories, pamphlets, and other published sources of information. Entries include: the title and name, address, and phone number of its publisher or distributor; editor's or author's name; publication date or frequency; price; number of pages; description of contents; toll-free or additional phone numbers; and fax numbers, when known. Publication titles appear in italics.

Newspapers, Magazines, and Journals. Lists items published on a serial basis. Entries include: the title and name, address, and phone number of its publisher or distributor; frequency; price; description of contents; toll-free or additional phone numbers; and fax numbers, when known. Publication titles appear in italics.

Audio/Visual Resources. Features audiocassettes, videocassettes, and filmstrips. Entries include: the title and name, address, and phone number of its distributor or producer; date; price; special formats; descriptive information; toll-free or additional phone numbers; and fax numbers, when applicable. Videocassette and audiocassette titles appear in italics.

Online and Database Services. Publicly available electronic databases, including websites that facilitate matching job hunters with openings are cited. Entries include: the name of the product or service; the name, address, and phone number of the distributor or producer; price; special formats or arrangements; descriptive information; toll-free or additional phone numbers; and fax numbers, when applicable. For websites: the online address (URL) is included along with descriptive information.

Software. This category notes software programs designed to help with various aspects of job hunting, such as resume preparation. Entries include: the name of the product or service; the name, address, and phone number of the distributor or producer; price; special formats or arrangements; hardware compatibility, if relevant; descriptive information; toll-free or additional phone numbers; and fax numbers, when applicable.

Other Sources. Varied resources such as special associations and organizations and job-hunting bibliographies, kits, and organizers are covered in this section. Citations for journal and newspaper articles are provided if a topic is relatively new. Entries include: the title of the publication or name of the organization, product, or service; the name, address, and phone number of the organization, publisher, distributor, or producer; editor's or author's name; publication date or frequency; price; special formats or arrangements; descriptive information; toll-free or additional phone numbers; and fax numbers, when applicable. Publication titles appear in italics. For article citations: the article title, publication date, and journal or newspaper title, as well as a description of the article.

Index to Information Sources

JHS provides a comprehensive Index to Information Sources that lists all publications, periodicals, associations, organizations, firms, online and database services, and other resources cited in Volumes One, Two, and Three. Entries are arranged alphabetically and are referenced by their entry numbers. Titles of publications, audiocassettes, and videocassettes appear in italics.

List of Profiled Professions and Occupations

This list outlines references to occupations and professions by job titles, alternate names contained within job titles, popular names, and synonymous and related names. Beginning page numbers for each occupation's profile are provided. Titles of profiles appear in boldface.

REFERENCE WORKS

13362 ■ *The 2-Hour Job Search*
Ten Speed Press
6001 Shellmound St.
Emeryville, CA 94608
Ph: (510)285-3000
Fax: (510)285-2979
URL: http://www.randomhouse.com

Steve Dalton. 2012. $12.99 (paper). 240 pages. Serves as a guide for job seekers to efficiently and effectively target potential employers and secure the essential first interview.

13363 ■ *5 Necessary Skills To Keep Your Career On Track*
Outskirts Press, Inc.
10940 S Parker Rd., No. 515
Parker, CO 80134
Fr: 888-672-6657
E-mail: info@outskirtspress.com
URL: http://www.outskirtspress.com

Richard S. Pearson. 2009. $15.95 (paper). 224 pages. Covers topics on creating the right mindset in maintaining continuous employment; ability to adapt and change; and communication skills. Teaches readers how to be proactive and cognizant; the importance of networking and finding a mentor; and how to deal with bad bosses.

13364 ■ *10 Insider Secrets to a Winning Job Search: Everything You Need to Get the Job You Want in 24 Hours or Less*
Career Press
3 Tice Rd.
PO Box 687
Franklin Lakes, NJ 07417-1322
Ph: (201)848-0310
Fax: (201)848-1727
Fr: 800-227-3371
URL: http://www.careerpress.com/
 ?section=home&product_id=56

Todd Bermont. 2004. $14.99. 216 pages. Step-by-step guide to getting the job you want; shares secrets to finding a job in any economy.

13365 ■ *50 Best Jobs for Your Personality*
JIST Publishing
875 Montreal Way
St. Paul, MN 55102
Fax: 800-547-8329
Fr: 800-648-5478
E-mail: info@jist.com
URL: http://www.jist.com/shop/
 product.php?productid=16547&cat=0&page=8

Michael Farr and Laurence Shatkin, PhD. 2009. $17.95. 480 pages. Used to help job seekers match their personality to the right career.

13366 ■ *101 Tips for Graduates*
Facts On File Inc.
132 W 31st St., 17th Fl.
New York, NY 10001
Ph: (212)967-8800
Fax: 800-678-3633
Fr: 800-322-8755
URL: http://www.infobasepublishing.com

Latest edition 2010. $35.00 for individuals. Covers: The key principles a graduate needs to know about work skills, communication skills, leadership skills, social skills, self-discipline, and demonstrating a positive attitude.

13367 ■ *150 Best Jobs for a Better World*
JIST Publishing
875 Montreal Way
St. Paul, MN 55102
Fr: 800-648-5478
E-mail: educate@emcp.com
URL: http://www.jist.com

Laurence Shatkin. 2008. $16.95 (softcover). 432 pages. Covers occupations that have job functions that directly affect lives and the world in positive ways regardless of employer. Contains job lists and job descriptions of careers in health, education, fine arts, public safety, social service, natural resources, and more. Lists the careers ranked by pay, growth, and openings.

13368 ■ *150 Best Jobs for a Secure Future*
JIST Publishing
875 Montreal Way
St. Paul, MN 55102
Fr: 800-648-5478
URL: http://www.jist.com

Laurence Shatkin. 2012. $17.95 (softcover). 432 pages. Contains 150 job listings that can sustain despite economic instability. Includes details about each job's pay, growth, openings, skills needed, education and training requirements, and highest-growth fields.

13369 ■ *150 Best Jobs for Your Skills*
JIST Publishing
875 Montreal Way
St. Paul, MN 55102
Fr: 800-648-5478
URL: http://www.jist.com

Laurence Shatkin. 2012. $17.95 (softcover). 432 pages. Contains 150 job listings that are suitable for job seekers' working skills. Includes details about earnings, growth, annual openings, work environment, and education requirements.

13370 ■ *150 Best Recession-Proof Jobs*
JIST Publishing
875 Montreal Way
St. Paul, MN 55102
Fr: 800-648-5478
E-mail: info@jist.com
URL: http://www.jist.com

Laurence Shatkin. 2009. $16.95 (softcover). 432 pages. Provides lists of recession-proof jobs by pay, growth, and openings and by education level, personality type, career clusters/interests, age, part-time work, and self-employment.

13371 ■ *200 Best Jobs for College Graduates, Fourth Edition*
JIST Publishing
875 Montreal Way
St. Paul, MN 55102
Fax: 800-547-8329
Fr: 800-648-5478
E-mail: info@jist.com
URL: http://www.jist.com/shop/
 product.php?productid=16462&cat=14&page=1

Michael Farr, Laurence Shatkin, Ph.D. 2009. $16.95. 432 pages. 200 jobs with the best pay, fastest growth, and most openings for people with associate's, bachelor's, and higher degrees.

13372 ■ *200 Best Jobs for Introverts*
JIST Publishing
875 Montreal Way
St. Paul, MN 55102
Fr: 800-648-5478
E-mail: info@jist.com
URL: http://www.jist.com

Laurence Shatkin. 2008. $8.47 (softcover). 432 pages. Includes 200 job descriptions that give details on jobs ranked by levels of quiet, solitary work, contact with others, autonomy, and direct contact with the public.

13373 ■ *200 Best Jobs Through Apprenticeships*
JIST Publishing
875 Montreal Way
St. Paul, MN 55102
Fax: 800-547-8329
Fr: 800-648-5478
E-mail: info@jist.com
URL: http://www.jist.com/shop/
 product.php?productid=16463&cat=14&page=1

Michael Farr and Laurence Shatkin, PhD. 2009. $24.95. 544 pages. Lists all 981 apprenticeships that are registered with the U.S. Department of Labor and explains how to become an apprentice, where the opportunities are, what the requirements are, and the pros and cons.

13374 ■ *250 Best-Paying Jobs*
JIST Publishing
875 Montreal Way
St. Paul, MN 55102
Fr: 800-648-5478
URL: http://www.jist.com

Michael Farr and Laurence Shatkin. 2010. $17.95 (softcover). 528 pages. Contains information on 250 best-paying jobs. Includes useful facts for each job such as updated data, career cluster and career pathway listing, beginning wage, and earnings growth potential.

13375 ■ *300 Best Jobs Without a Four-Year Degree, Third Edition*
JIST Publishing
875 Montreal Way
St. Paul, MN 55102
Fax: 800-547-8329
Fr: 800-648-5478
E-mail: info@jist.com
URL: http://www.jist.com/shop/
    product.php?productid=16615&cat=1322&page=9
Michael Farr, Laurence Shatkin, Ph.D. 2009. $17.95. 472 pages. 300 jobs with the best pay, fastest growth, and most openings with no four-year degree required.

13376 ■ *1000 Best Job Hunting Secrets*
Sourcebooks, Inc.
1935 Brookdale Rd., Ste. 139
Naperville, IL 60563
Ph: (630)961-3900
Fax: (630)961-2168
Fr: 800-727-8866
URL: http://www.sourcebooks.com
Diane Stafford and Moritza Day. 2004. $12.95. 461 pages. Provides information on how to: customize the resume to suit the job; protect yourself and keep your job search confidential; write a cover letter that gets you noticed; secure a second interview; and guarantee a positive reference.

13377 ■ *Adams Jobs Almanac*
Adams Media Corp.
57 Littlefield St.
Avon, MA 02322-1944
Ph: (508)427-7100
Fax: (508)427-6790
URL: http://www.adamsmediastore.com/product/68/5
Annual, Latest edition 9th. $10.00 for individuals. Covers: Job listings nationwide. Entries include: Firm or organization name, address, phone, name and title of contact; description of organization, headquarters location, typical titles for entry- and middle-level positions, educational backgrounds desired, fringe benefits offered, stock exchange listing, training programs, internships, parent company, number of employees, revenues, e-mail and web address, projected number of hires. Indexes: Alphabetical.

13378 ■ *The Almanac of American Employers 2012*
Plunkett Research, Ltd.
PO Drawer 541737
Houston, TX 77254-1737
Ph: (713)932-0000
Fax: (713)932-7080
E-mail: customersupport@plunkettresearch.com
URL: http://www.plunkettresearch.com
Jack W. Plunkett. 2011. $299.99. 731 pages. Features in-depth profiles of leading employers, employment forecasts and statistics, and trends in U.S. economy. Includes extensive lists of jobseeking-related websites and practical hints and guidelines for jobseekers.

13379 ■ *Atlanta JobBank*
Adams Media Corp.
57 Littlefield St.
Avon, MA 02322-1944
Ph: (508)427-7100
Fax: (508)427-6790
URL: http://www.adamsmedia.com
latest edition 15th. $17.95 for individuals. Covers: 3,900 employers in the state of Georgia, including Albany, Columbus, Macon, and Savannah. Entries include: Firm or organization name, address, local phone, toll-free phone, fax, description of organization, subsidiaries, other locations, recorded jobline, name and title of contact, typical titles for common positions, educational backgrounds desired, number of employees, benefits offered, training programs, internships, parent company, revenues, e-mail and

URL address, projected number of hires. Arrangement: Classified by industry. Indexes: Alphabetical.

13380 ■ *Best Career and Education Web Sites, Sixth Edition*
JIST Publishing
875 Montreal Way
St. Paul, MN 55102
Fax: 800-547-8329
Fr: 800-648-5478
E-mail: info@jist.com
URL: http://www.jist.com
Anne Wolfinger. 2009. $14.95. 224 pages. Provides URLs and objective reviews of the most helpful career and college-related sites on the Web; organized by category and target audience.

13381 ■ *Best Entry-Level Jobs, 2008*
The Princeton Review
2315 Broadway
New York, NY 10024
Ph: (212)874-8282
Fax: (212)874-0775
URL: http://www.princetonreview.com
Princeton Review. 2007. $16.95. 400 pages. Reveals where the best first job opportunities in the country are and what you need to do to get them.

13382 ■ *Best Jobs for the 21st Century, Fifth Edition*
JIST Publishing
875 Montreal Way
St. Paul, MN 55102
Fax: 800-547-8329
Fr: 800-648-5478
E-mail: info@jist.com
URL: http://www.jist.com
Michael Farr, Laurence Shatkin, Ph.D. 2012. $19.95. 704 pages. Reference book featuring "best jobs" list and detailed job descriptions organized according to interest area structure following the U.S. Department of Education career clusters.

13383 ■ *The Big Book of Jobs*
McGraw-Hill Professional
PO Box 182604
Columbus, OH 43272
Ph: 877-833-5524
Fax: (614)759-3749
URL: http://www.mhprofessional.com/
    product.php?cat=106&isbn=0071602046
2011. $19.00. 960 pages. Comprehensive and reliable source of career information on the market. Includes expert information on conducting an effective job search.

13384 ■ *Career Building: Your Total Handbook for Finding a Job and Making It Work*
HarperCollins Publishers
10 E 53rd St.
New York, NY 10022
Fr: 800-242-7737
URL: http://www.harpercollins.com
2009. $16.99 (paper). 288 pages. Covers topics on job hunting basics, hiring manager secrets, office survival advice, career transition, workplace statistics, and other related matters.

13385 ■ *The Career Clinic: Eight Simple Rules for Finding Work You Love*
AMACOM Publishing
c/o American Management Association
1601 Broadway
New York, NY 10019-7434
Ph: (212)586-8100
Fax: (518)891-0368
Fr: 800-714-6395
E-mail: pubs_cust_serv@amanet.org
URL: http://www.amacombooks.org
Maureen Anderson. 2008. $15.00 (paper). 224 pages. Features stories of career transitions that led to fulfill-

ment, meaning, and peace. Features suggestions on how people can make a successful career transition.

13386 ■ *Career Coward's Guide to Job Searching*
JIST Publishing
875 Montreal Way
St. Paul, MN 55102
Fr: 800-648-5478
E-mail: educate@emcp.com
URL: http://www.jist.com
Katy Piotrowski. 2008. $10.95 (softcover). 224 pages. Empowers job seekers to step outside their comfort zone by breaking down the job search process into small, attainable goals.

13387 ■ *Career Directions: The Path to Your Ideal Career*
McGraw-Hill Professional
1221 Avenue of the Americas
New York, NY 10020-1095
Ph: (212)904-2000
URL: http://www.mhprofessional.com
Donna Yena. 2010. $61.33 (paper). 336 pages. Provides job seekers with essential resources and techniques to develop a career plan, conduct a successful job search and succeed in a diverse workplace.

13388 ■ *Career Exploration on the Internet Set*
Facts On File Inc.
132 W 31st St., 17th Fl.
New York, NY 10001
Ph: (212)967-8800
Fax: 800-678-3633
Fr: 800-322-8755
URL: http://factsonfile.infobasepublishing.com
$49.90 for individuals. Covers: Descriptions and links to the most informative and useful career sites on the Internet.

13389 ■ *Career Ideas for Teens Set*
Facts On File Inc.
132 W 31st St., 17th Fl.
New York, NY 10001
Ph: (212)967-8800
Fax: 800-678-3633
Fr: 800-322-8755
URL: http://factsonfile.infobasepublishing.com
Published 2005. $240.00 for individuals; $216.00 for libraries. 8-volume set. Covers: A multitude of career possibilities based on a teenager's specific interests and skills and links his/her talents to a wide variety of actual professions.

13390 ■ *Career Opportunities Set*
Facts On File Inc.
132 W 31st St., 17th Fl.
New York, NY 10001
Ph: (212)967-8800
Fax: 800-678-3633
Fr: 800-322-8755
URL: http://factsonfile.infobasepublishing.com
Latest edition 2010. $1,158.30 for individuals; $1,287.00 for individuals. 25-volume set. Covers: In-depth profiles of approximately 60 to 100 jobs, providing thorough information on salary ranges, employment trends, necessary experience, advancement prospects, and helpful unions and associations.

13391 ■ *Career Skills Library—Communication Skills*
Facts On File Inc.
132 W 31st St., 17th Fl.
New York, NY 10001
Ph: (212)967-8800
Fax: 800-678-3633
Fr: 800-322-8755
URL: http://www.infobasepublishing.com
Latest edition 3rd; Published September, 2009. $25.95 for individuals. Covers: The importance of solid speaking, writing, listening, and conversational

skills for thriving in the workplace, plus additional communication skills that are useful in specific situations, such as techniques for conducting structured and productive meetings.

13392 ■ Career Skills Library—Leadership Skills
Facts On File Inc.
132 W 31st St., 17th Fl.
New York, NY 10001
Ph: (212)967-8800
Fax: 800-678-3633
Fr: 800-322-8755
URL: http://www.infobasepublishing.com

Latest edition 3rd; Published September, 2009. $25.95 for individuals. Covers: The qualities of all successful leaders, such as courteousness, compassion, decisiveness, and willingness to give and receive criticism.

13393 ■ Career Skills Library—Learning the Ropes
Facts On File Inc.
132 W 31st St., 17th Fl.
New York, NY 10001
Ph: (212)967-8800
Fax: 800-678-3633
Fr: 800-322-8755
URL: http://www.infobasepublishing.com

Latest edition 3rd; Published October, 2009. $25.95 for individuals. Covers: What to expect from the first day on the job, how to successfully navigate the workplace environment, preparing for some of the realities of work life, including dress codes, organizational hierarchies, co-worker conflicts and resolutions, and some basic rights of every employee.

13394 ■ Career Skills Library—Organization Skills
Facts On File Inc.
132 W 31st St., 17th Fl.
New York, NY 10001
Ph: (212)967-8800
Fax: 800-678-3633
Fr: 800-322-8755
URL: http://www.infobasepublishing.com

Latest edition 3rd; Published August, 2009. $25.95 for individuals. Covers: Time management, setting schedules, avoiding procrastination and time wasters, and organizing one's workplace.

13395 ■ Career Skills Library—Problem Solving
Facts On File Inc.
132 W 31st St., 17th Fl.
New York, NY 10001
Ph: (212)967-8800
Fax: 800-678-3633
Fr: 800-322-8755
URL: http://www.infobasepublishing.com

Latest edition 3rd; Published September, 2009. $25.95 for individuals. Covers: The difference between scientific and creative problem-solving techniques and outlines a five-step approach to dealing with dilemmas to apply to almost any situation.

13396 ■ Career Skills Library—Research and Information Management
Facts On File Inc.
132 W 31st St., 17th Fl.
New York, NY 10001
Ph: (212)967-8800
Fax: 800-678-3633
Fr: 800-322-8755
URL: http://www.infobasepublishing.com

Latest edition 3rd; Published October, 2009. $25.95 for individuals. Covers: Different ways of approaching research and information management, such as research methods, evaluating information for relevance, creating effective presentations, and managing information with spreadsheet and word processing software.

13397 ■ Career Skills Library Set
Facts On File Inc.
132 W 31st St., 17th Fl.
New York, NY 10001
Ph: (212)967-8800
Fax: 800-678-3633
Fr: 800-322-8755
URL: http://www.infobasepublishing.com

Latest edition 2009. $233.55 for individuals; $210.20. 9-volume set. Covers: The skills, traits, and attributes that are crucial to success in any field, including communication, problem solving, organization, and relating to others.

13398 ■ Career Skills Library—Teamwork Skills
Facts On File Inc.
132 W 31st St., 17th Fl.
New York, NY 10001
Ph: (212)967-8800
Fax: 800-678-3633
Fr: 800-322-8755
URL: http://www.infobasepublishing.com

Latest edition 3rd; Published July, 2009. $25.95 for individuals. Covers: The need for teams and how to achieve and encourage healthy team dynamics, including topics such as developing people skills, effectively setting goals and negotiating, appreciating diversity among team members, and resolving team conflicts.

13399 ■ The Career Within You
HarperCollins Publishers
10 E 53rd St.
New York, NY 10022
Ph: (212)207-7000
URL: http://www.harpercollins.com

Elizabeth Wagele and Ingrid Stabb. 2009. $17.99 (paper). 368 pages. Helps individuals determine the career type and forge the career path that suits their personality.

13400 ■ Change Your Job, Change Your Life: Careering and Re-Careering in the New Boom/Bust Economy
Impact Publications
9104 Manassas Dr., Ste. N
Manassas Park, VA 20111-5211
Ph: (703)361-7300
Fax: (703)335-9486
Fr: 800-361-1055
E-mail: query@impactpublications.com
URL: http://www.impactpublications.com

Ronald Krannich. Ninth edition, 2004. $21.95 (paper). 367 pages. Details trends in the marketplace, how to identify opportunities, how to retrain for them, and how to land jobs. Includes a chapter on starting a business. Contains index, bibliography, and illustrations.

13401 ■ College Majors Handbook with Real Career Paths and Payoffs, Second Edition
JIST Publishing
875 Montreal Way
St. Paul, MN 55102
Fax: 800-547-8329
Fr: 800-648-5478
E-mail: info@jist.com
URL: http://www.jist.com/shop/
   product.php?productid=16782&cat=14&page=2

Neeta P. Fogg, PhD; Paul E. Harrington, EdD; Thomas F. Harrington, PhD. 2012. $24.95. 656 pages. Gives job salary prospects for specific college majors, employment growth rates, and how many graduates go on to additional education, based on U.S. Census Bureau study.

13402 ■ Complete Idiot's Guide to Recession-Proof Careers
Alpha Books
c/o Penguin Group USA
375 Hudson St.
New York, NY 10014-3657

Ph: (212)366-2000
Fax: (212)366-2933
E-mail: ecommerce@us.penguingroup.com
URL: http://us.penguingroup.com

Jeff Cohen. 2010. $18.00 (paper). 352 pages. Presents essential information that will help job seekers choose a career for secure employment. Includes resources for job sites, fairs and organizations.

13403 ■ The Connecticut JobBank
Adams Media Corp.
57 Littlefield St.
Avon, MA 02322-1944
Ph: (508)427-7100
Fax: (508)427-6790
URL: http://www.adamsmediastore.com/product/
   183/6

Biennial, latest edition 3. $9.00 for individuals. Covers: Approximately 2,000 employers, career resources, industry associations, and employment services in Connecticut. Entries include: Company name, address, phone, fax, e-mail, and web address; names and titles of key personnel; number of employees; geographical area served; financial data; subsidiary names and addresses; description of services; Standard Industrial Classification (SIC) code. Indexes: Alphabetical.

13404 ■ Courting Your Career
JIST Publishing
875 Montreal Way
St. Paul, MN 55102
Fr: 800-648-5478
E-mail: educate@emcp.com
URL: http://www.jist.com

Shawn Graham. 2008. $6.47 (softcover). 208 pages. Contains anecdotes and advice appropriate for every stage of a typical job search - from what initially attracts job seekers to a potential employer to strategies for landing that dream job.

13405 ■ Cracking the Hidden Job Market
Ten Speed Press
6001 Shellmound St.
Emeryville, CA 94608
Ph: (510)285-3000
Fax: (510)285-2979
URL: http://www.randomhouse.com

Donald Asher. 2010. $14.99 (paper). 208 pages. Offers proven strategies for finding employment opportunities in any industry.

13406 ■ Cracking the New Job Market
AMACOM Publishing
c/o American Management Association
1601 Broadway
New York, NY 10019-7420
Fax: (212)903-8083
Fr: 800-250-5308
URL: http://www.amacombooks.org

R. William Holland. 2011. $17.95 (paper). Presents effective new job-hunting strategies to land a well-paying job.

13407 ■ Discovering Careers for Your Future Set
Facts On File Inc.
132 W 31st St., 17th Fl.
New York, NY 10001
Ph: (212)967-8800
Fax: 800-678-3633
Fr: 800-322-8755
URL: http://factsonfile.infobasepublishing.com

Latest edition 2008. $329.25 for individuals; $296.35 for individuals. 18-volume set. Covers: 20 careers in each volume and offering a comprehensive look at everything from how to start preparing while still in school to what the future might hold in terms of job prospects and salaries.

13408 ■ *The Don't Sweat Guide to Your Job Search: Finding a Career Your Really Love*
Hyperion Press
114 Fifth Ave.
New York, NY 10011
Ph: (212)207-7505
Fax: (212)207-7222
Fr: 800-242-7737
URL: http://www.hyperionbooks.com
$10.95 (paper). 208 pages. May 2004.

13409 ■ *Encyclopedia of Careers and Vocational Guidance, Fifteen Edition*
JIST Publishing
875 Montreal Way
St. Paul, MN 55102
Fax: 800-547-8329
Fr: 800-648-5478
E-mail: info@jist.com
URL: http://www.jist.com
2010. $249.95. 3,776 pages. Four-volume comprehensive career reference.

13410 ■ *Enhanced Occupational Outlook Handbook*
JIST Works
875 Montreal Way
St. Paul, MN 55102
Fax: 800-328-4564
Fr: 800-328-1452
E-mail: educate@emcp.com
URL: http://jist.emcpublishingllc.com
2009. $39.95 (softcover). 784 pages. Contains organized clusters of related jobs and up-to-date career information.

13411 ■ *Fearless Job Hunting*
New Harbinger Publications
5674 Shattuck Ave.
Oakland, CA 94609
Fr: 800-748-6273
URL: http://www.newharbinger.com
Bill J. Knaus, Sam Klarreich, Russell Grieger, and Nancy Knaus. 2010. $16.95 (paper). 216 pages. Offers powerful psychological techniques to handle job opportunities fearlessly and get hired as an exceptional employee.

13412 ■ *Getting the Job You Really Want*
Jist Works
875 Montreal Way
St. Paul, MN 55102
Fr: 800-648-5478
E-mail: info@jist.com
URL: http://www.jist.com/shop/
    product.php?productid=16727
J. Michael Farr. Sixth edition, 2011. $20.95 (paper). 240 pages. A step-by-step guide to career planning, job seeking, and job survival.

13413 ■ *The Google Resume: How to Prepare for a Career and Land a Job at Apple, Microsoft, Google, or any Top Tech Company*
John Wiley & Sons, Inc.
111 River St.
Hoboken, NJ 07030-5774
Ph: (201)748-6000
Fax: (201)748-6088
E-mail: info@wiley.com
URL: http://www.wiley.com
Gayle Laakmann McDowell. 2011. $22.95 (hardcover). 280 pages. Helps job seekers land a job in top companies such as Google, Apple and Microsoft. Includes tips and advice on resume-writing, interview preparation and other key concerns.

13414 ■ *Guerilla Marketing for Job Hunters 2.0: 1,001 Unconventional Tips, Tricks, and Tactics for Landing Your Dream Job*
John Wiley and Sons, Inc.
1 Wiley Dr.
Somerset, NJ 08875-1272

Fax: (732)302-2300
Fr: 800-225-5945
E-mail: custserv@wiley.com
URL: http://as.wiley.com
Jay Conrad Levinson, David E. Perry and Darren Hardy. 2010. $21.95. 315 pages. Provides steps to using a typically unconventional Guerilla approach covering all the basics of a winning campaign.

13415 ■ *Guerrilla Marketing for Job Hunters: 400 Unconventional Tips, Tricks, and Tactics for Landing Your Dream Job*
Wiley
111 River St.
Hoboken, NJ 07030-5774
Ph: (201)748-6000
Fax: (201)748-6088
E-mail: info@wiley.com
URL: http://as.wiley.com
Jay Conrad Levinson, David E. Perry. 2005. $19.95. 288 pages. Covers information about using the internet for research and job searches, performing a resume make-over and creating a resume, and branding and selling strengths in resumes, letters, e-mail, and interviews.

13416 ■ *Guide to Employment Web Sites*
Kennedy Information
1 Phoenix Mill Ln., 3rd Fl.
Peterborough, NH 03458
Ph: (603)924-1006
Fax: (603)924-4460
Fr: 800-531-0007
URL: http://www.kennedyinfo.com/hr/
    hrbookstore.html
Annual, Latest edition 2007-2008. $39.95 for individuals. Covers: Over 40,000 sites for locating high caliber job candidates. Entries include: Website address, duration of the site, visits per month, profile of frequent visitors, candidate visits, fees, number of records, resume acquisition, site features such as automatic notification of resume-job matches.

13417 ■ *Guide for the Pissed-off-Job-Seeker: Angry? Good! Use That Anger to Get Work!*
iUniverse, Inc.
1663 Liberty Dr.
Bloomington, IN 47403
Ph: (402)323-7800
Fax: (812)355-4085
Fr: 877-288-4677
URL: http://bookstore.iuniverse.com
Irv Zuckerman. May 2004. $14.95 (paper). 132 pages.

13418 ■ *Harper's Rules: A Recruiter's Guide to Finding a Dream Job and the Right Relationship*
Greenleaf Book Group LLC
PO Box 91869
Austin, TX 78709
Ph: (512)891-6100
Fax: (512)891-6150
Fr: 800-932-5420
E-mail: contact@greenleafbookgroup.com
URL: http://www.greenleafbookgroup.com
Danny Cahill. 2011. $21.95. 144 pages (hardcover). Contains tips for successful job hunting and career-building.

13419 ■ *Have No Career Fear: A College Grad's Guide to Snagging a Job, Trekking the Career Path, and Reaching Job Nirvana*
Natavi Guides
19 Stuyvesant Oval, Ste. 8E
New York, NY 10009
Fax: (866)425-4218
Fr: (866)425-4218
E-mail: info@nataviguides.com
URL: http://www.nataviguides.com
Ben Cohen-Leadholm, Rachel Skerritt, Ari Gerzon-Kessler. April 2005. $13.95 (paper). 224 pages.

13420 ■ *"Headhunter" Hiring Secrets: The Rules of the Hiring Game Have Changed... Forever!*
CreateSpace
7290 B. Investment Dr.
Charleston, SC 29418
E-mail: info@createspace.com
URL: http://www.createspace.com
Skip Freeman. 2010. $17.95 (paper). 348 pages. Reveals the hiring secrets of headhunters in today's job market.

13421 ■ *Hot Jobs: More Than 25 Careers With the Highest Pay, Fastest Growth, and Most New Job Openings*
College & Career Press
PO Box 300484
Chicago, IL 60630
Ph: (773)282-4671
URL: http://www.collegeandcareerpress.com
Andrew Morkes. 2010. $14.99 (paper). 224 pages. Covers various career profiles. Features an overview of the job and work environment, educational requirements, and personal skills. Includes tips on landing a job and winning interviews.

13422 ■ *How to Find the Work You Love*
Penguin
375 Hudson St.
New York, NY 10014
Ph: (212)366-2000
Fax: (212)366-2666
Fr: 800-847-5515
URL: http://us.penguingroup.com
Laurence G. Boldt. 2004. $13.00 (paper). 192 pages.

13423 ■ *How to Get a Great Job: A Library How-To Handbook*
Skyhorse Publishing
307 W 36th St., 11th Fl.
New York, NY 10018
Ph: (212)643-6816
Fax: (212)643-6819
URL: http://www.skyhorsepublishing.com
Editors of the American Library Association. 2011. $14.95 (paper). 176 pages. Offers expert advice on how to conduct proper research, build networks of friends and colleagues, put together a great resume, research industries that are constantly changing, prepare for an interview, negotiate a contract or a salary and other job-hunting tips.

13424 ■ *How to Get a Job & Keep It*
Ferguson Publishing Co.
132 W 31st St., 17th Fl.
New York, NY 10001
Fax: 800-678-3633
Fr: 800-322-8755
E-mail: custserv@factsonfile.com
URL: http://ferguson.infobasepublishing.com
Susan Morem. 2007. $35.00. 224 pages.

13425 ■ *How to Get a Job on Wall Street: Proven Ways to Land a High-Paying, High-Power Job*
McGraw-Hill Companies
PO Box 182604
Columbus, OH 43272
Fax: (614)759-3749
Fr: 877-833-5524
E-mail: customer.service@mcgraw-hill.com
URL: http://www.mcgraw-hill.com
Scott Hoover. 2011. $17.95. 176 pages. Contains sample questions and advice for passing interviews with old-fashioned knowledge, confidence and professionalism. Includes topics on reading balance sheets and income statements, concepts of finance, and company valuation basics.

13426 ■ *How to Get the Job You Desire*
Dorrance Publishing Company, Inc.
701 Smithfield St., 3rd Fl.
Pittsburgh, PA 15222

Ph: (412)288-4543
Fr: 800-788-7654
URL: http://www.dorrancebookstore.com/
   howtogetjoby.html

Peggy Redman. February 2004. $14.95 (paper). 42 pages.

13427 ▪ How to Succeed in Business Using LinkedIn: Making Connections and Capturing Opportunities on the World's 1 Business Networking Site
AMACOM Publishing
c/o American Management Association
1601 Broadway
New York, NY 10019-7434
Ph: (212)586-8100
Fr: 800-714-6395
E-mail: pubs_cust_serv@amanet.org
URL: http://www.amacombooks.org

Eric Butow and Kathleen Taylor. 2008. $19.95 (paper). 256 pages. Provides information about every aspect of the site, from getting registered and building a network to posing questions and creating groups. Helps readers learn how to: create a homepage so other users can find them; give and receive references; search for experts in any field; find leads; market business; look for and become a service provider; find and recruit for jobs; conduct business research; and discover people outside the networks.

13428 ▪ The Innovative Road to Greater Success in Job Hunting and Changing Careers
PublishAmerica
PO Box 151
Frederick, MD 21705
Ph: (301)695-1707
URL: http://www.publishamerica.net

Joan M. Enering. 2011. $19.95 (softcover). 94 pages. Serves as a guide for finding a job or changing careers. Includes tips on writing resumes and cover letters, getting dressed for a job interview, and the secret of the waiting area.

13429 ▪ Insider's Guide to Finding a Job
JIST Publishing
875 Montreal Way
St. Paul, MN 55102
Fax: 800-547-8329
Fr: 800-648-5478
E-mail: info@jist.com
URL: http://www.jist.com/shop/
   product.php?productid=16690&cat=0&page=1

Wendy S. Enelow and Shelly Goldman. 2005. $6.47. 256 Pages. First-hand advice from 66 top hiring managers, HR directors, and recruiters at the most sought-after companies in the U.S.

13430 ▪ The Job Hunting Handbook
Dahlstrom & Company
50 October Hill Rd.
Holliston, MA 01746-1308
Fax: 800-997-7444
Fr: 800-222-0009
E-mail: email@dahlstromco.com
URL: http://www.dahlstromco.com

Harry Dahlstrom. 2010. $6.99. 48 pages. Teaches job seekers how to prospect for jobs, write a cover letter, create a resume, prepare for and land interviews, market themselves, and win job offers.

13431 ▪ Job-Hunting Online
Ten Speed Press
1745 Broadway, 3rd Fl.
New York, NY 10019
Fax: (212)572-6066
E-mail: ecustomerservice@randomhouse.com
URL: http://www.randomhouse.com/crown

Mark Emery Bolles and Richard N. Bolles. 2008. $12.95 (paper). 208 pages. Serves as a guide to using job listings, message boards, research sites, the underweb, counseling, networking self-assessment tools, niche sites, or the internet. Helps job seekers

navigate information available on the internet to find the sites and avoid common pitfalls. Contains website recommendations and steps of a successful job hunt.

13432 ▪ Job Search and Career Checklists: 101 Proven Time-Saving Checklists to Organize and Plan Your Career Search
JIST Publishing
875 Montreal Way
St. Paul, MN 55102
Fax: 800-547-8329
Fr: 800-648-5478
E-mail: info@jist.com
URL: http://www.jist.com

Arlene S. Hirsch. 2005. $18.95. 208 pages. Job search workbook including checklists and task lists for assessing needs, initiating job searches, improving current jobs and exploring career options.

13433 ▪ Job Search: Career Planning Guide
Wadsworth Publishing
PO Box 6904
Florence, KY 41022
Fax: 800-487-8488
Fr: 800-354-9706
E-mail: esales@cengage.com
URL: http://www.cengage.com

Robert D. Lock. Fifth edition, 2005. $62.49 (paper). 384 pages. Assists the reader in a productive job search. Part of Career Planning Guide series.

13434 ▪ Job Search Magic: Insider Secrets from America's Career and Life Coach
JIST Publishing
875 Montreal Way
St. Paul, MN 55102
Fax: 800-547-8329
Fr: 800-648-5478
E-mail: info@jist.com
URL: http://www.jist.com

Susan Britton Whitcomb. 2006. $18.95. 512 pages. Job search manual offers basic foundations of a complete resume, cover letters, and strategies for getting the interview and embarking on a career path.

13435 ▪ The Job Search Solution: The Ultimate System for Finding a Great Job Now!
AMACOM
1601 Broadway
New York, NY 10019
Fax: (518)891-2372
Fr: 800-250-5308
E-mail: pubs_cust_serv@amanet.org
URL: http://www.amacombooks.org

Tony Beshara. 2012. $16.95 (paper). Addresses the challenges that confront job seekers. Provides readers with advice and tools needed to get hired. Includes interactive exercises and real-life examples, tips on: creating a personal 'brand' online; communicating with employers; and winning interviews.

13436 ▪ The Job Searcher's Handbook
Prentice Hall
c/o Pearson Education, Inc.
One Lake St.
Upper Saddle River, NJ 07458
URL: http://www.pearsonhighered.com

Carolyn R. Robbins. 2009. $42.20 (paper). 216 pages. Contains career development guides and effective job search techniques. Includes hands-on exercises.

13437 ▪ Job Searching with Social Media For Dummies
Wiley Publishing
10475 Crosspoint Blvd.
Indianapolis, IN 46256
Fax: 800-597-3299
Fr: 877-762-2974
URL: http://www.dummies.com

Joshua Waldman. 2011. $19.99 (paper). 360 pages.

Focuses on taking advantage of social media sites to research and find job opportunities, and secure the desired position. Includes in-depth coverage of topics such as creating effective online profiles and resumes, understanding online etiquette and necessary background on current social media sites.

13438 ▪ Job Seeker's Online Goldmine: A Step-by-Step Guidebook to Government and No-Cost Web Tools
JIST Publishing
875 Montreal Way
St. Paul, MN 55102
Fax: 800-547-8329
Fr: 800-648-5478
E-mail: info@jist.com
URL: http://www.jist.com

Janet E. Wall, EdD. 2006. $6.97. 240 pages. Handbook pulls together, in a single source, a wealth of online options that are not widely publicized because they're funded by tax dollars or nonprofit organizations.

13439 ▪ Job Seeker's Workbook
JIST Publishing
875 Montreal Way
St. Paul, MN 55102
Fax: 800-547-8329
Fr: 800-648-5478
E-mail: info@jist.com
URL: http://www.jist.com/shop/
   product.php?productid=1189&cat=0&page=1

Editors at JIST. 2007. $13.95. 80 pages. For job seekers with lower reading level or limited English skills. Includes interactive worksheets, charts and checklists.

13440 ▪ Knock 'em Dead 2012: The Ultimate Job Search Guide
Adams Media
57 Littlefield St.
Avon, MA 02322
Ph: (508)427-7100
E-mail: deskcopies@adamsmedia.com
URL: http://www.adamsmedia.com

Martin Yate. 2012. $11.53 (paper). 384 pages. Features advice on crafting resumes and leveraging social networking. Supplies information on the top job titles and tips on how to land positions in those fields.

13441 ▪ Knock 'Em Dead: The Ultimate Job Seeker's Handbook
Adams Media Corp.
4700 E Galbraith Rd.
Cincinnati, OH 45236
Ph: (513)531-2690
Fax: (513)531-4082
Fr: 800-289-0963
URL: http://www.adamsmediastore.com/product/
   1359/careers

Martin Yate. 2010. $15.95 (paper). 384 pages. Prepares the job seeker for the interview with advice on dress, manner, how to answer the toughest questions, and how to spot illegal questions. Discusses how to respond to questions of salary to maximize income. Features sections on executive search firms and drug testing.

13442 ▪ Major Employers of the Greater Philadelphia Region
Greater Philadelphia Chamber of Commerce
200 S Broad St., Ste. 700
Philadelphia, PA 19102
Ph: (215)545-1234
Fax: (215)790-3600
URL: http://www.greaterphilachamber.com/
   Resources.aspx?PageConten

$25.00 for members; $35.00 for nonmembers. Covers: over 500 top employers and pertinent information in each of the Greater Philadelphia's 11 counties. Arrangement: Alphabetical.

13443 ■ *Managing Brand You: 7 Steps to Creating Your Most Successful Self*
AMACOM Publishing
c/o American Management Association
1601 Broadway
New York, NY 10019-7434
Ph: (212)586-8100
Fax: (518)891-0368
Fr: 800-714-6395
E-mail: pubs_cust_serv@amanet.org
URL: http://www.amacombooks.org

Jerry S. Wilson and Ira Blumenthal. 2008. $21.95 (hardback). 256 pages. Provides readers a step-by-step guide for conducting a self analysis, creating a unique identity, defining objectives, discovering passions, creating a plan, putting that plan into action, and monitoring progress.

13444 ■ *Media Career Guide: Preparing for Jobs in the 21st Century*
Bedford/St. Martin's Press
Bedford, Freeman & Worth Publishing Group, LLC
41 Madison Ave.
New York, NY 10010
URL: http://www.bedfordstmartins.com

James Seguin and Sherri Hope Culver. 2011. $9.95 - students; $7.50 bookstores (paper). 128 pages. Guides readers through the process of researching, interviewing for, and landing a perfect media job. Offers career advice and practical tips from real media professionals.

13445 ■ *National JobBank*
Adams Media Corp.
57 Littlefield St.
Avon, MA 02322-1944
Ph: (508)427-7100
Fax: (508)427-6790
URL: http://www.adamsmediastore.com/product/national-jobbank-2010

Annual, Latest edition 2010. $475.00 for individuals. Covers: Over 20,000 employers nationwide. Entries include: Firm or organization name, address, local phone, toll-free phone, fax, contact name and title, description of organization, headquarters location, names of management, number of employees, other locations, subsidiaries, parent company, projected number of hires, training offered, internships, hours, recorded jobline, typical titles for common positions, educational backgrounds desired, stock exchange (if listed), fringe benefits offered. Several state and regional volumes are available and described separately. Arrangement: Geographical. Indexes: Geographical and classified by industry.

13446 ■ *New Guide for Occupational Exploration, Fourth Edition*
JIST Publishing
875 Montreal Way
St. Paul, MN 55102
Fax: 800-547-8329
Fr: 800-648-5478
E-mail: info@jist.com
URL: http://www.jist.com/shop/product.php?productid=3187&cat=14&page=4

Michael Farr, Laurence Shatkin PhD. 2006. Hardcover $24.97, softcover $19.97. Resource for matching interests to both job and learning options based on the 16 U.S. Department of Education clusters that connect learning to careers.

13447 ■ *The New Jersey JobBank*
Adams Media Corp.
57 Littlefield St.
Avon, MA 02322-1944
Ph: (508)427-7100
Fax: (508)427-6790
URL: http://www.adamsmediastore.com/product/857/6

Biennial, latest edition 4th. $17.95 for individuals. Covers: Approximately 4,000 employers, career resources, industry associations, and employment services in the Garden State. Entries include: Company name, address, phone, fax, email, and web address; names and titles of key personnel; number of employees; geographical area served; financial data; subsidiary names and addresses; description of services; standard industrial classification (sic) code. Indexes: Alphabetical.

13448 ■ *No One Will Hire Me: Avoid 17 Mistakes and Win the Job*
JIST Publishing
875 Montreal Way
St. Paul, MN 55102
Fr: 800-648-5478
URL: http://www.jist.com

Ron and Caryl Krannich, PhDs. Third edition. $15.95. 198 pages. Identifies 17 major mistakes and offers analyses, self-tests, exercises, and resources to avoid the error.

13449 ■ *Now Hiring, Apply Yourself*
Dahlstrom & Company
50 October Hill Rd.
Holliston, MA 01746-1308
Fax: 800-997-7444
Fr: 800-222-0009
E-mail: email@dahlstromco.com
URL: http://www.dahlstromco.com

Harry Dahlstrom. 2010. $5.00. 24 pages. Provides job hunters with step-by-step guidelines for the entire job application process.

13450 ■ *Occupational Outlook Handbook*
U.S. Bureau of Labor Statistics
2 Massachusetts Ave. NE Ste. 2135
Washington, DC 20212-0001
Ph: (202)691-5200
Fr: 800-877-8339
E-mail: oohinfo@bls.gov
URL: http://www.bls.gov/oco/home.htm

Biennial, Latest edition 2010-2011. $22.00 for individuals. Publication includes: Various occupational organizations that provide career information on hundreds of occupations. Entries include: For organizations—Organization name, address. Principal content of publication is profiles of various occupations, which include description of occupation, educational requirements, job outlook, and expected earnings. Arrangement: Organizations are classified by occupation.

13451 ■ *The Ohio JobBank*
Adams Media Corp.
57 Littlefield St.
Avon, MA 02322-1944
Ph: (508)427-7100
Fax: (508)427-6790
URL: http://www.adamsmediastore.com/product/858/6

Biennial, Latest edition 12th. $17.95 for individuals. Covers: 4,800 Employers and employment services in Ohio. Entries include: Firm or organization name, address, phone, name and title of contact; description of organization, headquarters location, typical titles for entry- and middle-level positions, educational backgrounds desired, fringe benefits offered, stock exchange listing, training programs, internships, parent company, number of employees, revenues, e-mail and web address, projected number of hires. Arrangement: Alphabetical.

13452 ■ *O*NET Dictionary of Occupational Titles, Third Edition*
JIST Publishing
875 Montreal Way
St. Paul, MN 55102
Fax: 800-547-8329
Fr: 800-648-5478
E-mail: info@jist.com
URL: http://www.jist.com/shop/product.php?productid=16182&cat=14&page=4

Michael Farr. 2007. Hardcover $24.97, softcover $19.97. 672 pages. Reference book of job descriptions and other information from the U.S. Department of Labor's O-NET database put into print form.

13453 ■ *Outwitting the Job Market: Everything You Need to Locate and Land a Great Position*
The Lyons Press
246 Goose Ln.
Guilford, CT 06437
Ph: (203)458-4500
Fax: 800-820-2329
Fr: 888-249-7586
E-mail: info@globepequot.com
URL: http://www.lyonspress.com

Chandra Prasad. May 2004. $13.95 (paper). 256 pages. Part of the Outwitting Series.

13454 ■ *Overnight Career Choice: Discover Your Ideal Job in Just a Few Hours*
JIST Publishing
875 Montreal Way
St. Paul, MN 55102
Fax: 800-547-8329
Fr: 800-648-5478
E-mail: info@jist.com
URL: http://www.jist.com

Michael Farr. 2011. $9.95. 200 pages. Guide for job seekers to discover their ideal career quickly.

13455 ■ *The Pocket Book of Job Search Data and Tips, Third Edition*
JIST Publishing
875 Montreal Way
St. Paul, MN 55102
Fax: 800-547-8329
Fr: 800-648-5478
E-mail: info@jist.com
URL: http://www.jist.com

Michael Farr. 2008. $46.95. 32 pages. Includes worksheets for personal information, job preferences, health information, school experience, other training, past employer contact information, work experience, and all other information required for employment applications.

13456 ■ *Quick Guide to College Majors and Careers*
JIST Publishing
875 Montreal Way
St. Paul, MN 55102
Fr: 800-648-5478
URL: http://www.jist.com/shop/product.php?productid=16497&cat=0&page=1

Laurence Shatkin, PhD. 2009. $18.95. 368 pages. Based on information from the O-NET database, this reference connects education to careers using self-assessment worksheets to help focus on college majors to investigate.

13457 ■ *The Quick Job Search, Fourth Edition*
JIST Publishing
875 Montreal Way
St. Paul, MN 55102
Fax: 800-547-8329
Fr: 800-648-5478
E-mail: info@jist.com
URL: http://www.jist.com/shop/product.php?productid=16504

Michael Farr. 2006. $39.95. 64 pages. Covers the basics on how to explore career options and conduct an effective job search; includes skills checklists, worksheets, and sample resumes.

13458 ■ *Recruiter's Guide*
American Association for Employment in Education
3040 Riverside Dr., Ste. 117
Columbus, OH 43221
Ph: (614)485-1111
Fax: (360)244-7802
E-mail: office@aaee.org
URL: http://www.aaee.org

Latest edition 2008. Covers: Lists of job and career fairs and the institutions which sponsor the programs or participate in programs sponsored by consortia. Entries include: Contact information, date and title of event, location, number of expected employers and candidates, percentage of minority candidates expected, employers fees, registration deadlines, e-mail and website addresses.

13459 ■ Seven-Step Job Search, Second Edition: Cut Your Job Search Time in Half
JIST Publishing
875 Montreal Way
St. Paul, MN 55102
Fax: 800-547-8329
Fr: 800-648-5478
E-mail: info@jist.com
URL: http://www.jist.com

Michael Farr. 2006. $8.95. 192 pages. Advice on finding a great job, from resumes to interviews.

13460 ■ Super Job Search: The Complete Manual for Job-Seekers and Career-Changers
Jamenair Ltd.
PO Box 241957
Los Angeles, CA 90024-9757
Ph: (310)470-6688
Fax: (310)470-8106
Fr: 800-581-5953
URL: http://www.superjobsearch.com/html/ameredition2.html

Peter Studner. Third edition, 2011. $22.95 (paper). 352 pages. A step-by-step guidebook for getting a job, with sections on getting started, how to present accomplishments, networking strategies, telemarketing tips, and negotiating tactics.

13461 ■ Taking Charge of Your Career Direction
Wadsworth Publishing
PO Box 6904
Florence, KY 41022
Fax: 800-487-8488
Fr: 800-354-9706
E-mail: esales@cengage.com
URL: http://www.cengage.com

Robert D. Lock. Fifth edition, 2005. Three volumes. 512 pages. $73.49. Provides guidance for the job search process.

13462 ■ Today's Hot Job Targets
JIST Publishing
875 Montreal Way
St. Paul, MN 55102
Fr: 800-648-5478
E-mail: info@jist.com
URL: http://www.jist.com

Michael Farr and Laurence Shatkin. 2007. $8.95 (softcover). 192 pages. Includes information on job tasks, projected growth, openings, salary, education required, and personality type. Gives guidance on obtaining training and education for in-demand jobs.

13463 ■ The Top 100: The Fastest-Growing Careers for the 21st Century
Ferguson
132 W 31st St., 17th Fl.
New York, NY 10001
Fax: 800-678-3633
Fr: 800-322-8755
E-mail: custserv@factsonfile.com
URL: http://www.infobasepublishing.com

2011. $75.00 (hardcover). 400 pages. Provides information on jobs projected to have the fastest growth, biggest opportunities and best earnings. Includes an overview of the most popular career fields.

13464 ■ Top 300 Careers
JIST Publishing
875 Montreal Way
St. Paul, MN 55102
Fax: 800-547-8329

Fr: 800-648-5478
E-mail: info@jist.com
URL: http://www.jist.com/shop/product.php?productid=16396&cat=0&page=1

U.S. Department of Labor. Twelfth edition. $19.95. 848 pages. Based on the latest edition of the Occupational Outlook Handbook, this reference includes information job seekers and students need to research careers, learn about pay, outlook, and education and skills needed to land a job.

13465 ■ Top Careers Set
Facts On File Inc.
132 W 31st St., 17th Fl.
New York, NY 10001
Ph: (212)967-8800
Fax: 800-678-3633
Fr: 800-322-8755
URL: http://factsonfile.infobasepublishing.com/

6-volume set, each volume profiling approximately 35 jobs available to college graduates within a chosen major. Entries include: Duties and responsibilities, necessary qualifications or certification requirements, salary ranges, types of employers, job outlook.

13466 ■ The Twitter Job Search Guide
JIST Publishing
875 Montreal Way
St. Paul, MN 55102
Fr: 800-648-5478
URL: http://www.jist.com

Susan Britton Whitcomb, Deb Dib and Chandlee Bryan. $14.95 (softcover). 192 pages. Serves as a guide for job seekers concerning the use and relevance of Twitter as a new tool for job searching.

13467 ■ The Ultimate Job Hunter's Guidebook
Cengage Learning
PO Box 6904
Florence, KY 41022-6904
Fax: 800-487-8488
Fr: 800-354-9706
URL: http://www.cengage.com

Susan Greene and Melanie Martel. 2012. $79.95 (spiralbound). 304 pages. Offers a concise coverage of essential jobhunting and career strategies. Includes tips on job searching using social media, samples of resumes and cover letters from a variety of career fields, experiential exercises and hands-on activities, and integrated technology resources.

13468 ■ Ultimate Job Hunting Secrets: Essential Tips, Tricks, and Tactics for Today's Job Seeker
AllCountyJobs.com LLC
674 Orchard St.
Trumbull, CT 06611
Fr: 800-399-6651
E-mail: info@allcountyjobs.com
URL: http://www.allcountyjobs.com/job-search-tools.html

C.M. Russell. 2005. $20. 115 pages. Provides timely job hunting strategies ranging from breakthrough ideas, to clever ways of networking, to unique apply methods.

13469 ■ The Very Quick Job Search: Get a Better Job in Half the Time
Jist Publishing
875 Montreal Way
St. Paul, MN 55102
Fr: 800-648-5478
E-mail: info@jist.com
URL: http://www.jist.com/shop/product.php?productid=2430&cat=0&page=1

J. Michael Farr. Third edition, 2004. $23.95. 544 pages.

13470 ■ Weddle's Recruiter's and Job Seeker's Guide to Association Web Sites
Paul & Co.
814 N Franklin St.
Chicago, IL 60610

Ph: (312)337-0747
Fax: (312)337-5985
Fr: 800-888-4741
URL: http://www.ipgbook.com

$49.95 for individuals; $54.95 for individuals. Covers: More than 2,000 associations from around the world. Entries include: resume database, discussion forum, and association who offers a job board. Indexes: By career field, industry, and Geographical location.

13471 ■ What Color Is Your Parachute
Ten Speed Press
6001 Shellmound St.
Emeryville, CA 94608
Ph: (510)285-3000
Fax: (510)285-2979
URL: http://www.randomhouse.com/crown/features/what-color-is-your-parachute/

Richard N. Bolles. 2011. $18.99. Publication cancelled. 336 pages. Subtitled: "A Practical Manual for Job-Hunters and Career-Changers". One of the best-known works on job hunting, this book provides detailed and strategic advice on all aspects of the job search.

NEWSPAPERS, MAGAZINES, AND JOURNALS

13472 ■ Career Magazine
HH Publishing
PO Box 54166
Atlanta, GA 30308
Ph: (404)604-4511
URL: http://www.thecareermag.com

Bimonthly. $15.00/hard copy; $17.99/year (online); $2.99/digital copy. Features articles in career advancement and other topics related to careers in general.

13473 ■ Job Choices
National Association of Colleges and Employers
62 Highland Ave.
Bethlehem, PA 18017-9085
Ph: (610)868-1421
Fax: (610)868-0208
Fr: 800-544-5272
URL: http://www.naceweb.org/Products/2011_Job_Choices_Packages.as

$13.95/year for nonmembers. Magazine focusing on job-search and career planning.

13474 ■ Journal of Job Placement
National Rehabilitation Association
633 S Washington St.
Alexandria, VA 22314
Ph: (703)836-0850
Fax: (703)836-0848
Fr: 888-258-4295
E-mail: info@natioanlrehab.org
URL: http://www.nationalrehab.org

Periodic. Employment journal.

13475 ■ Occupational Outlook Quarterly
U.S. Government Printing Office and Superintendent of Documents
Mail Stop: IDCC
732 N Capitol St. NW
Washington, DC 20401
Ph: (202)512-1800
Fax: (202)512-2104
Fr: (866)512-1800
URL: http://www.bls.gov/opub/ooq/ooqhome.htm

Quarterly. $30.00/year for two years; $15.00/year for individuals; $42.00/year for other countries, 2 years; $6.00/year for single issue; $8.40/year for other countries, single copy. Magazine providing occupational and employment information.

13476 ■ Packaging Horizons Online
Women in Packaging, Inc.
4290 Bells Ferry Rd., Ste. 106-17
Kennesaw, GA 30144-1300
Ph: (678)594-6872
URL: http://www.womeninpackaging.org/ph/ph1.html

Weekly. for Included in membership; $300.00/year for nonmembers, e-broadcast; $6,000.00/year for individuals. E-zine comprising career guidance tips, advice, and industry know how.

13477 ■ Professional Studies Review
St. John's University
8000 Utopia Pky.
Jamaica, NY 11439
Ph: (718)990-2000
URL: http://www.stjohns.edu/academics/
   undergraduate/professionals

Semiannual. $60.00/year for institutions; $35.00/year for individuals; $20.00/year for single issue. Peer-reviewed journal devoted to the pedagogic needs and research interests of those working within career-oriented disciplines.

13478 ■ Student Pharmacist
American Pharmacists Association
2215 Constitution Ave. NW
Washington, DC 20005-1707
Ph: (202)628-4410
Fax: (202)783-2351
Fr: 800-237-2742
URL: http://www.pharmacist.com/AM/
   Template.cfm?Section=Student_Ph

Bimonthly. $11.00/year for individuals; $12.00/year for members; $13.00/year for members; $14.00/year for Canada; $15.00/year for Canada and Mexico; $16.00/year for members; $17.00/year for individuals; $18.00/year for individuals; $19.00/year for individuals; $20.00/year for individuals. Magazine providing advice for pharmacy career planning.

13479 ■ Today's Officer
Military Officers Association of America
201 N Washington St.
Alexandria, VA 22314
Ph: (703)549-2311
Fr: 800-234-6622
URL: http://www.moaa.org/membership/pubs/pubs_
   todaysofficer/index

Quarterly. for Included in membership. Magazine that addresses issues important to new officers as well as officers transitioning to other careers.

AUDIO/VISUAL RESOURCES

13480 ■ Behind the Scenes: Industrial Field Trips
Cambridge Educational
PO Box 2053
Princeton, NJ 08543-2053
Ph: 800-257-5126
Fax: (609)671-0266
Fr: 800-468-4227
E-mail: custserv@films.com
URL: http://cambridge.films.com

VHS and DVD. $239.85.

13481 ■ Career Clusters 2 Series
JIST Publishing
875 Montreal Way
St. Paul, MN 55102
Fax: 800-547-8329
Fr: 800-648-5478
E-mail: info@jist.com
URL: http://www.jist.com/shop/
   product.php?productid=16274&cat=1317&page=2

2004. $399.80. 18 minutes each. Men and women with experience in their fields talk about their jobs and the kinds of skills and training they needed to successfully acquire them.

13482 ■ Career Clusters 3 Series
JIST Publishing
875 Montreal Way
St. Paul, MN 55102
Fax: 800-547-8329
Fr: 800-648-5478
E-mail: info@jist.com
URL: http://www.jist.com/shop/
   product.php?productid=16279

2004. $399.80. 18 minutes each. Experienced workers talk about their jobs and the kinds of skills and training needed to successfully acquire them.

13483 ■ Career Evaluation
Cambridge Educational
PO Box 2053
Princeton, NJ 08543-2053
Ph: 800-257-5126
Fax: (609)671-0266
Fr: 800-468-4227
E-mail: custserv@films.com
URL: http://cambridge.films.com

VHS and DVD. $89.95. 2007. 11 minutes. Program illustrates how to relate interests, skills, education, training, values, and lifestyle to specific occupations in the world of work.

13484 ■ Career Exploration: You're in the Driver's Seat
Cambridge Educational
PO Box 2053
Princeton, NJ 08543-2053
Ph: 800-257-5126
Fax: (609)671-0266
Fr: 800-468-4227
E-mail: custserv@films.com
URL: http://cambridge.films.com

VHS and DVD. $199.90. Covers mapping your career plan and tracking your interests and abilities.

13485 ■ Choices Today for Career Satisfaction Tomorrow
Cambridge Educational
PO Box 2053
Princeton, NJ 08543-2053
Ph: 800-257-5126
Fax: (609)671-0266
Fr: 800-468-4227
E-mail: custserv@films.com
URL: http://cambridge.films.com

VHS and DVD. $239.85. 30 minutes. Includes student/teacher manual. Topics covered are preparing for an occupation, investigating the world of work, and self-awareness.

13486 ■ The Complete Career Cluster
Cambridge Educational
PO Box 2053
Princeton, NJ 08543-2053
Ph: 800-257-5126
Fax: (609)671-0266
Fr: 800-468-4227
E-mail: custserv@films.com
URL: http://cambridge.films.com/id/13211/The_
   Complete_Career_Clusters.htm

VHS and DVD. $1,599.20. 2007. Covering 16 broad occupational categories, the Career Clusters system offers information on practically every job there is.

13487 ■ The Complete Job Search System
Cambridge Educational
PO Box 2053
Princeton, NJ 08543-2053
Ph: 800-257-5126
Fax: (609)671-0266
Fr: 800-468-4227
E-mail: custserv@films.com
URL: http://cambridge.films.com

VHS and DVD. 2007. $499.75. Individual titles cover career planning, career evaluation, finding a job, interviewing for a job, and succeeding on the job.

13488 ■ From Pink Slip to Paycheck Series: The Road to Reemployment
JIST Publishing
875 Montreal Way
St. Paul, MN 55102
Fax: 800-547-8329
Fr: 800-648-5478
E-mail: info@jist.com
URL: http://www.jist.com/shop/
   product.php?productid=3456

$549. 15 minutes. Five-video series produced especially for adult career changers, covering all essential job search topics: coping with job loss, planning the job search, networking, resumes, cover letters, and interviewing.

13489 ■ The Job Search
JIST Publishing
875 Montreal Way
St. Paul, MN 55102
Fr: 800-648-5478
E-mail: info@jist.com
URL: http://www.jist.com

2009. $129. 25 minutes. Covers ways to find job openings including contacting employers directly, posting resumes online, and using a network of contacts. Provides job search techniques and how to create a job search plan for every situation.

13490 ■ Job-Seeking Skills for Young People (DVD)
Impact Publications
9104 Manassas Dr., Ste. N
Manassas Park, VA 20111
Ph: (703)361-7300
Fax: (703)335-9486
URL: http://www.impactpublications.com

2009. $129.95. 27 minutes. Examines technology-based tools to help young job-seekers and the skills necessary to make those tools work. Includes guide on how to access the "hidden job" market through personal networking, usage of four main styles of the resume, advantages of mock interviews and the STAR system.

13491 ■ The National Job Bank
Adams Media
4700 E Galbraith Rd.
Cincinnati, OH 45236
Fr: (855)278-0402
URL: http://www.adamsmediastore.com

CD-ROM. 2011. $250.00. Includes company profiles of more than 20,000 employers throughout the United States. Features proven cover letters and resume samples.

13492 ■ The Real Work Begins
JIST Publishing
875 Montreal Way
St. Paul, MN 55102
Fr: 800-648-5478
E-mail: info@jist.com
URL: http://www.jist.com

2009. $129. 25 minutes. Teaches viewers how to keep the jobs they find and establish themselves as valuable employees in the workplace. Presents the do's and don'ts of on-the-job success as well as how to exceed an employer's expectations.

13493 ■ The Right Job for You
JIST Publishing
875 Montreal Way
St. Paul, MN 55102
Fr: 800-648-5478
E-mail: info@jist.com
URL: http://www.jist.com

2009. $129. 25 minutes. Teaches viewers to set short and long term goals, methods for researching job objectives that fit their skills and interests, and develop a career plan for achieving these goals.

13494 ■ *Secrets to Job Fair Success*
JIST Publishing
875 Montreal Way
St. Paul, MN 55102
Fr: 800-648-5478
E-mail: info@jist.com
URL: http://www.jist.com

2007. $129. 23 minutes. Covers job fair related topics such as preparing for the job fair, presenting yourself and what to bring, possible interview questions, networking advice, and advice from employers.

13495 ■ *The Very Quick Job Search Video, Revised Edition*
JIST Publishing
875 Montreal Way
St. Paul, MN 55102
Fr: 800-648-5478
URL: http://www.jist.com

Michael Farr. 2007. $159 (VHS), $149 (DVD). 35 minutes. Video overview of results-oriented self-directed job search techniques.

13496 ■ *The Video Guide to Occupational Exploration*
Cambridge Educational
PO Box 2053
Princeton, NJ 08543-2053
Ph: 800-257-5126
Fax: (609)671-0266
Fr: 800-468-4227
E-mail: custserv@films.com
URL: http://cambridge.films.com

VHS and DVD. $1,119.30. 14 video programs covering each occupational cluster. Organized according to the 12 interest areas developed by the U.S. Department of Labor.

13497 ■ *Vocational Visions Career Series*
Cambridge Educational
PO Box 2053
Princeton, NJ 08543-2053
Ph: 800-257-5126
Fax: (609)671-0266
Fr: 800-468-4227
E-mail: custserv@films.com
URL: http://cambridge.films.com/id/2166/Vocational_Visions_Career_Series.htm

VHS and DVD. 10 videos. $499.50. 15 minutes each. Topics include auto mechanic, band director, florist, park ranger, potter, chef, insurance agent, physical therapist, letter carrier, and paralegal.

13498 ■ *The World of Work*
JIST Publishing
875 Montreal Way
St. Paul, MN 55102
Fr: 800-648-5478
E-mail: info@jist.com
URL: http://www.jist.com

2009. $129. 25 minutes. Teaches viewers to recognize what they need from a job and what they have to offer an employer. Features tips for budgeting time and money, identifying job skills, and seeing through the eyes of an employer.

ONLINE AND DATABASE SERVICES

13499 ■ 2aJobGuide.com
E-mail: oswaldep@2ajobguide.com
URL: http://2ajobguide.com

Description: Works as a career assistant and career information guide. Provides resume resources, cover letters, and interview guidelines. Features links to venture capital and personal loans to start a business.

13500 ■ 4Jobs.com
URL: http://www.4jobs.com

Description: Lists available job openings from coast to coast. Offers a variety of career resources for individuals who wish to foster their professional growth.

13501 ■ AllStarJobs.com
URL: http://www.allstarjobs.com

Description: Provides online career resources for job seekers such as job boards, employment agencies, resumes sites, and career sections on employer websites.

13502 ■ America's Job Exchange
URL: http://www.americasjobexchange.com

Description: Seeks to provide everyday Americans with the job opportunities and career tools to find their dream careers. Specializes in non-executive jobs.

13503 ■ AppleOne.com
Fr: 800-564-5644
URL: http://www.appleone.com

Description: Search site with job databank, resume posting and online e-newsletter subscriptions. Applicants can also interview with prospective employers online. Registration is free.

13504 ■ The Career Czar
URL: http://www.careerczar.com

Description: Internet talk radio show that provides career advice, planning, and coaching.

13505 ■ Career.com
URL: http://www.career.com

Description: Users can perform job searches by company, location, discipline, and for new graduates. Other features include "Hot Jobs," CyberFair, and a resume save option.

13506 ■ CareerExposure.com
URL: http://careerexposure.com

Description: Serves as the general portal of the career network offering opportunities for college graduates to top C-level executives.

13507 ■ careerlink.com
URL: http://careerlink.com

Description: Serves as a career portal that features resume postings, job searches, upcoming career fairs, and related links.

13508 ■ CareerMag.com
URL: http://www.careermag.com

Description: Online magazine containing many columns, features and articles about job hunting. Also holds job listings for browsers. Main files include: Job Openings, Employers, Articles, Resume Bank, Career Forum, On Campus, Diversity, Be Your Own Boss, Job Fairs, Recruiter Directory, Consultant Directory, Products & Services, Relocation Resources, Career Links, Post Your Jobs. Has information section for self-employed and freelance workers.

13509 ■ CareerOneStop.org
Ph: 877-348-0502
E-mail: info@careeronestop.org
URL: http://www.careeronestop.org

Description: Career resources. Job seekers can post their resume and search for job openings.

13510 ■ CareerOverview.com
URL: http://www.careeroverview.com

Description: Assists aspiring career professionals, job seekers and students to make better and more informed career choices by providing them with relevant, reliable and up-to-date career and job information.

13511 ■ CareerPerfect.com
URL: http://www.careerperfect.com

Description: Provides links to career software and books; lists FAQ's on career planning, resumes, job searching, and interviewing; identifies online job databases; accepts resumes for posting.

13512 ■ CareersInFood.com
E-mail: cif@careersinfood.com
URL: http://www.careersinfood.com

Description: Serves as a job board for professionals in the food and beverage manufacturing industries. Features advertising opportunities, food/beverage companies, and other industry resources.

13513 ■ Careers.org
URL: http://www.careers.org

Description: Provides career resources, career guides, online education resources, and directories. Contains detailed information on over 1000 career occupations including wages, skills required, as well as links to colleges offering such training.

13514 ■ CareerTV.com
URL: http://careertv.com

Description: Functions as an internet and social media company specializing in streaming employer branding and career videos across the web.

13515 ■ CareerZing.com
E-mail: contact@careerzing.com
URL: http://www.careerzing.com

Description: Features a compilation of interviews with professionals in fields like marine biology, journalism, graphic design, architecture, writing, and teaching. Contains articles about building experience as well as links to more career resources.

13516 ■ Carousel Expo
URL: http://www.carouselexpo.com

Description: Serves as a job fair directory that lists job fairs, career fairs, and recruiters' open house in each state.

13517 ■ CollegeGrad.com
URL: http://www.collegegrad.com

Description: Site contains the online version of the College Grad Job Hunter-an entry level job search book. Main files include: Preparation, Resumes and Cover Letters, Job Postings, Interviews and Negotiations, New Job. Employers may also search for candidates fitting positions.

13518 ■ DiversityJobFairs.com
URL: http://www.diversityjobfairs.com

Description: Features a job search board, resume postings, and lists of career fairs.

13519 ■ EmploymentGuide.com
URL: http://www.employmentguide.com

Description: Serves as a job board that focuses on hourly and skilled full-time and part-time jobs, from entry-level to mid-management employment opportunities. Features local and online job fairs, college degree programs, training courses, and other resources for job seekers.

13520 ■ FindJobUSA
URL: http://www.findjobusa.com

Description: Features job listings, resume postings, recruitment services, and other career resources. Provides advice on writing resumes, proper dressing for an interview, how to behave and what to say during a job interview, and how to answer tough questions.

13521 ■ First Steps in the Hunt: Daily News for Online Job Hunters
E-mail: colleen@interbiznet.com
URL: http://www.interbiznet.com/hunt/index.html

Description: Database provides a wide variety of information on job hunting on the Internet, as well as links to other sources of information. Included are examples of online web page resumes and links to information about publishing them. Also includes current and archived articles, company job sites, and a listing of job hunting tools and products that may help in the job search. Main files include: Sponsors; Tools; Archives; Products; and Info.

13522 ■ FlipDog.com
URL: http://www.flipdog.com

Description: A Monster.com web site. Job search site with job board, resume posting, automated job finders with e-mail alert, resume coaching and broadcasting, career resource center and semimonthly newsletter. Registration is free.

13523 ■ Glassdoor.com
URL: http://www.glassdoor.com

Description: Serves as a clearinghouse for individuals seeking positions in various industries. Features salary information by company or by city, company reviews, interview questions by industry, and jobs by title, company, or by city.

13524 ■ Job-Hunt.org
URL: http://www.job-hunt.org

Description: Provides lists of resources and services for job hunting on the web. Lists job sites where job hunters can search for a job or leave a copy of their resume. Also lists sites that provide information/support in the job search process.

13525 ■ Jobalot.com
URL: http://www.jobalot.com

Description: Functions as a vertical search engine of various job opportunities from job boards and employers of various industries.

13526 ■ JobCentral.com
URL: http://www.jobcentral.com

Description: Serves as a direct employers job search engine for different industries and areas of interest.

13527 ■ Job.com
E-mail: jobseekersupport@job.com
URL: http://jobs.com

Description: Seekers can post resumes, search through job databank and use website "powertools" such as resume coaching and distribution, career direction report, personal salary report, online education and self-employment links, and more.

13528 ■ JobExpo.com
E-mail: jobseeker@jobexpo.com
URL: http://www.jobexpo.com

Description: Matches job seekers with employers who best match their skills and capabilities. Facilitates match ups in various fields such as professional sales, marketing, management, finance, telecommunication, healthcare, customer service, and information technology.

13529 ■ JobisJob.com
URL: http://www.jobisjob.com

Description: Works as a search engine for all job categories.

13530 ■ JobKeg.com
URL: http://www.jobkeg.com/a/jobs/find-jobs

Description: Serves as a search tool for the career-minded. Researches and filters employment listings and postings from employment websites and government agencies.

13531 ■ JobRadio.fm
URL: http://jobradio.fm

Description: Features career advice and jobcasts.

13532 ■ Jobs Careers 24
URL: http://www.jobscareers24.com

Description: Serves as a job search engine providing employment opportunities for various industries.

Provides access to job opportunities across different job boards.

13533 ■ JobSearchPage.com
E-mail: info@jobsearchpage.com
URL: http://www.jobsearchpage.com

Description: Serves as career-based search engine allowing job seekers to locate and apply for jobs from various fields and specialties. Lists niche job boards.

13534 ■ JobStar.org
E-mail: electrajobstar@earthlink.net
URL: http://jobstar.org

Description: Job search guide based in California. Includes career guides and information on local, national and international career counseling centers, resumes, salaries, and hidden jobs.

13535 ■ MBAcareers.com
URL: http://mbacareers.com

Description: Serves the Master of Business Administration (MBA) recruiting marketplace. Features C-level, executive and MBA jobs, MBA resume bank, job bank, post MBA jobs, and more.

13536 ■ MonsterTRAK
URL: http://college.monster.com/?wt.mc_
n=monstertrak

Description: College-targeted job hunting and recruiting site. Students and alumni may enter a user profile or resume to be reviewed by potential employers, or search job listings without doing so. Employers may enter full-time, part-time, temporary, and internship opportunities into the database to be reviewed by students and recent graduates, and may review resumes.

13537 ■ MyCareerSpace.com
E-mail: customersupport@mycareerspace.com
URL: http://mycareerspace.com

Description: Provides local and international jobs for various industries and specializations. Features relocation tools, career expos, resume services, and other career related resources.

13538 ■ NACElink Network
URL: http://www2.nacelink.com

Description: Works as a national recruiting network. Features web based recruiting and career services automation tools that serve the needs of colleges, employers, and job candidates.

13539 ■ National Career Fairs
URL: http://www.nationalcareerfairs.com

Description: Features various job openings and career fairs, career advice, tips on salary negotiation, interviewing skills, and networking.

13540 ■ NYU Stern School of Business
E-mail: ocd@stern.nyu.edu
URL: http://www.stern.nyu.edu

Description: Office of Career Development section of website provides career resources for business graduates, along with resume databases arranged by classes. Many resources restricted to Stern students and alumni.

13541 ■ PayScale, Inc.
E-mail: service@payscale.com
URL: http://www.payscale.com

Online resource provides detailed information concerning salary, vacation time, bonuses and commute time. Also gives tips for salary negotiation and career planning.

13542 ■ PhDs.org
URL: http://www.phds.org

Description: Provides job opportunities for the following PhD fields: life sciences, physical sciences, math, engineering, computer science, business,

finance, economic, social sciences, humanities, and education.

13543 ■ Placement USA
URL: http://www.placementusa.com

Description: Serves as an online job board and career resource for various industries and specialties. Features an automated system that allows users to create a personalized resume.

13544 ■ PlusJobs America
URL: http://www.us.plusjobs.com

Description: Serves as a clearinghouse for individuals seeking positions in various fields and industries.

13545 ■ Quintessential Careers
E-mail: randall@quintcareers.com
URL: http://www.quintcareers.com

Description: Job search mega-site that links to several job boards, provides information on every step of the job search process, and offers additional information on earning advanced degrees and certificates to increase one's value as a professional.

13546 ■ Recruiters Online Network
E-mail: recruitersonline@earthlink.net
URL: http://www.recruitersonline.com

Description: Site is used by over 8,000 recruiters, search firms, employment agencies, and employment professionals. Job seekers may read the Careers Online magazine, post resumes, and search jobs. Fee: Free to job seekers; fee for recruiters.

13547 ■ ResumeRobot.com
URL: http://www.resumerobot.com

Description: Helps in the process of passive searching and finding potential candidates who may not be listed on job boards or resume sites, but who may be open to new opportunities and are eager to hear proposals.

13548 ■ The Riley Guide
11218 Ashley Dr.
Rockville, MD 20852
Ph: (240)602-6043
E-mail: margaret@rileyguide.com
URL: http://www.rileyguide.com

Description: Job search portal site. Also contains resources on writing and distributing resumes, targeting employers, interviewing, salary negotiations and more.

13549 ■ Staffinglinks
E-mail: staff@staffinglinks.com
URL: http://www.staffinglinks.com

Description: Provides links to job search and career information. Features jobs, employment, interview tips, resumes, and other career resources.

13550 ■ Tech-centric.net
URL: http://www.tech-centric.net

Description: Serves as a job board for technology professionals. Enables job seekers to search for jobs locally or internationally and pinpoint the jobs that suit them based on keywords, skills, location, and information technology experience.

13551 ■ Top of Job Board
URL: http://1jobboard.com

Description: Features information about job vacancies, career opportunities, cover letters, resumes, letters of appreciation, letters of recommendation, curriculum vitae, and job interviews.

13552 ■ VolunteerCrossing.com
URL: http://www.volunteercrossing.com

Description: Provides lists of all available volunteer job openings across employer career webpages, job boards, organization's websites, newspaper classifieds and recruiter sites.

13553 ■ What Color Is Your Parachute? Job Hunters Bible
URL: http://www.jobhuntersbible.com

Description: Companion internet guide to the job-hunting book, What Color is Your Parachute? Includes lists of helpful links to other resources on the internet. Main files include: Jobs, Resumes, Counseling, Contacts, Research, Dealing With Depression.

13554 ■ Yahoo! Careers
701 1st Ave.
Sunnyvale, CA 94089
URL: http://us.careers.yahoo.com

Description: Contains over 360,000 jobs for job seekers to search and post resumes for, as well as weekly features, relocation resources, a daily column, and links to resume banks and services and temp agencies. Special sections are devoted to industry research, company research, advice, high tech jobs, and first jobs and internships.

SOFTWARE

13555 ■ CareerExplorer CD-ROM, Version 3.0
JIST Publishing
875 Montreal Way
St. Paul, MN 55102
Fax: 800-547-8329
Fr: 800-648-5478
E-mail: info@jist.com
URL: http://www.jist.com

2004. $295. Users can indicate their interests and get a list of the best 20 occupational matches in about 20 minutes.

13556 ■ PG Job Site Pro
PilotGroup Ltd.
5758 Yerington Ave.
Las Vegas, NV 89110
Fr: (866)620-1919
URL: http://www.jobsoftpro.com

Web-based software. $859 (one domain open source license with all modules), $679 (one domain basic license with all modules), $499 (one domain open source license without all modules), $299 (one domain basic license without all modules). Allows users to build a high-availability, user-friendly, commercial or free job board that can either be integrated with an existing web site or designed as a standal-one job board. Includes advanced management tools for both job seekers and employers.

OTHER SOURCES

13557 ■ Ady & Associates
115 N Neil St., Ste. 216
Champaign, IL 61820-4086
Ph: (217)359-8080
Fax: (217)359-8082

Personnel consulting firm provides outplacement and career management services, employee and applicant assessment, and general human resource consulting. Additional expertise available in staffing and employment strategy, employee and organization development, plus effective employee communications programs. Industries served: All.

13558 ■ Allied Search Inc.
2030 Union St., Ste. 206
PO Box 472410
San Francisco, CA 94123
Ph: (415)921-2200
Fax: (415)921-3900
E-mail: donmay@alliedsearchinc.com
URL: http://www.alliedsearchinc.com

Executive search firm which will search, locate, recruit, and place the very best professionals and executives with client companies nationwide.

13559 ■ Amansco Inc.
606 Liberty Ave., Ste. 201
Pittsburgh, PA 15222-3412
Ph: (412)281-5766
Fax: (412)281-5184
Fr: 800-245-1909
E-mail: adroom@bellrecruit.com
URL: http://www.belladvertisingservice.com

Executive search consultants active in all industries on worldwide basis.

13560 ■ Career Connections
934 Dunlap St.
PO Box 9331
Santa Fe, NM 87501
Ph: (505)983-9217
Fax: (505)983-8483
E-mail: barbaraconroy@earthlink.net

Provides individualized guidance in career planning, including job search strategies, assessment, goal-setting and networking strategies. Tailored networking techniques and strategies are employed to achieve specific aims. Ongoing support services include life/work coaching and consultations.

13561 ■ Career Management Alliance
1 Phoenix Mill Ln., Fl. 3
Peterborough, NH 03458
Ph: (603)924-1006
Fax: (603)924-4034
Fr: 800-531-0007
URL: http://www.careermanagementalliance.com

Description: Represents all sectors of the careers industry - career coaching, career counseling, resume writing, outplacement, college and university career development, government and military career transition, and human resources. Works to enhance professional talents to better serve individuals managing their careers and organizations managing their talents while strengthening the visibility and credibility of the entire careers industry.

13562 ■ Career Path
1240 Iroquois Ave., Ste. 100
Naperville, IL 60563
Ph: (630)369-3390
URL: http://www.career-path.info

Career planning consultants offering counseling in such areas as career development, career transition, and team building.

13563 ■ Clear Rock Inc.
Regus Business Ctr., 225 Franklin St., 26th Fl.
Boston, MA 02110
Ph: (617)217-2811
Fax: (617)217-2001
E-mail: info@clearrock.com

Focuses on executive and career development with an emphasis on coaching and outplacement. Approach focuses on individuals leadership, style, interpersonal relationships, career strategy, finances, stress, health and life balance.

13564 ■ First Transitions Inc.
1211 W 22nd St., Ste. 1006
Oak Brook, IL 60523
Ph: (630)571-3311
Fax: (630)571-5714
Fr: 800-358-1112
E-mail: admin@firsttransitions.com
URL: http://www.firsttransitions.com

Provides corporate sponsored career transition services. Firm offers executive coaching, executive assessment and evaluation, organizational career development, 360 degree evaluations and leadership assessment.

13565 ■ FREEdLANCE Group for Career & Workforce Innovation
1100 Washington Ave., Ste. 213
Carnegie, PA 15106
Ph: (412)429-7650
Fax: (412)429-7651

Fr: 877-937-6638
E-mail: info@freedlance.com

Specialized expertise in career and workforce development. Best practices and research-based innovations. Innovative stakeholder data accumulation, evaluation and analysis. Formal research methods or models and administration of testing, assessment and career case management systems; grant writing; contextual curriculum development and training, including career development facilitator certification training; independent pre and post testing; formal program evaluations; technological interventions.

13566 ■ Hill & Hill Consulting Inc.
12035 Cooperwood Ln.
Cincinnati, OH 45242
Ph: (513)984-8448
Fax: (513)856-5916

A career or life planning consulting firm specializing in helping persons to make successful career transitions and/or enhance their career. Clients include: associations, corporations, higher education and persons from diverse professions.

13567 ■ Institute for Urban Family Health
16 E 16th St.
New York, NY 10003
Ph: (212)633-0800
Fax: (212)691-4610
E-mail: info@institute2000.org
URL: http://www.institute2000.org

Services in organization development, recruitment and retention, training and career development, diversity initiatives and performance management.

13568 ■ J. Philip Associates Inc.
2120 Wilshire Blvd., Ste. 310
Santa Monica, CA 90403-5708
Ph: (310)453-7700
Fax: (310)453-4660
Fr: 877-925-5446
E-mail: info@allignteam.com
URL: http://www.allignteam.com

Firm specializes in business solutions, search and recruitment services, executive search, hire recruitment campaigns, outsourcing or development of internal recruitment organizations and retention programs. Developer of ALLIGN business program tool.

13569 ■ Job Search CD Series
JIST Publishing
875 Montreal Way
St. Paul, MN 55102
Fr: 800-648-5478
E-mail: info@jist.com
URL: http://www.jist.com/shop/web

$799. Each CD is focused on a particular skill needed for a successful job search.

13570 ■ The Murdock Group Holding Corp.
4084 South 300 West
Salt Lake City, UT 84107
Ph: (801)268-3232
Fax: (801)268-3289
Fr: 888-888-0892
E-mail: info@themurdockgroup.com

Specializes in providing full service career services and seminars for individuals and companies, including out-placements, 'The Hiring Series' and career expos.

13571 ■ Norma Zuber and Associates
3585 Maple St., Ste. 237
Ventura, CA 93003-9504
Ph: (805)656-6220
Fax: (805)654-1523
E-mail: nzubercdlp@msn.com
URL: http://www.normazubercareers.com

Counselor/consultant offers formal assessment, evaluation and private counseling to individuals to discover their unique personal characteristics and potentials. This is done by combining self-understanding and an understanding of the world of work through personal assessment and occupational and educational exploration. Services provide an individualized career profile developed in order to help one make appropriate and satisfying career choices or changes at any age. Provides services to business and industry for staff development and team building. Serves clients located in central California.

13572 ■ One Source Managed Solutions Inc.
1 Hollycrest Dr.
Brick, NJ 08723
Ph: (732)451-0035
Fax: (775)295-7475
E-mail: info@onesourcemanaged.com
URL: http://www.onesourcemanaged.com

A management consulting firm specializing in contract recruiting, executive search, contingency search.

13573 ■ Reaction Search International Inc.
2682 Bishop Dr., Ste. 208
San Ramon, CA 94583
Ph: (925)275-0727
Fr: 800-832-8268
E-mail: info@reactionsearch.com
URL: http://www.reactionsearch.com

Executive recruiters specializing in search, assessment, selection processes and employer services. Provides custom-designed staffing searches and arrangements render us a preferred provider of executive search services.

13574 ■ R.L. Stevens & Associates Inc.
800 South St., Ste. 295
Waltham, MA 02453
Ph: (781)647-4888
Fax: (781)647-2878
Fr: 800-721-9491
E-mail: jridge@rlstevens.com
URL: http://www.rlstevens.com

A career management firm that specializes in career marketing and outplacement.

13575 ■ RO-LAN Associates Inc.
725 Sabattus St.
Lewiston, ME 04240
Ph: (207)784-1010
Fax: (207)782-3446
E-mail: rlapointe@aol.com

Professional placement specialists for permanent and temporary positions. Also offers executive search and recruiting expertise, outplacements, complete resume

service, new business consulting and job and career transition coaching.

13576 ■ Sociometrics Corp.
170 State St., Ste. 260
Los Altos, CA 94022-2827
Ph: (650)949-3282
Fax: (650)949-3299
E-mail: socio@socio.com
URL: http://www.socio.com

Consulting firm offering program evaluation, needs assessment, personnel services and technical assistance and training. Company serves government and private industries worldwide.

13577 ■ TWC Group
2570 Blvd. of the Generals, Ste. 110
Audubon, PA 19403
Ph: (610)635-0101
Fax: (610)635-0304
Fr: (866)892-1500
E-mail: info@twcgroup.com
URL: http://www.twcgroup.com

Provides complete recruitment and HR outsourcing services that enable companies to build competitive advantage through workforce recruitment and retention.

REFERENCE WORKS

13578 ■ 5 Necessary Skills To Keep Your Career On Track
Outskirts Press, Inc.
10940 S Parker Rd., No. 515
Parker, CO 80134
Fr: 888-672-6657
E-mail: info@outskirtspress.com
URL: http://www.outskirtspress.com

Richard S. Pearson. 2009. $15.95 (paper). 224 pages. Covers topics on creating the right mindset in maintaining continuous employment; ability to adapt and change; and communication skills. Teaches readers how to be proactive and cognizant; the importance of networking and finding a mentor; and how to deal with bad bosses.

13579 ■ Best Answers to 202 Job Interview Questions
JIST Publishing
875 Montreal Way
St. Paul, MN 55102
Fr: 800-648-5478
E-mail: educate@emcp.com
URL: http://www.jist.com

Daniel Porot and Frances Bolles Haynes. 2007. $17.95 (softcover). 238 pages. Contains interview questions, sample answers, checklists of do's and don'ts, and a mini quiz to help readers understand why some answers are better than others. Help users learn what type of answers interviewers are really looking for when they ask a particular question.

13580 ■ The Career Adventure: Your Guide to Personal Assessment, Career Exploration, and Decision Making
Prentice Hall
1 Lake St.
Upper Saddle River, NJ 07458
Fr: 800-922-0579
URL: http://www.prenticehall.com

Susan M. Johnston. $33.40 (4th ed.). 240 pages. Covers career planning in a step-by-step process of self-assessment and decision making. Offers expanded use of electronic and internet resources, an update of Maslow's Hierarchy, and a new perspective on decision making.

13581 ■ Career, Aptitude and Selection Tests: Match Your IQ, Personality and Abilities to Your Ideal Career
Kogan Page Publishers
1518 Walnut St., Ste. 1100
Philadelphia, PA 19102
Ph: (215)928-9112
Fax: (215)928-9113
E-mail: info@koganpage.com
URL: http://www.koganpageusa.com

Jim Barrett. 2009. $17.95 (3rd ed.). 192 pages. Covers career guidance, preparation and personal performance improvement. Features IQ tests and questionnaires to help job-seekers identify strengths and scientifically interpret the jobs best suited for them. Also provides an opportunity to prepare for the types of psychometric, or aptitude, tests likely to be encountered during the job search.

13582 ■ Career Flow: A Hope-Centered Approach to Career Development
Prentice Hall
c/o Pearson Education, Inc.
One Lake St.
Upper Saddle River, NJ 07458
URL: http://www.pearsonhighered.com

Spencer G. Niles, Norman E. Amundson and Roberta Neault. 2010. $37.80 (paper). 264 pages. Presents creative, innovative, and useful strategies for addressing career challenges.

13583 ■ Career Match
AMACOM Publishing
c/o American Management Association
1601 Broadway
New York, NY 10019-7434
Ph: (212)586-8100
Fr: 800-714-6395
E-mail: pubs_cust_serv@amanet.org
URL: http://www.amacombooks.org

Shoya Zichy and Ann Bidou. 2007. $15.00 (paper/softback). 256 pages. Contains a ten-minute self-assessment test that helps readers determine their personality style and discover a range of career choices that best fit them. Includes chapters for each personality type, explanations of career options and real-life stories of people who have found fulfillment in a job that suits their personality.

13584 ■ The Career Within You
HarperCollins Publishers
10 E 53rd St.
New York, NY 10022
Ph: (212)207-7000
URL: http://www.harpercollins.com

Elizabeth Wagele and Ingrid Stabb. 2009. $17.99 (paper). 368 pages. Helps individuals determine the career type and forge the career path that suits their personality.

13585 ■ Effective Immediately
Ten Speed Press
6001 Shellmound St.
Emeryville, CA 94608
Ph: (510)285-3000
Fax: (510)285-2979
URL: http://www.randomhouse.com

Emily Bennington and Skip Lineberg. 2010. $14.99 (paper). Teaches readers how to excel at their first job and boost their careers. Serves as a guide on how to transform an individual from entry-level employee into a skilled and invaluable professional.

13586 ■ Employment Personality Tests Decoded
Career Press
220 West Pkwy., Unit 12
Pompton Plains, NJ 07444
Ph: (201)848-0310
Fax: (201)848-1727
Fr: 800-227-3371
E-mail: sales@careerpress.com
URL: http://www.careerpress.com

Anne Hart and George Sheldon. 2007. $16.99 (paper). 216 pages. Features details on why corporations require personality tests and how to prepare for them. Teaches readers how to solve problems, get results, and simplify answers for clarity.

13587 ■ The Everything Career Tests Book: 10 Tests to Determine the Right Occupation for You
Adams Media
4700 E Galbraith Rd.
Cincinnati, OH 45236
URL: http://www.adamsmediastore.com/product/the-everything-career-tests-book

A. Bronwyn Llewellyn. 2007. $10.36 (paper). 224 pages. Determines an individual's career path through ten different tests that reveal the work habits, affinities and interests of an individual. Features values test, skills test, interests test, personality test, work environment test, location test, work/life balance test, entrepreneurial ability test, managerial ability test and emotional intelligence test.

13588 ■ Get the Career you Want: A Teach Yourself Guide
McGraw-Hill Professional
c/o The McGraw-Hill Companies
PO Box 182604
Columbus, OH 43272
Fax: (614)759-3749
Fr: 877-833-5524
URL: http://www.mhprofessional.com

Karen Mannering. 2011. $15.00 (paperback). 208 pages. Helps candidates achieve their dream job.

13589 ■ I Want to Do Something Else, But I'm Not Sure What It Is: Find a Job That's Fit for You
9104 Manassas Dr., Ste. N
Manassas Park, VA 20111
Ph: (703)361-7300
Fax: (703)335-9486
URL: http://www.impactpublications.com/iwanttodosomethingelsebutimnotsurewhatitis.aspx

Ron and Caryl Krannich, Ph.Ds. 2005. $15.95. 208 pages. Provides a tool kit for determining what one should do in his or her next stage in life. Includes self-assessment devices, online assistance, a directory of community resources and an action plan for landing a new job based on a clear sense of purpose and a pattern of accomplishments.

13590 ■ Information Technology: Field Guides to Finding a New Career Set, 20-Volumes
Facts On File
132 W 31st St., 17th Fl.
New York, NY 10001
Fax: 800-678-3633
Fr: 800-322-8755
E-mail: custserv@factsonfile.com
URL: http://factsonfile.infobasepublishing.com
Amanda Kirk. 2009. $39.95 (hardcover). 152 pages. Provides readers with the tools necessary to take their career in a new direction in the information technology field. Features tips and advice for career changers looking to navigate their way into a career in information technology. Offers interviews with professionals working in the field, self-assessment questions, and more.

13591 ■ IQ and Aptitude Tests
Kogan Page Publishers
1518 Walnut St., Ste. 1100
Philadelphia, PA 19102
Ph: (215)928-9112
Fax: (215)928-9113
E-mail: info@koganpage.com
URL: http://www.koganpageusa.com
Philip Carter. 2011. $14.95 (paper). 224 pages. Contains practice questions with answers, explanations, and a guide to assessing performance. Provides questions that are organized into four IQ tests together with verbal, spatial, and numerical aptitude tests. Includes tests of word meanings, grammar and comprehension, advanced verbal aptitude, logical analysis, mental arithmetic, numerical sequences, and number problems.

13592 ■ The Other Kind of Smart
AMACOM Publishing
c/o American Management Association
1601 Broadway
New York, NY 10019-7434
Ph: (212)586-8100
Fax: (518)891-0368
Fr: 800-714-6395
E-mail: pubs_cust_serv@amanet.org
URL: http://www.amacombooks.org
Harvey Deutschendorf. 2009. $17.95 (paper/softback). 224 pages. Shows readers how to increase emotional intelligence and overcome the barriers that prevent realization of true potential. Offers tools that will bring results and shows how to develop stress tolerance, cultivate empathy, increase flexibility with co-workers, boost assertiveness, and resolve problems successfully.

13593 ■ The Pathfinder: How to Choose or Change Your Career for a Lifetime of Satisfaction and Success
Touchstone
c/o Simon & Schuster, Inc.
1230 Ave. of the Americas
New York, NY 10020
Ph: (212)698-7000
URL: http://www.simonandschuster.com
Nicholas Lore. 2012. $16.99 (paper). 448 pages. Guides professionals through the career transition process. Offers self-tests, diagnostic tools and career design methods to help professionals embark on a new career, entrepreneurial path or ideal job in the present field. Includes tips on landing a fitting job through personal marketing and networking.

13594 ■ Picture Interest Career Survey
JIST Publishing
875 Montreal Way
St. Paul, MN 55102
Fr: 800-648-5478
E-mail: educate@emcp.com
URL: http://www.jist.com
Robert P. Brady. 2011. $46.95. Helps people with limited reading ability or special needs to explore their career interests and find a job that fits. Enables people to identify occupational interests by using pictures of people at work rather than text-based items. Includes streamlined instructions, an updated design, some modified pictures for greater clarity, and expanded validity information.

13595 ■ Reinvention: How to Make the Rest of Your Life the Best of Your Life
AMACOM Publishing
c/o American Management Association
1601 Broadway
New York, NY 10019-7434
Ph: (212)586-8100
Fax: (518)891-0368
Fr: 800-714-6395
E-mail: pubs_cust_serv@amanet.org
URL: http://www.amacombooks.org
Brian Tracy. 2009. $21.95 (hardback). 224 pages. Provides readers with a series of exercises they can use to focus on what they really want for themselves such as taking control of their careers; turning unexpected shakeups and turbulence into positive occasions for growth; improving earning ability; developing the self-confidence to take the kind of risks that lead to rapid advancement; deciding on and getting the job they really want; setting goals for their lives; writing resumes and getting results; and determining salary range.

13596 ■ Writing your NSPS Self-Assessment, Second Edition
The Resume Place, Inc.
89 Mellor Ave.
Baltimore, MD 21228
Ph: (410)744-4324
Fax: (410)744-0112
Fr: 888-480-8265
E-mail: resume@resume-place.com
URL: http://www.resume-place.com
Kathryn K. Troutman and Nancy H. Segal. 2009. $28.95 (softcover). 186 pages. Serves as a guide to writing accomplishments for the Department of Defense employees and supervisors. Includes an appendix that details four complete NSPS self-assessment samples.

NEWSPAPERS, MAGAZINES, AND JOURNALS

13597 ■ Journal of Career Assessment
Sage Publications
2455 Teller Rd.
Thousand Oaks, CA 91320
Ph: (805)499-9774
Fax: (805)499-0871
Fr: 800-818-7243
E-mail: journals@sagepub.com
URL: http://jca.sagepub.com
Quarterly. Journal covers the various techniques, tests, inventories, rating scales, interview schedules, surveys and direct observational methods used in scientifically-based practice and research to provide an improved understanding of career decision-making.

AUDIO/VISUAL RESOURCES

13598 ■ The World of Work
JIST Publishing
875 Montreal Way
St. Paul, MN 55102
Fr: 800-648-5478
E-mail: info@jist.com
URL: http://www.jist.com
2009. $129. 25 minutes. Teaches viewers to recognize what they need from a job and what they have to offer an employer. Features tips for budgeting time and money, identifying job skills, and seeing through the eyes of an employer.

ONLINE AND DATABASE SERVICES

13599 ■ AnalyzeMyCareer.com
URL: http://www.analyzemycareer.com
Description: Serves as a career portal with services that assess an individual's personality, aptitude abilities and occupational interests. Provides career assessment tests that provide a rationale through which one can make informed career decisions that are based on the individual's talents, achievements, career interests and personality.

13600 ■ ArizonaMentor.org
E-mail: support@arizonamentor.org
URL: http://www.arizonamentor.org
Description: Student services website representing the colleges and universities of Arizona. Provides career assessment services that match jobs with the applicant's abilities and personality.

13601 ■ Brainbench.com
URL: http://www.brainbench.com
Description: Offers pre-employment testing, assessment and screening services and products, as well as employment screening and testing.

13602 ■ Career Assessment Center
URL: http://www.careerassessment.com
Description: Identifies an individual's personality traits that are most compatible with specific jobs as well structures and cultures of organizations that are more appropriate for specific personalities.

13603 ■ Career Gate Test
URL: http://www.careergatetest.com
Description: Provides a personal report which describes an individual's personality and points out the occupations that suit one's character.

13604 ■ The Career Key
URL: http://www.careerkey.org
Description: Provides a career test that matches the user's personality with the appropriate careers. Offers help with career options, career change, career search, job skills and choosing a college major or training program.

13605 ■ Career Liftoff
E-mail: info@careerliftoff.com
URL: http://www.careerliftoff.com
Description: Offers career planning and career guidance tools for job market and college students. Provides an on-line career assessment tool to assess career interests. Includes profile and narrative reports.

13606 ■ Career Success Center
URL: http://www.careersuccesscenter.com
Description: Provides employers with tools and services needed to post jobs, internships and volunteer opportunities. Provides job seekers with career advice, educational resources and job listings.

13607 ■ CareerEvolution.com
URL: http://www.careerevolution.com
Description: Offers tools for career acceleration, including an online career test that provides an instant in-depth personality overview showing strengths and career scores; detailed comparison reports in each career application that present actionable insights; and an online virtual career coaching program that helps improve one's weakest skills.

13608 ■ CareerFitter.com
URL: http://www.careerfitter.com
Description: Gives insights into what career an individual should pursue and how to operate best at work. Provides career tests that are designed by professionals to help individuals determine which personality profile they fit into.

13609 ■ CareerLeader.com
URL: http://www.careerleader.com

Description: Functions as a web-based assessment tool. Offers careers counseling and self assessment programs. Measures the user's interests, abilities and what he/she finds most motivating in work.

13610 ■ CareerMaze.com
URL: http://www.careermaze.com

Description: Provides users with an assessment of their vocational strengths and weaknesses, interests and capabilities.

13611 ■ CareerPlanner.com
URL: http://www.careerplanner.com

Description: Provides online career testing as well as information on life planning and finding the ideal career. Offers downloadable career guides that give tips on how to get the right interviews and land the right jobs.

13612 ■ Chico State Career Center
E-mail: careercenter@csuchico.edu
URL: http://www.csuchico.edu/careers

Description: Assists students and alumni through all phases of career development to bridge the transition between the academic environment and the world of work.

13613 ■ Dream Job Coaching
URL: http://www.dreamjobcoaching.com/resources/career-resources

Description: Focuses on helping people find the perfect job that aligns with their passions and natural talents. Provides simple tools for the evaluation of current levels of satisfaction and identification of the best approach to meet specific needs. Provides resources and links for job opportunities.

13614 ■ JobDiagnosis.com
E-mail: support@jobdiagnosis.com
URL: http://www.jobdiagnosis.com/registration.htm

Description: Offers a free career test that yields a complimentary job diagnosis that analyzes skills in terms of industry and job position. Includes industry matching, industry outlook, job position matching, job position outlook, report sent via email, unlimited access and job search access.

13615 ■ JVIS.com
URL: http://www.jvis.com

Description: Assists high school students, college students and adults with education and career planning. Uses multivariate statistical procedures and computer-based optimizing procedures for selection of students' vocational interests.

13616 ■ Keirsey Temperament Sorter and Temperament Web Site
E-mail: keirsey@orci.com
URL: http://www.keirsey.com

Description: Online personality questionnaire that identifies temperament and interest traits that may be applied towards career searches.

13617 ■ LiveCareer.com
URL: http://www.livecareer.com

Description: Career interest test designed to help make career decisions and to learn more about oneself. Includes career advice such as changing careers, choosing the right school, entrepreneurship, career snapshots and more. Specifically designed to be taken online.

13618 ■ MyPlan.com
URL: http://www.myplan.com

Description: Provides students and professionals an online resource for career and college information. Offers services including career profiles, career videos, salary data, college profiles and information on majors and degrees.

13619 ■ TestingRoom.com
URL: http://www.testingroom.com

Description: Provides online tests and profiling that help users discover careers that fit them and strategies toward achieving satisfaction in work and life. Offers tests that yield results on self-discovery such as career interest profiler, personality index and career values scale.

13620 ■ WomensCareerChannel.com
URL: http://womenscareerchannel.com

Description: Serves as a career site for women who are seeking employment opportunities. Offers jobs, resumes and career tools to help match users to the right career.

OTHER SOURCES

13621 ■ Career Assessment Goddess
6670 Crystal Lake Rd.
Three Lakes, WI 54562
Ph: (866)884-4055
E-mail: susan@assessmentgoddess.com
URL: http://www.assessmentgoddess.com

Description: Offers career assessment training and career counseling programs for individuals, entrepreneurs, career coaches and companies.

13622 ■ The Center for Professional Development
University of Hartford
50 Elizabeth St.
Hartford, CT 06105
Ph: (860)768-5619
E-mail: cpd@hartford.edu
URL: http://www.hartford.edu/cpd

Description: Enables individuals to identify and explore life choices and to empower them to attain their career goals through counseling, education, training and support.

13623 ■ MAPP Assessment
7400 Metro Blvd., Ste. 350
Edina, MN 55439
Ph: (952)921-9368
E-mail: info@assessment.com
URL: http://www.assessment.com

Description: Provides online assessment that seeks to guide, motivate and empower people to achieve their greatest educational and career potential.

REFERENCE WORKS

13624 ■ 5 Necessary Skills To Keep Your Career On Track
Outskirts Press, Inc.
10940 S Parker Rd., No. 515
Parker, CO 80134
Fr: 888-672-6657
E-mail: info@outskirtspress.com
URL: http://www.outskirtspress.com

Richard S. Pearson. 2009. $15.95 (paper). 224 pages. Covers topics on creating the right mindset in maintaining continuous employment; ability to adapt and change; and communication skills. Teaches readers how to be proactive and cognizant; the importance of networking and finding a mentor; and how to deal with bad bosses.

13625 ■ 12 Steps to a New Career: What to Do When You Want to Make a Change Now!
Career Press
220 West Pkwy., Unit 12
Pompton Plains, NJ 07444
Ph: (201)848-0310
Fax: (201)848-1727
Fr: 800-227-3371
E-mail: sales@careerpress.com
URL: http://www.careerpress.com

Carl J. Wellenstein. 2009. $16.99 (paper). 272 pages. Guides professionals through the process of job and career changes. Includes real-life examples and advice on suitable career options and navigation of the job market. Features techniques on effective communication, networking, and development of a strategic plan.

13626 ■ 30-Day Job Promotion
JIST Publishing
875 Montreal Way
St. Paul, MN 55102
Fr: 800-648-5478
E-mail: educate@emcp.com
URL: http://www.jist.com

Susan Britton Whitcomb. 2007. $8.95 (softcover). 208 pages. Gives experienced professionals and first-time workers insider strategies for standing out and demonstrating their value to employers. Features scripts and tips for asking for a promotion. Includes a discussion on career branding and advice for career success.

13627 ■ 100 Fastest-Growing Careers
JIST Publishing
875 Montreal Way
St. Paul, MN 55102
Fr: 800-648-5478
E-mail: educate@emcp.com
URL: http://www.jist.com

Michael Farr. 2010. $17.95 (softcover). 408 pages. Assists job seekers and students in finding everything they need to research fast-growing careers. Includes descriptions of 100 jobs alphabetically, the seven steps that cut job search time, sample targeted resumes by professional resume writers, and assessment matching skills.

13628 ■ 101 Best Ways to Land a Job in Troubled Times
McGraw-Hill Professional
c/o The McGraw-Hill Companies
PO Box 182604
Columbus, OH 43272
Fax: (614)759-3749
Fr: 877-833-5524
URL: http://www.mhprofessional.com

Jay A. Block. 2009. $14.95 (paperback). 208 pages. Helps approach job transition through a campaign of discovery in order to achieve career objectives.

13629 ■ 150 Best Jobs Through Military Training
JIST Publishing
875 Montreal Way
St. Paul, MN 55102
Fr: 800-648-5478
E-mail: educate@emcp.com
URL: http://www.jist.com

Laurence Shatkin. 2008. $19.95 (softcover). 432 pages. Focuses on the military jobs bridging to civilian careers. Covers military occupations and its civilian counterparts with detailed job descriptions. Contains lists that are organized by pay, growth, openings, part-time work, self-employment, gender, interest, and personality type. Includes lists of occupations held by veterans and the fields in which veterans work.

13630 ■ 150 Best Low-Stress Jobs
JIST Publishing
875 Montreal Way
St. Paul, MN 55102
Fr: 800-648-5478
E-mail: info@jist.com
URL: http://www.jist.com

Laurence Shatkin. 2008. $16.95 (softcover). 432 pages. Helps readers find job satisfaction through rewarding and low-stress work. Includes low-stress jobs that are ranked by stress factors and by pay, growth, openings, personality type, interests, education level, gender, age, part-time work, and self-employment.

13631 ■ 150 Best Recession-Proof Jobs
JIST Publishing
875 Montreal Way
St. Paul, MN 55102
Fr: 800-648-5478
E-mail: info@jist.com
URL: http://www.jist.com

Laurence Shatkin. 2009. $16.95 (softcover). 432 pages. Provides lists of recession-proof jobs by pay, growth, and openings and by education level, person-ality type, career clusters/interests, age, part-time work, and self-employment.

13632 ■ 200 Best Jobs for Introverts
JIST Publishing
875 Montreal Way
St. Paul, MN 55102
Fr: 800-648-5478
E-mail: info@jist.com
URL: http://www.jist.com

Laurence Shatkin. 2008. $8.47 (softcover). 432 pages. Includes 200 job descriptions that give details on jobs ranked by levels of quiet, solitary work, contact with others, autonomy, and direct contact with the public.

13633 ■ Career Comeback: Repackage Yourself to Get the Job You Want
Hachette Book Group
237 Park Ave.
New York, NY 10017
Fr: 800-759-0190
E-mail: privacy@hbgusa.com
URL: http://www.hachettebookgroup.com

Lisa Johnson Mandell. 2010. $24.99 (hardcover). 256 pages. Provides tips in seeking a career.

13634 ■ Career Coward's Guide to Changing Careers
JIST Publishing
875 Montreal Way
St. Paul, MN 55102
Fr: 800-648-5478
E-mail: educate@emcp.com
URL: http://www.jist.com

Katy Piotrowski. 2008. $10.95 (softcover). 240 pages. Features information on changing careers. Contains details on identifying several career options, making a choice about the best career, creating a career-change plan, and transitioning into a new career.

13635 ■ Career Directions: The Path to Your Ideal Career
McGraw-Hill Professional
1221 Avenue of the Americas
New York, NY 10020-1095
Ph: (212)904-2000
URL: http://www.mhprofessional.com

Donna Yena. 2010. $61.33 (paper). 336 pages. Provides job seekers with essential resources and techniques to develop a career plan, conduct a successful job search and succeed in a diverse workplace.

13636 ■ Careers after the Armed Forces: How to Decide on the Right Career and Make a Successful Transition
Kogan Page Publishers
1518 Walnut St., Ste. 1100
Philadelphia, PA 19102
Ph: (215)928-9112

Fax: (215)928-9113
E-mail: info@koganpage.com
URL: http://www.koganpageusa.com

Jon Mitchell. 2009. $17.95 (paper). 160 pages. Offers career options for men and women who leave the U.S. military for other work. Features exercises, tools, case studies, and tips designed to ease the transition from active duty to the civilian workforce. Includes advice on resume preparation, interview techniques, working with job recruiters, and evaluating job offers.

13637 ■ Change Your Job, Change Your Life: Careering and Re-Careering in the New Boom/Bust Economy
Impact Publications
9104 Manassas Dr., Ste. N
Manassas Park, VA 20111-5211
Ph: (703)361-7300
Fax: (703)335-9486
Fr: 800-361-1055
E-mail: query@impactpublications.com
URL: http://www.impactpublications.com

Ronald Krannich. Ninth edition, 2004. $21.95 (paper). 367 pages. Details trends in the marketplace, how to identify opportunities, how to retrain for them, and how to land jobs. Includes a chapter on starting a business. Contains index, bibliography, and illustrations.

13638 ■ College Majors and Careers
Facts On File Inc.
132 W 31st St., 17th Fl.
New York, NY 10001
Ph: (212)967-8800
Fax: 800-678-3633
Fr: 800-322-8755
URL: http://www.infobasepublishing.com

Irregular, latest edition 6th; Published December, 2008. $35.00 for individuals. Publication includes: Lists of organizations and other sources of information on choosing a college field of concentration and a subsequent career path. Entries include: Organization name, address, phone. Principal content of publication is descriptions of 60 of the most popular major fields and discussions of their attributes.

13639 ■ Combat Leader to Corporate Leader
ABC-CLIO
130 Cremona Dr.
Santa Barbara, CA 93117
Fax: (866)270-3856
Fr: 800-368-6868
URL: http://www.abc-clio.com

Chad Storlie. 2010. $34.95. 184 pages (hardcover). Features military-to-civilian career transition, and how to use their military experiences and training to succeed in civilian careers.

13640 ■ Complete Idiot's Guide to Career Advancement
Alpha Books
c/o Penguin Group
375 Hudson St.
New York, NY 10014-3658
Ph: (212)366-2372
Fax: (212)366-2933
Fr: 800-847-5515
E-mail: dawn.werk@pearsoned.com
URL: http://us.penguingroup.com

Marc Dorio. 2009. $18.95 (paper). 336 pages. Features a step-by-step guide to finding a new career. Helps readers explore the various job-search resources available to job seekers. Includes career-profile comparisons, salary and compensation information, and tips on developing short and long term goals.

13641 ■ Expert Resumes for Baby Boomers
JIST Publishing
875 Montreal Way
St. Paul, MN 55102

Fr: 800-648-5478
E-mail: educate@emcp.com
URL: http://www.jist.com

Louise M. Kursmark and Wendy S. Enelow. 2007. $16.95 (softcover). 288 pages. Presents written sample resumes for people facing career crossroads: advancing, downsizing, retiring, returning to work after an absence, changing careers, starting their own business, and more. Includes step-by-step instructions and strategies for writing perfectly targeted and professional resumes for all situations.

13642 ■ Expert Resumes for Military-to-Civilian Transitions
JIST Publishing
875 Montreal Way
St. Paul, MN 55102
Fr: 800-648-5478
URL: http://www.jist.com

Wendy S. Enelow. 2009. $16.95 (softcover). 304 pages. Provides information on job search strategies, sound resume-writing advice, and tips for creating and using electronic resumes. Features a collection of professionally written resumes designed for veterans and ex-military job seekers.

13643 ■ How to Find the Work You Love
Penguin
375 Hudson St.
New York, NY 10014
Ph: (212)366-2000
Fax: (212)366-2666
Fr: 800-847-5515
URL: http://us.penguingroup.com

Laurence G. Boldt. 2004. $13.00 (paper). 192 pages.

13644 ■ Information Technology: Field Guides to Finding a New Career Set, 20-Volumes
Facts On File
132 W 31st St., 17th Fl.
New York, NY 10001
Fax: 800-678-3633
Fr: 800-322-8755
E-mail: custserv@factsonfile.com
URL: http://factsonfile.infobasepublishing.com

Amanda Kirk. 2009. $39.95 (hardcover). 152 pages. Provides readers with the tools necessary to take their career in a new direction in the information technology field. Features tips and advice for career changers looking to navigate their way into a career in information technology. Offers interviews with professionals working in the field, self-assessment questions, and more.

13645 ■ The Innovative Road to Greater Success in Job Hunting and Changing Careers
PublishAmerica
PO Box 151
Frederick, MD 21705
Ph: (301)695-1707
URL: http://www.publishamerica.net

Joan M. Enering. 2011. $19.95 (softcover). 94 pages. Serves as a guide for finding a job or changing careers. Includes tips on writing resumes and cover letters, getting dressed for a job interview, and the secret of the waiting area.

13646 ■ Internet and Media: Field Guides to Finding a New Career
Facts On File
132 W 31st St., 17th Fl.
New York, NY 10001
Fax: 800-678-3633
Fr: 800-322-8755
E-mail: custserv@factsonfile.com
URL: http://factsonfile.infobasepublishing.com

Amanda Kirk. 2009. $39.95 (hardcover). 168 pages. Offers advice for individuals who wish to transition into the fields of internet and media. Provides an overview of careers in this industry as well as self-assessment questions and interviews with profes-

sionals in the field. Contains tips for career changers and a section that helps readers identify important skills or qualities necessary to transition into, and succeed, in the internet and media fields.

13647 ■ Life After the Military: A Handbook for Transitioning Veterans
Government Institutes
4501 Forbes Blvd., Ste. 200
Lanham, MD 20706
Ph: (301)459-3366
Fax: (301)429-5748
URL: http://rowman.com

Janelle Hill, Cheryl Lawhorne, Don Philpott. 2011. $34.95 (hardback). 324 pages. Discusses many issues that transitioning veterans are faced with such as finding employment, going back to school, managing finances, special benefits available to veterans and a host of other issues the transitioning veteran is likely to face when making the move to civilian life.

13648 ■ Military to Federal Career Guide
The Resume Place, Inc.
89 Mellor Ave.
Baltimore, MD 21228
Ph: (410)744-4324
Fax: (410)744-0112
Fr: 888-480-8265
E-mail: resume@resume-place.com
URL: http://www.resume-place.com

Kathryn Troutman, Paulina Chen and Brian Moore. 2010. $14.95 (paper, CD-ROM included). 130 pages. Serves as a guide for military veterans who want to start a career in the federal government. Provides tips on how to design a federal resume that will translate a veteran's military skills and competencies into the federal skills, keywords and qualifications.

13649 ■ Nonprofits and Government: Field Guides to Finding a New Career
Facts On File
132 W 31st St., 17th Fl.
New York, NY 10001
Fax: 800-678-3633
Fr: 800-322-8755
E-mail: custserv@factsonfile.com
URL: http://factsonfile.infobasepublishing.com

Amanda Kirk. 2009. $39.95 (hardcover). 176 pages. Guides career changers in exploring career possibilities in the nonprofits and government fields. Contains tips and advice from professionals. Provides readers with an overview of nonprofits and government, ways to map out career goals for the future, and self-assessment questions.

13650 ■ Occupational Outlook Handbook
U.S. Bureau of Labor Statistics
2 Massachusetts Ave. NE Ste. 2135
Washington, DC 20212-0001
Ph: (202)691-5200
Fr: 800-877-8339
E-mail: oohinfo@bls.gov
URL: http://www.bls.gov/oco/home.htm

Biennial, Latest edition 2010-2011. $22.00 for individuals. Publication includes: Various occupational organizations that provide career information on hundreds of occupations. Entries include: For organizations—Organization name, address. Principal content of publication is profiles of various occupations, which include description of occupation, educational requirements, job outlook, and expected earnings. Arrangement: Organizations are classified by occupation.

13651 ■ The Pathfinder: How to Choose or Change Your Career for a Lifetime of Satisfaction and Success
Touchstone
c/o Simon & Schuster, Inc.
1230 Ave. of the Americas
New York, NY 10020
Ph: (212)698-7000
URL: http://www.simonandschuster.com

Nicholas Lore. 2012. $16.99 (paper). 448 pages.

Guides professionals through the career transition process. Offers self-tests, diagnostic tools and career design methods to help professionals embark on a new career, entrepreneurial path or ideal job in the present field. Includes tips on landing a fitting job through personal marketing and networking.

13652 ■ Physician's Pathways to Non-Traditional Careers and Leadership Opportunities

Springer Science+Business Media LLC
233 Spring St.
New York, NY 10013-1578
Ph: (212)460-1500
Fax: (212)460-1575
URL: http://www.springer.com

Richard D. Urman and Jesse M. Ehrenfeld. 2012. $39.95. 385 pages (softcover). Serves as a guide for medical professionals and medical students considering additional or new career outside of their field.

13653 ■ Second Chance: How Career Changers Can Find a Great Job

ABC-CLIO
PO Box 1911
Santa Barbara, CA 93116-1911
Fax: (866)270-3856
Fr: 800-368-6868
E-mail: customerservice@abc-clio.com
URL: http://www.abc-clio.com

Mary E. Ghilani. 2010. $34.95 (hardcover). 184 pages. Provides tips and strategies to help midlife career changers identify the best career-change options. Includes career exercises and worksheets; examples of work skills, job descriptions and self-marketing scripts; and resource guide to careers, job-search and educational websites.

13654 ■ Seven Steps to a Rewarding Transitional Career: Getting Work in a Tough Economy

HRD Press
22 Amherst Rd.
Amherst, MA 01002-9709
Ph: (413)253-3488
Fax: (413)253-3490
Fr: 800-822-2801
E-mail: info@hrdpress.com
URL: http://www.hrdpress.com

Richard J. Pinsker. 2009. $29.95. Serves as a guide for those who are interested in pursuing a transitional career.

13655 ■ Taking Charge of Your Career Direction

Wadsworth Publishing
PO Box 6904
Florence, KY 41022
Fax: 800-487-8488
Fr: 800-354-9706
E-mail: esales@cengage.com
URL: http://www.cengage.com

Robert D. Lock. Fifth edition, 2005. Three volumes. 512 pages. $73.49. Provides guidance for the job search process.

13656 ■ Ten Insider Secrets Career Transition Workshop: Your Complete Guide to Discovering the Ideal Job!

10 Step Publications
1151 N State Pkwy., No. 253
Chicago, IL 60610
Ph: (312)493-0582
URL: http://www.10stepjobsearch.com

Todd Bermont. January 2004. $14.95. 108 pages.

13657 ■ Your Career and Life Plan Portfolio

JIST Publishing
875 Montreal Way
St. Paul, MN 55102
Fr: 800-648-5478
E-mail: info@jist.com
URL: http://www.jist.com

Editors at JIST. 2008. $15.95 (softcover). 144 pages. Features a career planning program. Teaches individuals how to organize and present portfolio contents. Helps job seekers increase their skills, take control of their job search, plan their careers, and present what they have to offer an employer in a way that will get them noticed.

13658 ■ Your Dream Job Game Plan

JIST Publishing
875 Montreal Way
St. Paul, MN 55102
Fr: 800-648-5478
E-mail: info@jist.com
URL: http://www.jist.com

Molly Fletcher and Steve Kincaid. 2009. $14.95 (softcover). 224 pages. Offers advice for individuals who wish to discover and achieve an ideal career.

13659 ■ Your Next Career, Second Edition

JIST Publishing
875 Montreal Way
St. Paul, MN 55102
Fr: 800-648-5478
E-mail: info@jist.com
URL: http://www.jist.com

Gail Geary. 2009. $14.95 (softcover). 256 pages. Provides strategies for creating traditional, non-traditional, and entrepreneurial second careers that provide excitement and fulfillment. Helps readers discover their career passions and interests, as well as measure their fit for self-employment. Contains case studies, interview questions and answers, and a directory of additional resources to help navigate the job search.

13660 ■ Your Next Move: The Leader's Guide to Navigating Major Career Transitions

Harvard Business Publishing
60 Harvard Way
Boston, MA 02163
Fr: 800-988-0886
E-mail: custserv@hbsp.harvard.edu
URL: http://hbr.org

Michael D. Watkins. 2009. $26.95 (hardcover). 240 pages. Serves as a resource for manager or executive seeking to maintain career momentum. Provides guidelines on how one can survive and thrive in all the major transitions that he/she will face during his/her career. Includes real-life examples and case studies.

NEWSPAPERS, MAGAZINES, AND JOURNALS

13661 ■ Career Magazine

HH Publishing
PO Box 54166
Atlanta, GA 30308
Ph: (404)604-4511
URL: http://www.thecareermag.com

Bimonthly. $15.00/hard copy; $17.99/year (online); $2.99/digital copy. Features articles in career advancement and other topics related to careers in general.

13662 ■ Civilian Jobs News

Civilian Jobs, LLC.
1825 Barrett Lakes Blvd., Ste. 300
Kennesaw, GA 30144
Ph: (678)819-4198
Fax: (678)819-5162
Fr: (866)801-4418
E-mail: info@civilianjobs.com
URL: http://www.civilianjobnews.com

Bimonthly. $12/year. Features practical information for the military person transitioning from the military and seeking a civilian job.

AUDIO/VISUAL RESOURCES

13663 ■ Best Recession-Proof Jobs

JIST Publishing
875 Montreal Way
St. Paul, MN 55102
Fr: 800-648-5478
E-mail: educate@emcp.com
URL: http://www.jist.com

2009. $149.00. 30 minutes. Includes information on how to successfully transition into a recession-proof job. Helps viewers learn and develop the skills needed for these recession-proof occupations. Provides insights about job security and future trends.

13664 ■ Getting Fired, Getting Hired: Job Hunting From A to Z

Career Lab
8310 S Valley Hwy., Ste. 300
Englewood, CO 80112-5815
Ph: (303)790-0505
Fax: (303)790-0606
Fr: 800-723-9675
E-mail: wsfrank@careerlab.com
URL: http://www.careerlab.com/craig_lincoln/startup_
    fired_hired.htm

Six-part video series.

13665 ■ The Real Work Begins

JIST Publishing
875 Montreal Way
St. Paul, MN 55102
Fr: 800-648-5478
E-mail: info@jist.com
URL: http://www.jist.com

2009. $129. 25 minutes. Teaches viewers how to keep the jobs they find and establish themselves as valuable employees in the workplace. Presents the do's and don'ts of on-the-job success as well as how to exceed an employer's expectations.

ONLINE AND DATABASE SERVICES

13666 ■ CareerLeader.com

Fr: (866)438-1485
E-mail: help@careerleader.com
URL: http://www.careerleader.com

Description: Online career assessment tool for job seekers, emphasis on business careers. Fee: Several levels of assessment available; starts at $95.

13667 ■ CivilianJobs.com

E-mail: info@civilianjobs.com
URL: http://civilianjobs.com

Description: Offers an online recruiting solution for candidates that are currently transitioning out of the military as well as military veterans with varying amounts of business experience.

13668 ■ Keirsey Temperament Sorter and Temperament Web Site

E-mail: keirsey@orci.com
URL: http://www.keirsey.com

Description: Online personality questionnaire that identifies temperament and interest traits that may be applied towards career searches.

SOFTWARE

13669 ■ EmploymentTalk

Insala
1331 Airport Fwy., Ste. 313
Euless, TX 76040
Ph: (817)355-0939
Fax: (817)355-0746
E-mail: info@insala.com
URL: http://www.employmenttalk.com

A career transition system/database tool that is used

by outplacement and career management firms in their practice, client delivery, and consultant management services. Available in multiple languages and easily customizable.

OTHER SOURCES

13670 ■ Career Planning and Adult Development Network (CPADN)
543 Vista Mar Ave.
Pacifica, CA 94044
Ph: (650)773-0982
E-mail: admin@careernetwork.org
URL: http://www.careernetwork.org

Description: Counselors, trainers, consultants, therapists, educators, personnel specialists, and graduate students who work in business, educational, religious, and governmental organizations, and focus on career planning and adult development issues. Seeks to: establish a link between professionals working with adults in a variety of settings; identify and exchange effective adult development methods and techniques; develop a clearer understanding of the directions and objectives of the career planning and the adult development movement. Keeps members informed of developments in career decision-making, career values clarification, preretirement counseling, dual-career families, job search techniques, and mid-life transitions. Cosponsors professional seminars; maintains biographical archives.

13671 ■ Career Transitions, LLC
4101 Edison Lakes Pkwy., Ste. 200
Mishawaka, IN 46545
Ph: (574)968-1860
Fax: (574)968-1871
Fr: 800-800-3617
URL: http://www.careertransitionsllc.com

Description: Provides contract staffing as well as professional search, recruiting, and outplacement services.

13672 ■ MilitaryStars
PO BOX 276
Tallevast, FL 34270
Ph: (941)684-0133
Fr: 800-775-1415
E-mail: info@militarystars.com
URL: http://www.militarystars.com

Description: Provides military veteran employment through military job fair and career expos, and military hiring events. Assists transitioning military and veterans in finding civilian jobs via regional career expos throughout the United States.

13673 ■ New Ways to Work (NWW)
103 Morris St., Ste. A
Sebastopol, CA 95472
Ph: (707)824-4000
Fax: (707)824-4410
E-mail: newways@newwaystowork.org
URL: http://www.newwaystowork.org

Description: Helps communities build systems that connect schools, community organizations and businesses, and improve the services, educational programs and support the community provides for its youth. Engages and supports local communities in the invention and renewal of connected, comprehensive youth-serving systems.

13674 ■ Peter K. Studner Associates
Jamenair Ltd.
PO Box 241957
Los Angeles, CA 90024-9757
Ph: (310)470-6688
Fax: (310)470-8106
Fr: 800-581-5953
URL: http://www.superjobsearch.com

Description: Provides outplacement services helping individuals in career transitions through all stages of preparation to identify, attain, negotiate and achieve their next opportunity.

13675 ■ *The Guide to Internet Job Searching*
The McGraw-Hill Companies
PO Box 182604
Columbus, OH 43272
Fax: (614)759-3749
Fr: 877-883-5524
E-mail: customer.service@mcgraw-hill.com
URL: http://www.mhprofessional.com

Margaret Riley Dikel, Frances E. Roehm. $16.95. 2008. 288 pages. Helps readers develop an effective Internet job application, quickly locate major job listing sites in each career area, and use the computer to search for job opportunities.

13676 ■ *Guide to Internet Job Searching, 2008-2009 Edition*
JIST Publishing
875 Montreal Way
St. Paul, MN 55102
Fax: 800-547-8329
Fr: 800-648-5478
E-mail: info@jist.com
URL: http://www.jist.com

Margaret Riley Dikel and Frances E. Roehm. 2008. $16.95. 288 pages. Describes how to find and use online bulletin boards, job listings, recruiter information, discussion groups, and resume posting services.

13677 ■ *Headhunters Revealed*
Hunter Arts Publishing
PO Box 66578E
Los Angeles, CA 90066
Ph: (310)842-8864
Fax: (310)842-8868
URL: http://www.headhuntersrevealed.com

Quarterly. $14.95 for individuals; $12.50 for out of country. Covers: Online career sites, career associations, and organizations.

13678 ■ *How to REALLY use LinkedIn*
BookSurge Publishing
7290 B Investment Dr.
Charleston, SC 29418
Fr: (866)308-6235
E-mail: pr@booksurge.com
URL: http://www.booksurge.com

Jan Vermeiren. 2009. $19.95 (paper). 200 pages. Demonstrates how LinkedIn can be a powerful tool for job seekers.

13679 ■ *Internet Your Way To a New Job (Third Edition)*
Happy About
20660 Stevens Creek Blvd., Ste. 210
Cupertino, CA 95014
Ph: (408)257-3000
E-mail: questions@happyabout.info
URL: http://www.happyabout.com

Alison Doyle. 2009. $16.96 (paper). 128 pages. Provides information on the process of online job searching, professional branding, social and professional networking, and career building with advice, tips, and techniques on how to effectively find a new job and grow a career.

13680 ■ *Plunkett's Employers' Internet Sites with Careers Information: The Only Complete Guide to Careers Websites Operated by Major Employers*
Plunkett Research, Ltd.
PO Box 541737
Houston, TX 77254-1737
Ph: (713)932-0000
Fax: (713)932-7080
E-mail: customersupport@plunkettresearch.com
URL: http://www.plunkettresearch.com

Jack W. Plunkett. Revised, 2004. $229.99 (includes CD-ROM). Provides profiles of Internet sites for major employers. Job hunters can use the profiles or indexes to locate the Internet job sites that best fit their needs. 681 pages.

13681 ■ *Professional's Job Finder*
Planning Communications
7215 Oak Ave.
River Forest, IL 60305-1935
Ph: (708)366-5200
Fax: (708)366-5280
Fr: 888-366-5200
E-mail: projf@planningcommunications.com
URL: http://www.planningcommunications.com/jf/index.htm

$7.58 for individuals; $18.95. Covers: Over 3,003 sources of jobs in the private sector of the United States, including job matching services, job hotlines, periodicals and directories, Internet job sites, salary surveys, databases, and electronic online job services. Includes coupons for over $200 in discounts and free job resources. Entries include: For job services—Name, sponsor or operator name, address, phone, length of registration period, cost, description (including number of job vacancies listed). For publications—Title, publisher name, address, phone, frequency of publication, price, description (including number of job vacancies listed). Arrangement: Classified by occupational specialty; geographical by state. Indexes: Subject.

ONLINE AND DATABASE SERVICES

13682 ■ 6Figurejobs.com
E-mail: info@6figurejobs.com
URL: http://www.6figurejobs.com

Description: Provides executives and experienced professionals with access to some of the most exclusive executive jobs, executive recruiters and career management tools available. Includes tools for both posting and viewing jobs, resume refinement, company research and more.

13683 ■ 911hotjobs.com Employment Portal
E-mail: contact@911hotjobs.com
URL: http://www.911hotjobs.com

Description: Online site for those seeking job opportunities in public safety. Testing requirements and job postings are available to those seeking employment in law enforcement, fire careers, and EMS services.

13684 ■ Academic Careers Online
E-mail: info@academiccareers.com
URL: http://www.academiccareers.com

Description: Serves as an academic job site for teaching jobs, education jobs, research jobs, and professional jobs in education and academia.

13685 ■ Academic Employment Network
URL: http://www.academploy.com

Description: Online position announcement service. Lists available positions in colleges, primary and secondary educational institutions for faculty, staff, and administrative professionals. Fee: Free searching and browsing features.

13686 ■ Academic360.com
URL: http://www.academic360.com

Description: Site is a collection of internet resources gathered for the academic job hunter. Contains links to over 1,400 colleges and universities that advertise job openings online. Positions listed are not limited to teaching positions.

13687 ■ Accountantjobs.com
URL: http://www.accountantjobs.com

Description: Serves as a job site network and online portal for accounting careers worldwide. Features job postings, advertisements, resume access and other resources intended to provide both employers and job seekers their online recruitment needs.

13688 ■ AccountExecutiveManager.com
URL: http://www.accountexecutivemanager.com

Description: Provides career and employment opportunities for aspiring account executive managers. Offers links, job and resume postings and more.

13689 ■ AccountingClassifieds.com
URL: http://www.accountingclassifieds.com

Description: Serves as a specialized career site providing employment opportunities focused on the accounting industry.

13690 ■ Accounting.com
E-mail: info@accounting.com
URL: http://www.accounting.com

Description: Job board for those seeking accounting jobs. Employers may also post positions available. Contains directory of CPA firms, discussion forum for job seekers, CPE resources, news bulletins and accounting links.

13691 ■ AccountingCrossing.com
URL: http://www.accountingcrossing.com

Description: Offers collection of accounting jobs, including CPA, finance manager, corporate accountant, and forensic accounting positions. Features industry-specific articles relating to job searches and developments in the accounting industry.

13692 ■ AccountingJobsite.com
URL: http://www.accountingjobsite.com

Description: Provides listings of accounting jobs, accounting clerk jobs, accounting auditing jobs, and other accounting employment opportunities.

13693 ■ AccountingJobsToday.com
URL: http://www.accountingjobstoday.com

Description: Functions as a job resource for accounting and finance professionals worldwide. Offers several career resources including accounting job descriptions, sample accounting resumes, salary tools and education.

13694 ■ AccountingProfessional.com
E-mail: info@careermarketplace.com
URL: http://www.accountingprofessional.com

Description: Acts as a job search and recruiting site for accountants, CPAs and related financial jobs. Provides resources for both job seekers and employers.

13695 ■ ActuarialCrossing.com
URL: http://www.actuarialcrossing.com

Description: Offers a collection of research actuarial jobs worldwide. Focuses on the hiring needs of actuarial professionals and actuarial company in the United States.

13696 ■ Actuary.com
URL: http://www.actuary.com

Description: Actuarial professionals. Focuses on serving as a major resource center for the actuarial community at large. Provides information regarding exams, seminars, actuarial news, actuarial recruiters, actuary job postings, discussion forums, actuarial schools, links to many resources, leading actuarial companies information and more.

13697 ■ Acupuncture Today
E-mail: advertising@acupuncturetoday.com
URL: http://www.acupuncturetoday.com

Description: Provides the latest news, articles and featured items that are of interest to, and can be implemented by, the acupuncture and Oriental medicine profession.

13698 ■ Acupuncture.com
URL: http://www.acupuncture.com

Description: Serves as a gateway to Chinese medicine, health and wellness by featuring articles and research about acupuncture, resources, vendor opportunities, employment opportunities, strategic partnerships, programs and others services.

13699 ■ Ad Age TalentWorks
URL: http://adage.com/section/talentworks/474

Description: Provides a database of advertising jobs and resources for both job seekers and employers. Includes a collection of news and analysis regarding goings-on in the world of advertising.

13700 ■ Adjunctnation.com
URL: http://adjunctadvocate.com

Description: Focuses on faculty job postings within higher education for both part-time, as well as full-time temporary college faculty appointments.

13701 ■ AdminAssistantJobs.com
URL: http://www.adminassistantjobs.com

Description: Features job opportunities and resume searching and posting for administrative assistants.

13702 ■ AdminCrossing.com
URL: http://www.admincrossing.com

Description: Offers a wide database of research administrative job openings worldwide. Includes openings from Fortune 500 and Fortune 1000 companies.

13703 ■ Adoption Forums
URL: http://forums.adoption.com

Description: Includes job postings for adoption professionals.

13704 ■ AdRecruiter.com
URL: http://www.adrecruiter.com

Description: Provides job opportunities for professionals in the marketing and advertising industry.

13705 ■ AdvertiseCareers.com
URL: http://www.advertisecareers.com

Description: Provides job opportunities for marketing professionals.

13706 ■ AdvertisingCrossing.com
URL: http://www.advertisingcrossing.com

Description: Offers job opportunities in the advertising fields, including jobs for executives, managers, assistants, and entry-level workers.

13707 ■ AdvertisingIndustryJobs.com
URL: http://www.advertisingindustryjobs.com

Description: Features job opportunities, resume searching and postings for advertising professionals.

13708 ■ AerospaceCrossing.com
URL: http://www.aerospacecrossing.com

Description: Consolidates jobs from employer websites, job portals, and aerospace websites.

13709 ■ AerospaceEngineer.com
URL: http://www.aerospaceengineer.com

Description: Provides job opportunities in the aerospace engineering field.

13710 ■ AgCareers.com
URL: http://www.agcareers.com

Description: Serves as an agriculture employment search engine. Supplies human resource services to the agriculture, food, natural resources and biotechnology industry.

13711 ■ AgentsandSalesManagers.com
URL: http://www.agentsandsalesmanagers.com

Description: Online job search for agents and sales managers. Includes job, resume posting and more.

13712 ■ AgriculturalCrossing.com
URL: http://www.agriculturalcrossing.com

Description: Provides a database of agricultural job openings worldwide. Includes openings in Fortune 500 and Fortune 1000 companies.

13713 ■ AgricultureJobs.com
URL: http://www.agriculturejobs.com

Description: Provides new job openings for Agriculturists in addition to research into the farming, fishing and forestry employment markets. Maintains a career articles section written and frequented by industry professionals.

13714 ■ AIJobs.net
URL: http://www.aijobs.net

Description: Features artificial intelligence jobs and careers, resumes search and postings.

13715 ■ AirlineCareer.com
Ph: (978)615-3190
E-mail: jbelotti@airlinecareer.com
URL: http://www.airlinecareer.com

Web-based training center. Provides flight attendant job placement services.

13716 ■ AllAboutNannyCare.com
URL: http://nannybizreviews.com

Description: Provides expert assistance in recruitment, screening and retention of quality in-home caregivers and the creation of successful nanny/family relationships. Provides a variety of resources and connection to the larger childcare community. Offers a variety of exclusive tools to help caregivers and families find the right job/nanny match.

13717 ■ AmericaJobNetwork.com
URL: http://www.americajobnetwork.com

Description: Serves as a career opportunity resource and job search engine that covers all industries.

13718 ■ American Academy of Ophthalmology Professional Choices Career Center
American Academy of Ophthalmology
655 Beach St.
PO Box 7424
San Francisco, CA 94120-7424
Ph: (415)561-8500
Fax: (415)561-8533
E-mail: pchoices@aao.org
URL: http://www.aao.org/careers

Description: A site providing regularly updated ophthalmology positions. Applicants for jobs contact the AAO with resume, cover letter, and listing reference number. Job hunters may post resumes for free. Employers may post 90-day job listings at the rate of $335 for members, $535 for nonmembers.

13719 ■ American Academy of Physician Assistants Career Opportunities
2318 Mill Rd., Ste. 1300
Alexandria, VA 22314-1352
Ph: (703)836-2272
Fax: (703)684-1924
E-mail: aapa@aapa.org
URL: http://www.aapa.org/your_pa_career.aspx

Description: Online newsletter of the AAPA. Job opportunities may be searched by state or type. Members may also post position wanted on AAPA website.

13720 ■ American Accounting Association Placement Advertising
5717 Bessie Dr.
Sarasota, FL 34233-2399
Ph: (941)921-7747
Fax: (941)923-4093
E-mail: info@aaahq.org
URL: http://careercenter.aaahq.org/home/
index.cfm?site_id=7376

Description: Visitors may apply for membership to the Association at this site. Main files include: Placement Postings, Placement Submission Information, Faculty Development, Marketplace, more.

13721 ■ American Association of Anatomists Career Center
9650 Rockville Pike
Bethesda, MD 20814-3998
Ph: (301)634-7910
Fax: (301)634-7965
E-mail: exec@anatomy.org
URL: http://aaatoday.org/content/career-center

Description: Job advertisers include academic sites in the U.S. and Canada. Job seekers may review these posted jobs through "Positions Offered" or post their own needs under "Positions Wanted." Offerings for Postdoctoral Positions also available. Contains Career Resources sections and links to online career resources.

13722 ■ American Chemical Society Career Sources
E-mail: help@acs.org
URL: http://portal.acs.org

Description: Offers online interviewing between employers and potential employees, postings for positions available and situations wanted, and regularly updated career advice and information for American Chemical Society members only.

13723 ■ American Institute of Aeronautics and Astronautics Career Planning and Placement Services
1801 Alexander Bell Dr., Ste. 500
Reston, VA 20191-4344
Ph: (703)264-7500
Fax: (703)264-7551
Fr: 800-639-2422
E-mail: custserv@aiaa.org
URL: http://www.aiaa.org

Description: Site for AIAA members to place recruitment advertisements, browse career opportunities listings, post resumes, and seek additional employment assistance. Non-members may become members though this site.

13724 ■ American Institute of Biological Sciences Classifieds
1444 I St. NW, Ste. 200
Washington, DC 20005
Ph: (202)628-1500
Fax: (202)628-1509
URL: http://www.aibs.org/classifieds

Description: Section of the American Institute of Biological Sciences website used for posting available positions, research awards and fellowships, and other classified ads.

13725 ■ American Library Association Education and Employment
50 E Huron
Chicago, IL 60611
Fr: 800-545-2433
URL: http://www.ala.org/ala/educationcareers/employment/index.cfm

Description: Contains links to monthly job and career leads lists posted in American Libraries and College & Research Libraries NewsNet and other sources, as well as a Conference Placement Service and accreditation information.

13726 ■ American Oil Chemists Society Career Opportunities
2710 S Boulder
Urbana, IL 61802-6996
Ph: (217)359-2344
Fax: (217)351-8091
E-mail: general@aocs.org
URL: http://www.aocs.org/aocsbox/jobtarget/index.cfm

Description: Section of the AOCS homepage intended to aid members in finding jobs in the oil chemistry field. Job areas include analytical, health and nutrition, processing, surfactants and detergents, general fats and oils/chemistry, and others. Jobs may be posted and searched.

13727 ■ American Society of Landscape Architects JobLink
E-mail: membership@asla.org
URL: http://www.asla.org

Description: A job-search site of the American Society of Landscape Architects. Fee: Resume postings cost $100 (nonmembers) for a two-month listing. Job postings cost $600 (nonmembers) or $300 (members) for a one-month listing.

13728 ■ American Society of Plant Biologists Job Bank
15501 Monona Dr.
Rockville, MD 20855-2768
Ph: (301)251-0560
Fax: (301)279-2996
E-mail: info@aspb.org
URL: http://my.aspb.org/networking

Description: A service of the American Society of Plant Biologists, intended to aid its members in locating jobs and job resources. Site lists new jobs weekly in its job bank. Fee: A fee of $150 is charged for all academic/government/industry permanent positions

and for all positions, regardless of rank, posted by private companies. Postdoctoral positions; research/technical positions (non-Ph.D.); and assistantships, fellowships, and internships at universities and not-for-profit agencies are published for a fee of $25.

13729 ■ Answers4Dancers.com
URL: http://www.answers4dancers.com

Description: Provides resources such as listings of auditions and jobs, tips and secrets, tools and training, videos, and success stories to job seekers in the dance and choreography industry.

13730 ■ AppleOne.com
Fr: 800-564-5644
URL: http://www.appleone.com

Description: Search site with job databank, resume posting and online e-newsletter subscriptions. Applicants can also interview with prospective employers online. Registration is free.

13731 ■ ArchaeologyFieldwork.com
URL: http://www.archaeologyfieldwork.com/AFW

Description: Provides an archaeology resource database that includes employment listings, resume and CV postings, job hunt, archaeology announcements, and archaeology volunteer opportunities. Features other resources such as a forum for discussions on wages and per diem in CRM, working conditions, professional organizations and unions, and other issues of interest for field archaeologists.

13732 ■ Archinect.com
E-mail: jobs@archinect.com
URL: http://archinect.com

Description: Functions as an online destination for progressive-design oriented students, architects, educators and fans. Brings together designers from around the world to introduce new ideas from all disciplines.

13733 ■ ArchitectureCrossing.com
URL: http://www.architecturecrossing.com

Description: Offers a comprehensive collection of architectural job openings worldwide. Includes job listings from top companies and from virtually every employer career webpage and job board in America.

13734 ■ ArtJob Online
E-mail: artjob@westaf.org
URL: http://www.artjob.org

Description: Contains up-to-date national and international listings of arts employment and related opportunities in the arts: full- and part-time employment, internships, grants, public art projects, and residencies. User can search by region, art discipline, type of organization. Fee: Subscribers pay $25 for 3 months, $40 for six months and $75 for one year.

13735 ■ Asylum Law
E-mail: info@probono.net
URL: http://www.probono.net/asylum

Description: Supports lawyers who are providing pro bono assistance to individuals seeking asylum in the United States. Contains online support and resources for participating lawyers including news, a calendar of trainings and events, online listings of new cases for volunteers and an online library of training manuals, briefs and practice materials.

13736 ■ AttorneyJobs.com
URL: http://attorneyjobs.com

Description: Provides a database of current attorney and law-related job opportunities, contract opportunities, and practice development options. Offers advice and assistance to lawyers in all employment sectors, at all levels of experience, and in all stages of their careers.

13737 ■ Audiology Online
URL: http://www.audiologyonline.com

Description: Exists as an online resource in the field

of hearing healthcare. Strives to be the primary information resource for the benefit of the patients, the profession and the audiology industry.

13738 ■ AuditorCrossing.com
URL: http://www.auditorcrossing.com

Description: Offers a wide collection of top auditor job openings. Includes listings from Fortune 500 and Fortune 1000 companies.

13739 ■ AuthenticJobs.com
URL: http://www.authenticjobs.com

Description: Provides information for web and creative professionals and the companies seeking to hire them. Provides full-time and freelance job opportunities for designers and developers.

13740 ■ Automation.com
URL: http://www.automation.com

Description: Offers complimentary press releases, articles, and publication services for industrial automation and process control professionals.

13741 ■ AutomotiveCrossing.com
URL: http://www.automotivecrossing.com

Description: Offers a comprehensive collection of researched job openings in the automotive field. Includes free job postings, free job searching, free resuming posting, free resume searching, and job management tools.

13742 ■ AutoPersonnel.com
URL: http://www.autopersonnel.com

Description: Specializes in automotive staffing covering sales, office management, accounting, technicians and other positions.

13743 ■ Aviation Jobs Online
URL: http://www.aviationjobsonline.com

Description: Provides list of various jobs within the aviation industry.

13744 ■ AWN Career Connection
E-mail: jobs@awn.com
URL: http://jobs.awn.com

Description: Exists to provide the professional and enthusiast communities an assembly of animation resources. Allows job seekers to anonymously seek or investigate new career opportunities, while providing recruiters, HR personnel and other employment personnel a set of tools to find, assess and discretely contact those job seekers.

13745 ■ BankInfoSecurity.com
E-mail: advertising@bankinfosecurity.com
URL: http://www.bankinfosecurity.com

Description: Serves as a reference tool that promotes education on security issues. Reinforces the need for maintaining customer data confidentiality and integrity. Provides resources for individuals who want to work in the field such as interview tips, job postings, salary and hiring information and a resume center.

13746 ■ BankJobs.com
URL: http://www.bankjobs.com

Description: Posts jobs and resumes for the banking and finance industry. Allows users to post, preview and search jobs for free.

13747 ■ Benchfolks.com
URL: http://www.benchfolks.com

Description: Provides a one-stop shop for IT professionals, companies/clients and vendors/suppliers by catering to their employment needs. Caters to individual needs like professional standing in terms of qualification, level of expertise, experience gained and requirement of the industry.

13748 ■ Best Jobs USA
URL: http://www.bestjobsusa.com

Description: Employment search engine and database offering employment ads from @IT1Employment Review Magazine@IT2. Main files include: Career Guide (job opportunities, resume posting, career fairs, company profiles); HR Solutions (trends, statistics, resume searching); News to Peruse (industry information and news).

13749 ■ BillingJobs.com
URL: http://www.billingjobs.com

Description: Features billing jobs, billing resumes, accounts payable jobs, and billing careers.

13750 ■ BiologyJobs.com
URL: http://www.biologyjobs.com

Description: Provides resource for job seekers and employers who are interested in the life sciences. Includes listings of resumes and job openings.

13751 ■ BiomedicalEngineer.com
URL: http://www.biomedicalengineer.com

Description: Features biomedical engineering jobs and products to biomedical engineers.

13752 ■ BioSpace.com
E-mail: support@biospace.com
URL: http://www.biospace.com

Description: Serves as an online community for industry news and careers for life science professionals. Provides biospace news, career events, recruitment and job seeking opportunities for professionals in the biotechnology and pharmaceutical industries.

13753 ■ BiotechCrossing.com
URL: http://www.biotechcrossing.com

Description: Offers a collection of active biotech job listings. Includes the lists of employer career pages, job websites, association websites, newspaper classifieds and recruitment sites.

13754 ■ Blue Coat Systems Career Center
URL: http://www.bluecoat.com/company/careers

Description: Helps clients deliver the business-critical applications needed to enhance productivity, ensure a proactive line of defense and align network investments with business requirements.

13755 ■ BlueSuitMom.com
E-mail: info@bluesuitmom.com
URL: http://www.bluesuitmom.com/career

Description: An online database containing over 300,000 searchable job postings, including those in professional organizing. Offers career advice for the professional organizer.

13756 ■ BrokerHunter.com
URL: http://www.brokerhunter.com

Description: Serves as an Internet-based recruiting solution in the rapidly changing financial services industry. Provides job listings serving the securities, insurance and banking sectors.

13757 ■ BusinessAnalystCrossing.com
URL: http://www.businessanalystcrossing.com

Description: Offers business analyst job listings. Includes entry level business analyst, technical and business analyst jobs.

13758 ■ BusinessWeek.com
URL: http://jobs.businessweek.com/a/all-jobs/list

Description: Provides job listings and career opportunities. Searches career opportunities by title, industry, company or location. Covers job opportunities in all fields.

13759 ■ CabinCrewJobs.com
URL: http://www.cabincrewjobs.com

Description: Offers detailed information about how

to successfully launch a career in the airline industry. Includes career resources such as tips on resume writing, interviews, training, salaries, job benefits and more.

13760 ■ California Society of Certified Public Accountants Classifieds
1800 Gateway Dr., Ste. 200
San Mateo, CA 94404-4072
Fr: 800-922-5272
E-mail: info@calcpa.org
URL: http://www.calcpa.org/classifieds/public/search.aspx

Description: An accounting job search tool for CPAs in California. Details steps to become a CPA, provides job search posting opportunities for seekers and candidates' pages for employers looking to fill positions.

13761 ■ Career Mag
URL: http://www.careermag.com

Description: Searchable database with resume bank. Main files include: Post Your Jobs; Post Internships; Relocation Assistance Center, Resume Writing Advice; Featured Employers.

13762 ■ CareerBuilder.com
URL: http://www.careerbuilder.com

Description: Job-seekers may search job board through several different career headers, such as field of interest, location or keyword search; may also post resume to Career Builder database. Employers and recruiters may log on to post jobs and review resumes. Also contains resume and career resources, e-mail alerts.

13763 ■ Career.com
URL: http://www.career.com

Description: Users can perform job searches by company, location, discipline, and for new graduates. Other features include "Hot Jobs," CyberFair, and a resume save option.

13764 ■ Careerfield.org
URL: http://www.careerfield.org

Description: Serves as a job search engine that covers all industries. Allows users to find jobs across the United States.

13765 ■ CareerJet.com
URL: http://www.careerjet.com

Description: Maps the selection of job offerings available on the internet in one database by referencing job listings from company websites, recruitment agency websites and large recruitment specialist sites. Lists job offerings by industry and by location.

13766 ■ CareerMag.com
URL: http://www.careermag.com

Description: Online magazine containing many columns, features and articles about job hunting. Also holds job listings for browsers. Main files include: Job Openings, Employers, Articles, Resume Bank, Career Forum, On Campus, Diversity, Be Your Own Boss, Job Fairs, Recruiter Directory, Consultant Directory, Products & Services, Relocation Resources, Career Links, Post Your Jobs. Has information section for self-employed and freelance workers.

13767 ■ CareerMatrix.com
URL: http://www.careermatrix.com

Description: Provides free resources for job seekers and an employer information page including company logos, company profile and link to all the jobs posted.

13768 ■ CareerOneStop.org
Ph: 877-348-0502
E-mail: info@careeronestop.org
URL: http://www.careeronestop.org

Description: Career resources. Job seekers can post their resume and search for job openings.

13769 ■ CareerOverview.com
URL: http://www.careeroverview.com

Description: Assists aspiring career professionals, job seekers and students to make better and more informed career choices by providing them with relevant, reliable and up-to-date career and job information.

13770 ■ CareerPark.com
E-mail: info@careerpark.com
URL: http://www.careerpark.com

Description: Offers job search resources, job postings, and a resume database to help candidates in their career planning.

13771 ■ CareerPerfect.com
URL: http://www.careerperfect.com

Description: Provides links to career software and books; lists FAQ's on career planning, resumes, job searching, and interviewing; identifies online job databases; accepts resumes for posting.

13772 ■ CareerPharm.com
URL: http://www.careerpharm.com

Description: Exclusively serves the hospital and health system markets. Offers three ways for job seekers and advertisers to connect: online, in print or at a recruiting event.

13773 ■ CareerSite.com
E-mail: 400-support@careersite.com
URL: http://www.careersite.com

Description: Offers resources for career information, including personalized search agents, automatic matching of jobs against resume, and expert advice on all aspects of the job hunting process.

13774 ■ CatholicJobs.com
URL: http://www.catholicjobs.com

Description: Features free job listings for Catholic organizations, as well as free job searches and career tools for anyone seeking employment.

13775 ■ CertifiedHomeHealthAide.net
URL: http://www.certifiedhomehealthaide.net

Description: Lists job openings for home health aid professionals. Includes job and resume posting and other services.

13776 ■ ChefCrossing.com
URL: http://www.chefcrossing.com

Description: Shows job listings from employer career pages, job websites, association websites, newspaper classified ads and recruiter sites.

13777 ■ ChefJobs.com
E-mail: info@chefjobs.com
URL: http://www.chefjobs.com

Description: Provides resources to career and recreational culinary education programs worldwide.

13778 ■ ChemicalEngineer.com
E-mail: info@careermarketplace.com
URL: http://www.chemicalengineer.com

Description: Serves as an employment center where job seekers can find many job opportunities in the field of chemical engineering.

13779 ■ ChemIndustry.com
E-mail: info@chemindustry.com
URL: http://www.chemindustry.com

Description: Directory and search engine for chemical and related industry professionals. Provides specialized search services for chemical names, jobs, market research and consultants.

13780 ■ ChildcareJobs.net
URL: http://www.childcarejobs.net

Description: Features job opportunities, resume search, postings and employment for childcare workers.

13781 ■ Chronicle of Higher Education Career Network
1255 Twenty-Third St. NW, 7th Fl.
Washington, DC 20037
Ph: (202)466-1000
Fax: (202)452-1033
E-mail: help@chronicle.com
URL: http://chronicle.com/section/Jobs/61

Description: Provided by the Chronicle of Higher Education, a fully searchable online listing of jobs currently available at universities and colleges in the U.S. and abroad. Position listings include faculty, research, administrative and executive openings. Also provides an e-mail notification service for specific jobs, job market news, and links.

13782 ■ ChurchJobs.net
URL: http://www.churchjobs.net

Description: Allows job seekers to search national church jobs, Christian jobs, other ministry jobs and pastor jobs and positions. Offers users the ability to create custom job and resume listings.

13783 ■ ChurchStaffing.com
URL: http://www.churchstaffing.com

Description: Provides information for churches and church staff members in the area of personnel and staff relations.

13784 ■ Civil Engineering Jobs
URL: http://www.civilengineeringjobs.com

Description: Job postings for all civil engineering disciplines including positions in traffic/transportation.

13785 ■ CivilEngineeringCentral.com
URL: http://www.civilengineeringcentral.com

Description: Serves as niche for job board and resume database devoted exclusively to the civil engineering community-from the professionals who visit the site, to the companies, agencies or job recruiters who advertise job opportunities on the site. Offers unique opportunity to reach premier civil engineering professionals without the waste.

13786 ■ CivilEngineeringCrossing.com
URL: http://www.civilengineeringcrossing.com

Description: Locates jobs inside user's niche, conducting a more streamlined job search. Provides instant access to a comprehensive pool of listings based on particular area of focus.

13787 ■ CivilEngineerUSA.com
URL: http://www.civilengineerusa.com

Description: Serves as a career site for civil engineering professionals. Provides listings of jobs, career opportunities, and products to civil engineers and resources for both job seekers and employers.

13788 ■ Classified Solutions Group, Inc.
PO Box 1542
Radio City Station
New York, NY 10101-1542
Ph: (646)416-6665
Fax: (212)604-9361
URL: http://www.classifiedsolutionsgroup.com

Description: Job board where seekers may search for jobs, recruit a job search agent to assist them, and take advantage of relocation tools. Provides links to specific field information and diversity-concentrated sites.

13789 ■ ClearedConnections.com
URL: http://www.clearedconnections.com

Online resource lists jobs for those security-cleared professionals including counterintelligence specialists.

13790 ■ Clutterbug.net
URL: http://www.clutterbug.net

Description: Acts as an online clearinghouse of information for those interested in becoming profes-

sional organizers. Also maintains a directory of professional organizers.

13791 ■ CollegeGrad.com
URL: http://www.collegegrad.com

Description: Site contains the online version of the College Grad Job Hunter-an entry level job search book. Main files include: Preparation, Resumes and Cover Letters, Job Postings, Interviews and Negotiations, New Job. Employers may also search for candidates fitting positions.

13792 ■ CollegeRecruiter.com
URL: http://www.collegerecruiter.com
Job listings.

13793 ■ ComplianceCrossing.com
URL: http://www.compliancecrossing.com

Description: Features a comprehensive collection of compliance job openings. Includes listings from Fortune 500 and Fortune 1,000 companies.

13794 ■ ComputerJobs.com
URL: http://www.computerjobs.com

Description: Provides listings of computer-related job opportunities.

13795 ■ Computerworld Careers
URL: http://www.computerworld.com/careertopics/careers

Description: Offers career opportunities for IT (information technology) professionals. Job seekers may search the jobs database, register at the site, and read about job surveys and employment trends. Employers may post jobs.

13796 ■ Computing Research Association Job Announcements
1828 L St. NW, Ste. 800
Washington, DC 20036-4632
Ph: (202)234-2111
Fax: (202)667-1066
E-mail: info@cra.org
URL: http://www.cra.org/ads

Description: Contains dated links to national college and university computer technology positions.

13797 ■ Contract Job Hunter
E-mail: staff@cjhunter.com
URL: http://www.cjhunter.com

Description: Contains information on immediate and anticipated contract job openings throughout the United States, Canada, and overseas. All jobs listed are temporary technical jobs that are usually higher paying than similar direct jobs. Jobs database is updated every hour. Hosts Subscribers' Lounge, advertisers section, a guest area, and links. Also directory of contract staffing firms.

13798 ■ ControllerAccountingManager.com
URL: http://www.controlleraccountingmanager.com

Description: Lists job and career opportunities for aspiring controller accounting managers. Offers links, job listings, resume resources and more.

13799 ■ Coordinators' Corner
E-mail: nancy@coordinatorscorner.com
URL: http://www.coordinatorscorner.com

Description: Offers access to articles on managing a wedding consultant business. Provides information from the industry's top experts.

13800 ■ Coroflot.com
URL: http://www.coroflot.com

Description: Provides networking and promotional tools, and an employer directory for the design industry.

13801 ■ CounselingCrossing.com
URL: http://www.counselingcrossing.com

Description: Offers instant access to a comprehen-

sive pool of job listings in the counseling field. Shows jobs from employer career pages, job websites, association websites, newspaper classified ads and recruiter sites.

13802 ■ Counsel.net
URL: http://counsel.net

Description: Provides employment resources for the legal industry such as chatboards, legal jobs, classified ads, legal forums, practice areas, attorney marketing and more.

13803 ■ Court Reporters Board of California
E-mail: jennifer.haupert@dca.ca.gov
URL: http://www.courtreportersboard.ca.gov

Description: Provides users of the Judicial System protection by disseminating information and through regulating and testing of the qualifications, performance, and ethical conduct of CSRs and entities regulated by the Board.

13804 ■ CourtReporterNet.com
URL: http://www.courtreporternet.com

Description: Provides directory of court reporting firms worldwide.

13805 ■ CPAjobs.com
URL: http://www.cpajobs.com

Description: Serves as a job site network that lists several accounting and finance jobs for Certified Public Accountants. Features employment listings for CPAs at all levels of their careers.

13806 ■ CSC CareerSource
URL: http://www.csc.com/careersus

Description: Virtual recruiting site listing employment opportunities in the project management field.

13807 ■ Dance.net
URL: http://www.dance.net

Description: Strives to offer dancers a place on the internet to learn about all dance forms and meet fellow students, dancers, instructors, coaches, choreographers, and studio owners. Provides a database of jobs.

13808 ■ DatabaseAnalyst.com
E-mail: info@careermarketplace.com
URL: http://www.databaseanalyst.com

Description: Features database analyst jobs and products for the software development industry.

13809 ■ Delta T Group
E-mail: cfassl@deltatg.com
URL: http://www.delta-tgroup.com

Description: Specialized contract temporary staffing source for healthcare professionals in the fields of social service, psychiatry, mental health, and substance abuse. Organizations may request services and staffing; job seekers may view services provided, submit a resume, or peruse jobs available.

13810 ■ DentalAssistantJobs.com
E-mail: targetedjobsites@yahoo.com
URL: http://www.dentalassistantjobs.com

Description: Features job opportunities, resume search, postings and employment for dental assistant professionals.

13811 ■ Design Engineer Jobzone
URL: http://designengineerjobzone.com/site/2791/about.htm

Description: Database of job openings for design engineers. Lists the latest jobs from top companies in the field.

13812 ■ Designer Today
URL: http://designertoday.com/Home.aspx

Bimonthly. Online graphic design magazine for graphic designers. Features graphic design and related tutorials, graphic design software and hardware product reviews, resources for graphic design training, graphic design jobs as well as the latest in graphic design news.

13813 ■ Dice.com
URL: http://www.dice.com

Description: Job search database for computer consultants and high-tech professionals, listing thousands of high tech permanent contract and consulting jobs for programmers, software engineers, systems administrators, web developers, and hardware engineers. Also free career advice e-mail newsletter and job posting e-alerts.

13814 ■ DietitianCentral.com
URL: http://www.dietitiancentral.com

Description: Provides information on nutrition jobs, dietician jobs, dietician directory, and jobs in dietetics. Provides information on becoming a dietitian, current and projected national earning averages, job outlook and nature of work.

13815 ■ The Digital Financier
URL: http://www.dfin.com

Description: Job postings from financial companies. Offers links to major job search websites. Has leads for further training and allows companies to post its own job links.

13816 ■ DiversityWorking.com
URL: http://diversityworking.com

Description: Career opportunity resource and job engine for the culturally diverse marketplace.

13817 ■ DocJungle.com
URL: http://www.docjungle.com

Description: Serves as job board built specifically for physicians, doctors, and surgeons. Provides CV posting, job search and career development resources for physicians.

13818 ■ EconCareers.com
URL: http://www.econcareers.com

Description: Serves job seekers with backgrounds in economics, mathematics quantitative methods and econometrics.

13819 ■ EditingCrossing.com
URL: http://www.editingcrossing.com

Description: Shows jobs from employer career pages, job websites, association websites, newspaper classified ads and recruiter sites. Includes editing jobs from all Fortune 500 and Fortune 1,000 companies.

13820 ■ Education America Networks
URL: http://www.educationamerica.net

Description: Education employment network for the United States. Provides information and employment opportunities specifically related to the education industry.

13821 ■ eFinancialCareers.sg
URL: http://www.efinancialcareers.sg

Description: Provides accounting and finance professionals with career opportunities, news and advice, and a variety of tools to market themselves and manage a new job search.

13822 ■ ElectricalAgent.com
URL: http://www.electricalagent.com

Description: Lists job opportunities for electricians such as electrical jobs, apartment maintenance jobs, facilities maintenance jobs and other industry related positions.

13823 ■ ElectricalEngineerJobs.com
URL: http://www.electricalengineerjobs.com

Description: Lists electrical engineer jobs from all over the U.S. Allows users to post resumes and career profiles and search jobs by location. Provides

information about degree programs, resume writing, interview tips and salaries.

13824 ■ ElectronicsEngineer.com
URL: http://www.electronicsengineer.com

Description: Serves as job board for electronics engineering employers showcasing open jobs and products to electronics engineers and to the EE community.

13825 ■ ElitePharmacyJobs.com
URL: http://www.elitepharmacyjobs.com

Description: Provides job seekers with a relevant, current and comprehensive list of pharmacy industry employment opportunities on the internet. Serves as a resource for job seekers, employers and recruiters.

13826 ■ EmployMED: Healthcare Job Listings
E-mail: customerservice@evalumed.com
URL: http://www.evalumed.com/EmployMed.aspx

Description: Lists practice opportunities throughout North America for all medical specialties. Contains job listings directory. Posting option is available for those who wish to advertise jobs. Fee: $25 per month per posting for minimum of two months.

13827 ■ Employment Resources for People with Disabilities
E-mail: familyvillage@waisman.wisc.edu
URL: http://www.familyvillage.wisc.edu/general/employmt.htm

Description: Site offering employment and career-related links to job seekers with disabilities.

13828 ■ Employment Spot
URL: http://www.employmentspot.com

Help wanted advertisements for professional positions, including those in the genetics field. Users can search for positions by city, state or industry.

13829 ■ ENews Monitor
E-mail: editor@bensonmarketing.com
URL: http://bensonmarketing.com/services/enews-monitor-signup

Email news clipping service about the wine industry delivers specific category subscriptions for the wine lover, retailer, restaurateur, wholesaler, winery, grape grower and media.

13830 ■ EnvironmentalCrossing.com
URL: http://www.environmentalcrossing.com

Description: Provides a collection of environmental job listings. Includes lists of employer career pages, job websites, association websites, newspaper classifieds and recruitment sites.

13831 ■ EnvironmentalEngineer.com
URL: http://www.environmentalengineer.com

Description: Provides environmental engineering job listings and products to environmental engineers.

13832 ■ Epidemiologist.com
URL: http://www.epidemiologist.com

Description: Serves as an online source of information for professional epidemiologists, including job listings in the field.

13833 ■ EpidemiologyCareers.com
URL: http://epidemiologycareers.com

Description: Provides a database of epidemiology jobs and resources for job seekers. Includes job title, company, location, job type, salaries, employer and recruiters.

13834 ■ Escoffier.com
URL: http://escoffier.com

Description: Offers a collection of chef job openings, recreational culinary educational resources, resume writing services and career advice for job seekers.

13835 ■ Event Planner Directory 123
Fr: 800-379-4626
URL: http://www.eventplannerdirectory123.com

Description: Directory of various vendor resources.

13836 ■ ExecuNet.com
295 Westport Ave.
Norwalk, CT 06851
Fr: 800-637-3126
E-mail: member.services@execunet.com
URL: http://www.execunet.com

Description: Job site dedicated to the $150,000+ executive job seeker. Members may access job bank, recruiter and employer information, have their resumes reviewed, attend networking meetings, and access cutting-edge career information and references. Fee: Must become member to access services, cost is $219 for six-month membership.

13837 ■ ExecutivesOnly.com, Inc.
100 Jefferson Blvd.
3 Jefferson Pl., Ste. 310
Warwick, RI 02888
Fax: (401)921-6429
Fr: 877-804-5627
E-mail: support@executivesonly.com
URL: http://www.executivesonly.com

Description: Job site specializing in executive positions netting an annual salary of $100K or more. Members can view job bank and set up daily e-mail alerts. They may also choose to recruit the help of a senior adviser who can help review resumes and distribute them to recruiters. Fee: Must become member to access services.

13838 ■ FASEB Career Resources
9650 Rockville Pike
Bethesda, MD 20814-3998
Ph: (301)634-7000
Fax: (301)634-7001
E-mail: careers@faseb.org
URL: http://www.faseb.org/MARC-and-Professional-Development/Career-Resources.aspx

Description: A career opportunity site combined with a development service that attempts to pair applicants at all career levels with employers who hire biomedical scientists and technicians. Biomedical career development is highlighted through career resource tools. Main files include: Careers Online DataNet, Career Online Classified.

13839 ■ FashionCareerCenter.com
URL: http://www.fashioncareercenter.com

Description: Collects and maintains job seeker and company information through voluntary posting of information. Features fashion schools and colleges, fashion jobs, and career advices.

13840 ■ FCS - The 1st Choice in Psychiatric Recruitment
1711 Ashley Cir., Ste. 6
Bowling Green, KY 42104-5801
Fax: (270)782-1055
Fr: 800-783-9152
E-mail: admin@fcspsy.com
URL: http://www.fcspsy.com

Description: Physician search firm specializing in the recruitment of psychiatrists. After the applicant fills out an interest survey, a tailored search is run on the jobs database. Confidential and free.

13841 ■ FedWorld Federal Job Search
National Technical Information Service
5301 Shawnee Rd.
Alexandria, VA 22312
Ph: (703)605-6000
Fr: 800-553-6847
E-mail: helpdesk@fedworld.gov
URL: http://www.fedworld.gov

Description: Database containing employment information in the public sector. Listings include address, job title and information, contact information, geographic location, and data of availability, among others. Main files include: NTIS Federal Job Opportunities; Atlanta Regional Federal Jobs; Chicago Regional Federal Jobs; Dallas Regional Federal Jobs; Philadelphia Regional Federal Jobs; San Francisco Regional Federal Jobs; Washington DC Regional Federal Jobs; National Federal Jobs; S&S Federal Positions Available; Public Health Service Positions; Federal Jobs Listed by State; Atlantic Overseas; Pacific Overseas; Puerto Rico; Virgin Islands; Information on Downloading Files; Federal Jobs EMail Forum; Exit to Main Menu; and Enter Jobs File Library. Free.

13842 ■ Financial Job Network
PO Box 55431
Sherman Oaks, CA 91403
Ph: (818)905-5272
E-mail: info@fjn.com
URL: http://www.fjn.com

Description: Contains information on international and national employment opportunities for those in the financial job market. Job listings may be submitted, as well as resumes. Main files include: Testimonials, Calendar, Corporate Listings, FJN Clients, more. Free to candidates.

13843 ■ FinancialServicesCrossing.com
URL: http://www.financialservicescrossing.com

Description: Offers a collection of top financial services job openings carefully researched by analysts. Provides instant access to a comprehensive pool of listings in the industry of financial services.

13844 ■ FindAMechanic.com
URL: http://www.findamechanic.com

Description: Connects employers with mechanics and technicians. Focuses on auto, truck, diesel, equipment and/or marine mechanics and other positions in the industry.

13845 ■ FindaPilot.com
URL: http://www.findapilot.com

Description: Exists as a niche pilot jobs website. Provides a database of pilot jobs, allows posting of employments ads, and features a pilot directory.

13846 ■ Fire Career Assistance
URL: http://www.firecareerassist.com

Description: Provides a wide range of career services for fire fighters through features that include job openings, fire fighter qualifications, physical fitness test, firefighter oral board questions, written exams, firefighter interviews and others.

13847 ■ Fire Service Employment
URL: http://www.fireserviceemployment.com

Description: Gives special focus on EMTs and firefighters. Provides free recruitment information, links to fire service websites, firefighter and EMS job posting for employers, firefighter testing and interview tips and fire service career advice.

13848 ■ Firefighter-Jobs.com
URL: http://www.firefighter-jobs.com

Description: Exists as an online job site that lists various city, state or federal firefighting or EMT jobs. Includes other important employment information for aspiring firefighters such as a guide for professional resume writing and preparing for an interview.

13849 ■ Firehouse.com
URL: http://www.firehouse.com

Description: Provides fire rescue professionals with career services through features that include job openings, forums, products, news, members information, images, trainings, and events. Features a job board that covers company information, position type, position title, requirements, and salary.

13850 ■ FireJobs.com
URL: http://www.firejobs.com

Description: Seeks to find new firefighter employment for recruit firefighters just out of the academy and those who are already firefighters and want to move to a different department.

13851 ■ FiremenJobs.com
URL: http://www.firemenjobs.com

Description: Exists as an online firefighter job search site that provide its members with a database of updated jobs. Includes preparation tips, exam books, list of fire departments and schools and other career services.

13852 ■ FireRescue1.com
URL: http://www.firerescue1.com

Description: Serves as an online career portal that provides firefighters with the information and resources that make them better able to protect their communities and stay safer on the job. Serves as a growing network where firefighting personnel and aspiring professionals can find relevant news, watch online videos, locate important training information and product purchases, and interact with each other.

13853 ■ First Steps in the Hunt: Daily News for Online Job Hunters
E-mail: colleen@interbiznet.com
URL: http://www.interbiznet.com/hunt/index.html

Description: Database provides a wide variety of information on job hunting on the Internet, as well as links to other sources of information. Included are examples of online web page resumes and links to information about publishing them. Also includes current and archived articles, company job sites, and a listing of job hunting tools and products that may help in the job search. Main files include: Sponsors; Tools; Archives; Products; and Info.

13854 ■ FlightAttendantJobsite.com
URL: http://www.flightattendantjobsite.com

Description: Serves as an online career resource for flight attendants. Allows job seekers to post their resumes and features other career resources such as job search and interviewing, self-assessment tools and more.

13855 ■ FlipDog.com
URL: http://www.flipdog.com

Description: A Monster.com web site. Job search site with job board, resume posting, automated job finders with e-mail alert, resume coaching and broadcasting, career resource center and semi-monthly newsletter. Registration is free.

13856 ■ FoodServicesCrossing.com
URL: http://www.foodservicescrossing.com

Description: Features job listings for the food services industry.

13857 ■ Freeality Online Career and Job Search
E-mail: freeality@juno.com
URL: http://www.freeality.com/jobst.htm

Description: Listing of career-related search engines, along with links to other career resources.

13858 ■ FreelancePhotoJobs.com
URL: http://www.freelancephotojobs.com

Description: Offers daily freelance photography jobs to help freelance photographers.

13859 ■ FreelanceWriting.com
URL: http://www.freelancewriting.com

Description: Career resource for freelance writing professionals. Includes listings of freelance writing jobs, articles, writing contests, writing events, and more.

13860 ■ FreshWebJobs.com
URL: http://www.freshwebjobs.com

Description: Serves as job board for web professionals providing freelance and full-time jobs.

13861 ■ Fuel Cells 2000
1100 H St. NW, Ste. 800
Washington, DC 20005
Ph: (202)785-4222
Fax: (202)785-4313
E-mail: jennifer@fuelcells.org
URL: http://www.fuelcells.org

Description: Provides news, educational resources, and job postings.

13862 ■ FundraisingCrossing.com
URL: http://www.fundraisingcrossing.com

Description: Provides a comprehensive collection of researched fundraising job openings. Provides instant access to listings based on particular area of focus. Includes ads from Fortune 500 and Fortune 1,000 companies.

13863 ■ FuneralNet.com
Fr: 800-721-8166
E-mail: info@funeralnet.com
URL: http://www.funeralnet.com

Description: General mortuary science information site contains Funeral Careers section with information on continuing education and classifieds section with postings for internship and employment opportunities.

13864 ■ Gables Search Group, Inc.
E-mail: info@gablessearch.com
URL: http://www.gablessearch.com

Description: Online job search group that provides employment opportunities for legal, accounting and finance, information technology, sales/marketing and engineering positions. Provides placement for full and part-time permanent positions, in addition to temporary to permanent placements.

13865 ■ GadBall.com
URL: http://www.gadball.com

Description: Online job search that covers all industries. Features discussion forums to provide opportunities for networking and sharing. Allows free resume posting and distribution.

13866 ■ Gamasutra
CMP Media LLC
600 Harrison St., 5th Fl.
San Francisco, CA 94107
Ph: (516)562-5000
E-mail: help@gamasutra.com
URL: http://www.gamasutra.com

Online resource provides up-to-date information about the video game industry as well as job listings, resumes, and featured companies.

13867 ■ GameJobs.com
URL: http://www.gamejobs.com

Description: Provides jobs in the video and computer gaming industry.

13868 ■ GasWork.com: The Largest Internet Anesthesia Employment Resource
E-mail: support@gaswork.com
URL: http://www.gaswork.com

Description: The largest anesthesia employment resource. Lists positions for anesthesiologists, CRNA's, and more. Visitors may post or search jobs.

13869 ■ Genetics Society of America: Positions Open
URL: http://www.genetics-gsa.org

Description: Listing of position announcements formerly published in Genetics. Members may e-mail job listings to the site to be posted.

13870 ■ GeologistCareers.com
URL: http://www.geologistcareers.com

Description: Online job search that provides information and resources for geologists.

13871 ■ Get Audiology Jobs
URL: http://www.getaudiologyjobs.com

Description: Serves as a one-step resource for finding and filling audiology positions. Allows employers to post job openings free of charge while also allowing job seekers to search through audiology job listings.

13872 ■ Get Robotics Jobs
URL: http://www.getroboticsjobs.com/about.php

Description: Serves as a community for robotics job seekers. Provides an easy-to-use resume template to make the job application process easy and convenient.

13873 ■ Get School Counselor Jobs
URL: http://www.getschoolcounselorjobs.com

Description: Serves as a one-stop resource for finding and filling school counselor positions.

13874 ■ GetDesktopPublishingJobs.com
URL: http://www.getdesktoppublishingjobs.com

Description: Provides resources for finding and filling desktop publishing positions. Offers job postings and employment opportunities worldwide.

13875 ■ GetElectricianJobs.com
URL: http://www.getelectricianjobs.com

Description: Offers electrician job postings and employment opportunities.

13876 ■ GetEntryLevelAttorneyJobs.com
URL: http://www.getentrylevelattorneyjobs.com

Description: Provides online job search for entry level attorney professionals.

13877 ■ GetEpidemiologistJobs.com
URL: http://www.getepidemiologistjobs.com

Description: Provides a resource for finding and filling epidemiologist positions.

13878 ■ GetImmigrationAttorneyJobs.com
URL: http://www.getimmigrationattorneyjobs.com

Description: Provides online job searches for immigration law professionals. Gives free weekly job listings via email.

13879 ■ GetPhotographyJobs.com
URL: http://www.getphotographyjobs.com

Description: Offers online photography job postings and employment services.

13880 ■ GlamourJob.com
E-mail: info@glamourjob.com
URL: http://glamjob.com

Description: Provides lists of resources and services for job search on the web. Lists job sites where employees can search for a job or post their resume.

13881 ■ GobsOfJobs.com
URL: http://www.gobsofjobs.com

Acts as an interactive career site devoted to the hardware, software and information technology industries. Functions as a career management tool for job candidates and employers.

13882 ■ Graduate School of Library and Information Science Resources
University of Illinois at Urbana-Champaign
501 E Daniel St.
MC 493
Champaign, IL 61820-6211
Ph: (217)333-3280
Fax: (217)244-3302
Fr: 800-982-0914
E-mail: gslis@uiuc.edu
URL: http://www.lis.illinois.edu

Description: Database contains links to site posting library science related jobs available.

13883 ■ GrantsNet
E-mail: membership@aaas.org
URL: http://sciencecareers.sciencemag.org/funding

Description: Grant-locating site intended for scientists in training who may become vulnerable in an era of competitive funding. Includes a directory of over 600 programs with contact information within a searchable database.

13884 ■ Great Insurance Jobs
URL: http://www.greatinsurancejobs.com

Description: Contains varied insurance positions. Job seekers may browse employee profiles, post resumes, and read descriptions of hundreds of recently-posted insurance jobs.

13885 ■ GreatAupair.com
URL: http://www.greataupair.com

Description: Exists as a website created for matching nannies and au pairs with families worldwide. Offers a way for host families, nannies and au pairs to easily find their matches.

13886 ■ GreatPharmacyJobs.com
URL: http://www.greatpharmacyjobs.com

Description: Presents employment opportunities across the United States and North America. Uses a distributed advertising system that provides unique content and unique jobs.

13887 ■ GuideToHealthcareSchools.com
E-mail: privacy@degreepages.com
URL: http://www.guidetohealthcareschools.com

Online resource lists education and training in the healthcare industry.

13888 ■ Guru.com
5001 Baum Blvd., Ste. 760
Pittsburgh, PA 15213
Fax: (412)687-4466
Fr: 888-687-1316
URL: http://www.guru.com

Description: Job board specializing in contract jobs for creative and information technology professionals. Also provides online incorporation and educational opportunities for independent contractors along with articles and advice.

13889 ■ Headhunt.com: The Counsel Network
URL: http://www.thecounselnetwork.com

Description: Job search and career resource site for attorneys. Search for jobs, post profile, contact recruiters and consultants, download PDF career guides, and more. Registration is free.

13890 ■ Health Care Job Store
395 South End Ave., Ste. 15-D
New York, NY 10280
Ph: (561)630-5201
E-mail: jobs@healthcarejobstore.com
URL: http://www.healthcarejobstore.com

Description: Job sites include every job title in the healthcare industry, every healthcare industry and every geographic location in the U.S.

13891 ■ Health Care Recruitment Online
E-mail: info@healthcarerecruitment.com
URL: http://healthcarerecruitment.com

Description: Helps seekers find healthcare positions through on-line postings with national staffing companies and hospital partners. Main files include: Featured Employers, Job Search, Immediate Openings, Relocating, Career Management, State boards, and more.

13892 ■ Health Search USA
Fax: (602)650-0664
Fr: 800-899-2200
E-mail: info@healthsearchusa.com
URL: http://www.healthsearchusa.com

Description: A site for national physician recruitment.

Offers job postings classified by region and salary comparison.

13893 ■ HealthCareerWeb.com
URL: http://www.healthcareerweb.com

Description: Advertises jobs for healthcare professionals. Main files include: Jobs, Employers, Resumes, Jobwire. Relocation tools and career guidance resources available.

13894 ■ HealthCareProfessional.com
URL: http://www.healthcareprofessional.com

Description: Provides jobs for directors, executives, managers, and supervisors in the health care industry.

13895 ■ HealthcareSource Job Board
URL: http://jobs.healthcaresource.com

Description: Healthcare human resources professionals. Provides employers and job seekers with resources for all areas of the healthcare field.

13896 ■ HealthEconomics.com
URL: http://www.healtheconomics.com

Description: Health outcomes professionals. Lists internet resources focused on health outcomes and health care value. Provides a world-wide list of resources on outcomes research, health economics, pharmacoeconomics, managed care, value in medicine, health-related quality of life, performance assessment, and quality of care.

13897 ■ HealthNewsDigest.com
E-mail: contact@healthnewsdigest.com
URL: http://healthnewsdigest.com/news

Description: Electronic news network. Covers breaking news and features on health, science and the environment. Lists jobs from all areas of the healthcare arena.

13898 ■ Heidrick & Struggles Management Search
233 S Wacker Dr.
Willis Tower, Ste. 4200
Chicago, IL 60606-6303
Ph: (312)496-1200
URL: http://www.heidrick.com/pages/default.aspx

Description: Executive search firm that will distribute registered resumes to recruiters with suitable positions available.

13899 ■ HelpWanted.com
E-mail: admin@helpwanted.com
URL: http://www.helpwanted.com

Description: Site providing job postings, resume service, and listing of employment agencies and recruiters. Caters to job seekers, employers, and agencies.

13900 ■ HigherEdJobs.com
E-mail: jobseeker@higheredjobs.com
URL: http://www.higheredjobs.com

Description: Exists as a job database focused exclusively on college and university positions. Provides a recruitment tool that adds value to the job seeker and recruiter by offering cost-effective, innovative, useful, and timely services.

13901 ■ Hiredface.com
URL: http://www.hiredface.com

Description: Serves as a career opportunity resource and job search engine for all industries. Allows job seekers to search by title, keywords or location.

13902 ■ HireDiversity.com
E-mail: hd@hirediversity.com
URL: http://www.hirediversity.com

Description: Exists as an online service for diversity recruitment and career development. Provides services and networking opportunities while linking under-represented candidates with Fortune 1000 corporations, government agencies, and non-profit/educational institutions.

13903 ■ Honor First
URL: http://www.honorfirst.com

Description: Serves as the unofficial website of the United States Border Patrol. Includes information on how to apply, pay and benefits, hiring process, study guides for the examination, and class schedules. Provides links to other sites with information on becoming a border patrol agent.

13904 ■ HoopCoach.org
URL: http://www.hoopcoach.org

Serves as a source for NBA, NCAA, NAIA, and high school basketball coaching jobs. Features salary information and networking opportunities with other coaches.

13905 ■ Hospitality Jobs Online
URL: http://www.hospitalityonline.com

Description: Enables hospitality industry job seekers to find career information, information about employers and tips and techniques to help them succeed. Provides daily updates of hotel jobs, resort jobs, restaurant jobs and club jobs nationwide.

13906 ■ Hospitality Link
URL: http://www.hospitalitylink.com

Online job site for the wine and hospitality industry.

13907 ■ HospitalPharmacyJobs.com
URL: http://www.hospitalpharmacyjobs.com/Public/Index.aspx

Description: Exists as an online job site focused entirely and exclusively on pharmacists interested in beginning or expanding their careers in hospital pharmacy. Provides a database of available hospital pharmacy positions located nationwide by location and positions of interest.

13908 ■ Hotel Jobs Network
E-mail: info@hoteljobsnetwork.com
URL: http://www.hoteljobsnetwork.com/home

Online job site for the hospitality industry.

13909 ■ Hotel Online
E-mail: contactus@hotel-online.com
URL: http://www.hotel-online.com

Description: Provides news, trends, discussion forums, employment opportunities, and classified advertising for the hospitality industry.

13910 ■ Hound.com
URL: http://www.hound.com

Description: Lists unadvertised job listings from employer websites. Enables job seekers to perform detailed job searches across a range of categories to find specific jobs that suit their interests and experience.

13911 ■ HPCareer.Net
URL: http://www.hpcareer.net/index.jsp

Description: Serves professionals in the health promotion related fields including health education, wellness, health, and fitness. Provides industry-specific career services for members/subscribers.

13912 ■ HSCareers.com
E-mail: info@hscareers.com
URL: http://www.hscareers.com

Description: Offers employment and human services niche site to assist human service professionals.

13913 ■ HumanResourcesCentral.com
URL: http://www.humanresourcescentral.com

Description: Provides job opportunities for human resource professionals.

13914 ■ HVAC-Industry.com
URL: http://www.hvac-industry.com

Description: Provides job opportunities and products to the heating ventilation and air conditioning industry.

13915 ■ iHireAccounting
URL: http://www.ihireaccounting.com

Description: Serves as a job site network that lists thousands of accounting jobs and includes exclusive job postings, internet job boards, newspapers and classified ads.

13916 ■ iHireOptometry
URL: http://www.ihireoptometry.com

Description: Offers nationwide career opportunities for candidates as well as posting options for employers.

13917 ■ Illinois Certified Public Accountant Society Career Center
550 W Jackson, Ste. 900
Chicago, IL 60661-5716
Ph: (312)993-0407
Fax: (312)993-9954
Fr: 800-993-0407
URL: http://www.icpas.org/hc-career-center.aspx?id=2178

Description: Offers job hunting aid to members of the Illinois CPA Society only. Opportunity for non-members to join online. Main files include: Overview of Services, Resume Match, Career Seminars, Career Resources, Free Job Listings, Per Diem Pool, and Career Bibliographies.

13918 ■ IMcareer.com
URL: http://www.imcareer.com

Description: Serves as a job board for internal medicine physicians and jobs for sub-specialty of internal medicine.

13919 ■ IMDiversity.com
URL: http://www.imdiversity.com

Description: Provides jobs for underrepresented minorities and other diverse job seekers. Offers a job bank that lists diversity sensitive employers. Includes other job search features such as customized resume and career management tools.

13920 ■ Immigration Advocates Network
URL: http://www.immigrationadvocates.org

Description: Provides an online resource and communication site to enhance and unify the work of the nation's immigrants' rights organizations.

13921 ■ Immigration Assistant
URL: http://www.immigration-usa.com

Description: Computer program that combines U.S. immigration law reference materials, learning tools and all the immigration forms that an immigrant might need.

13922 ■ Immigration.com
URL: http://www.immigration.com

Description: Supports the immigrant community by providing information and resources. Provides extensive visa information, legal services, and general legal advice to high technology and other businesses, and negotiates and drafts high-tech contracts. Provides links to resources that immigrants and other individuals can use to start a life in the United States.

13923 ■ Indeed.com
URL: http://www.indeed.com

Description: Job search database that covers all industries. Lists jobs by title, company and location. Search results includes salary information/salary range for the particular industry. Provides posting trends for all industries.

13924 ■ IndustrialEngineer.com
URL: http://www.industrialengineer.com

Description: Provides industrial engineering job listings and products to industrial engineers.

13925 ■ InformationTechnologyCrossing.com
URL: http://www.informationtechnologycrossing.com

Description: Provides information on IT jobs.

13926 ■ Institute of Food Technologists - IFT Career Center
525 W Van Buren, Ste. 1000
Chicago, IL 60607
Ph: (312)782-8424
Fax: (312)782-8348
Fr: 800-438-3663
E-mail: info@ift.org
URL: http://www.ift.org

Description: Offers job information and resources for those considering the Food Science and Technology field. Employers may post for full- or part-time positions and have the option of receiving a resume file of current job seekers. IFT members may register for a six-month confidential service to have their credentials reviewed by food industry employers. Job seekers who list credentials will receive the monthly Jobs Available bulletin. Main files include: Employment and Salary Information, How to Find Your First Job in the Food Sciences, Resources for Non-US Job Seekers, and more.

13927 ■ InsuranceJobs.com
E-mail: info@insurancejobs.com
URL: http://www.insurancejobs.com

Description: Offers employment and careers in the insurance industry.

13928 ■ InsuranceUnderwritingWeb.com
E-mail: info@insuranceunderwritingweb.com
URL: http://www.insuranceunderwritingweb.com

Description: Assists underwriters in finding employment and job postings.

13929 ■ IntelligenceCareers.com
Fax: (703)995-0863
Fr: 800-919-8284
E-mail: customerservice@intelligencecareers.com
URL: http://www.intelligencecareers.com

Provides an online job search for intelligence positions by state, U.S. Forces overseas, and worldwide.

13930 ■ InteriorDesignJobs.com
URL: http://interiordesignjobs.sellisp.com/Default.asp

Description: Provides sources of employment information for professionals in the interior design industry.

13931 ■ Internet Career Connection
URL: http://www.iccweb.com

Description: Online career and employment guidance agency. Site's services include: Help Wanted USA-job seekers can access one million help wanted ads; U.S. Government Employment Opportunities; Worldwide Resume/Talent Bank-job seekers can post resumes. Employers may view over 50,000 resumes and career advice articles.

13932 ■ IT Classifieds
URL: http://www.itclassifieds.com

Description: Serves as career site for information technology professionals.

13933 ■ ITworld
URL: http://www.itworld.com

Description: Participatory site that acts as a forum for IT professionals and technology vendors to discuss challenges and solutions in the IT world.

13934 ■ JobBank USA
URL: http://www.jobbankusa.com

Description: Serves as an online resource for job

seekers, employers, recruiters, and human resource professionals.

13935 ■ Job.com
E-mail: jobseekersupport@job.com
URL: http://jobs.com

Description: Seekers can post resumes, search through job databank and use website "powertools" such as resume coaching and distribution, career direction report, personal salary report, online education and self-employment links, and more.

13936 ■ JobCop.com
URL: http://www.jobcop.com

Description: Lists job openings and career development opportunities in police and law enforcement. Sorts jobs according to department/bureau and state.

13937 ■ JobFind.com
E-mail: jobfind@jobfind.com
URL: http://www.bostonherald.com/jobfind

Description: Job site that includes job search board, resume posting with HTML capabilities, "inbox" for e-mail job alerts, corporate profiles, job fair search and career resources.

13938 ■ Jobfront
URL: http://www.jobfront.com

Description: Serves as a job search engine that covers all industries.

13939 ■ JobHunt: On-Line Job Meta-list
E-mail: info@job-hunt.org
URL: http://www.job-hunt.org

Description: Database containing list of career search websites from various sources in the United States. Main files include: Categories: Academia; Classified Ads; Companies; General; Newsgroup Searches; Recruiting Agencies; Science, Engineering, and Medicine. Other Job Resources: Commercial Services; Other Meta-lists; Reference Material; Resume Banks; University Career Resource Centers. Also contains links to other job sites and free PDF file on choosing a career search site.

13940 ■ Jobirn
E-mail: jobirn@jobirn.com
URL: http://jobirn.com/Jobs-and-Careers.php

Description: Acts as a referral network that connects applicants with employees inside the company where they would like to work. Makes connecting easy through services such as video conferencing and chat.

13941 ■ JobPharm.com
URL: http://www.jobpharm.com

Description: Features a "JobGarden" that lists various pharmacy jobs and other career service facilities. Uses a database where users can either browse through the listings or search to narrow down job choices.

13942 ■ Jobs4Actuary.com
URL: http://www.jobs4actuary.com

Description: Provides users with advanced job search tools and employment resources for career advancement. Offers actuarial recruiting service and actuarial job database.

13943 ■ Jobs4Gems.com
URL: http://jobs4gems.com

Description: Serves as a web location for employment opportunities in the jewelry industry. Includes services that allow job seekers to work with professionals in the jewelry industry and gain employment at the top jewelry companies.

13944 ■ Jobs4HR.com
URL: http://www.jobs4hr.com

Description: Provides job opportunities for human resource professionals.

13945 ■ Jobserve
URL: http://www.jobserve.us

Description: Advertises jobs from all over the world. Matches the skills and location of every job seeker.

13946 ■ JobsForLoanOfficers.com
URL: http://jobsforloanofficers.com

Description: Serves the mortgage, real estate, financial services, insurance, title, and related industries. Provides tips, training, and advice to mortgage, real estate, and related professionals.

13947 ■ JobsInSports.com
URL: http://www.jobsinsports.com

Description: Provides an online database of sports jobs and internships. Features a resume bank for sports industry employers.

13948 ■ JobsOT.com
URL: http://www.jobsot.com

Description: Provides solutions for finding job opportunities and job candidates dedicated specifically to the occupational therapy profession.

13949 ■ JobsSLP.com
E-mail: customerservice@jobsslp.com
URL: http://www.jobsslp.com

Description: Serves as job board dedicated specifically to the speech and audiology profession.

13950 ■ JobStar.org
E-mail: electrajobstar@earthlink.net
URL: http://jobstar.org

Description: Job search guide based in California. Includes career guides and information on local, national and international career counseling centers, resumes, salaries, and hidden jobs.

13951 ■ Jobvertise.com
URL: http://www.jobvertise.com

Description: Provides a database of jobs and resumes.

13952 ■ JobWeb.com
URL: http://www.jobweb.com

Description: Site is maintained by the National Association of Colleges and Employers (NACE). Provides career-related information and job listings to college students and graduates.

13953 ■ JournalismNext.com
E-mail: info@journalismnext.com
URL: http://www.journalismnext.com

Description: Exists as a community website for minority journalists and media professionals. Allows employers to post job openings while also allowing job seekers to search through job listings.

13954 ■ Juju Job Search Engine
URL: http://www.job-search-engine.com/jobs?k=winemaking

Online listing of jobs, particularly those in the wine industry.

13955 ■ JustTechJobs.com
E-mail: support@justtechjobs.com
URL: http://www.justtechjobs.com

Description: Serves as a jobsite that provides employers with a technology specific focus and provides job seekers with job postings aimed at those specific tech jobs. Offers a community of 15 million tech professionals and also supports several technology websites.

13956 ■ Law.com: Court Reporter Directory
URL: http://www.almexperts.com/litigation/Court%20Reporters/LitExpert/1125822

Description: An online directory for those seeking services of court reporters.

13957 ■ Law.com: Law Jobs
URL: http://www.lawjobs.com

Description: Visitors can post job openings for attorneys, legal support staff and temporary workers. Also resources for legal recruiters and temporary staffing agencies.

13958 ■ LawCrossing.com
URL: http://www.lawcrossing.com

Description: Offers a collection of active legal jobs. Monitors the hiring needs of legal employers including law firms, corporations, government offices and public interest organizations in the United States.

13959 ■ Lawyers Weekly
URL: http://lawyersweeklyclassifieds.com

Description: Provides legal employment opportunities on the web. Maintains job listings from law firms, legal recruiters and corporate legal departments throughout the country, with new listings posted weekly.

13960 ■ Learn About Robots
URL: http://www.learnaboutrobots.com

Description: Specifically designed for individuals intending to learn about robots and robotics engineering. Provides information to assist people in learning about robots. Covers a varied scope about robotics from robot vision, motion control, research and forward kinematics.

13961 ■ LegalStaff.com
URL: http://www.legalstaff.com

Description: Provides list of legal and law-related jobs. Offers free searches, job agent feature, and the opportunity to post qualifications for employers to review.

13962 ■ Library and Information Technology Association Job Listing
E-mail: lita@ala.org
URL: http://www.ftrf.org/ala/mgrps/divs/lita/professional/jobs/index.cfm

Description: Contains weekly postings of available library jobs. Searchable by region.

13963 ■ Library Job Postings on the Internet
E-mail: sarah@libraryjobpostings.org
URL: http://www.libraryjobpostings.org

Description: Employers may post library position announcements. Also contains links to around 250 library employment sites and links to library-related e-mail lists. Positions are searchable by region and type of library.

13964 ■ Life Coach Directory
URL: http://www.life-coach-directory.com

Description: Serves as a directory of life coaching resources for individuals interested in life coaching. Covers a variety of topics regarding life coaching such as certifications, strategies, courses and careers.

13965 ■ Lifecoaching.com
URL: http://www.lifecoaching.com

Description: Serves as an information resource for both life coaches and clients. Provides life coaching resources, life coaching quizzes and other vital tools for any individual intending to becoming a life coach.

13966 ■ LIScareer.com
URL: http://www.liscareer.com

Description: Offers career development resources for librarians, information professionals, students and those considering a career in library and information science. Includes practical advice contributed by information professionals, links to online resources and information about print resources.

13967 ■ LISJobs.com
URL: http://www.lisjobs.com

Description: Provides career information for librarians and information professionals. Offers more resources beyond job hunting such as career development resources that are intended to help clients continue to grow as professionals.

13968 ■ Locate Jobs Network
URL: http://www.locatejobsnetwork.com

Description: Consists of niche job boards covering various industries.

13969 ■ LocatorJobs.com
URL: http://www.locatorjobs.com

Description: Features job postings focused on the utilities industry.

13970 ■ MailmanStuff.com
E-mail: mailman@rollanet.org
URL: http://www.mailmanstuff.com

Description: Shared resources for letter carriers.

13971 ■ Mandy's International Film and TV Production Directory
E-mail: directory@mandy.com
URL: http://www.mandy.com/1/filmtvjobs.cfm

Description: Employment site intended for film and TV professionals. Employers may post free Jobs Offered listings. Job seekers may post free Jobs Wanted ads.

13972 ■ Marketing Career Network
Fr: 888-491-8833
URL: http://www.marketingcareernetwork.com

Description: Online recruitment resource that aligns employers with professional marketing membership organizations. Brings together audiences from every marketing discipline and connects them through a single job board network.

13973 ■ MarketingCrossing.com
URL: http://www.marketingcrossing.com

Description: Offers collection of marketing jobs, including marketing director, marketing analyst, marketing content writer, and associate brand manager positions. Features industry-specific articles relating to job searches and developments in the marketing industry.

13974 ■ MarketingHire.com
URL: http://www.marketinghire.com

Description: Provides users with access to marketing jobs, advertising jobs and public relations jobs from respected employers. Enables employers and recruiters to reach a highly targeted audience of qualified marketing, advertising, PR, research and sales professionals.

13975 ■ MarketingJobForce.com
URL: http://www.marketingjobforce.com

Description: Online destination for professionals looking to enhance their careers in marketing.

13976 ■ MarketingJobs.com
URL: http://www.marketingjobs.com

Description: Provides professional jobs across the United States in sales, marketing, and advertising. Includes jobs from entry to executive level.

13977 ■ MarketResearchCareers.com
URL: http://www.marketresearchcareers.com

Description: Focuses exclusively on the market research industry. Offers a comprehensive database of resumes and jobs dedicated to market research professionals. Provides online services to fill marketing research jobs with a selection of qualified professionals.

13978 ■ MBA Careers
3934 SW Corbett Ave.
Portland, OR 97239
Ph: (503)221-7779
Fax: (503)221-7780
E-mail: eric@careerexposure.com
URL: http://mbacareers.com

Description: Job site that provides resume posting, databank search and e-mail alert services to MBA and other advanced graduate degree holders.

13979 ■ MDSPots.com
E-mail: info@mdspots.com
URL: http://www.mdspots.com

Description: Helps physicians locate new practice and job opportunities. Offers free access to physician employment opportunities, free CV posting, customized job search capabilities and real time e-mail notifications of new physician employment opportunities.

13980 ■ MedExplorer.com
E-mail: medmaster@medexplorer.com
URL: http://www.medexplorer.com

Description: Employment postings make up one module of this general medical site. Other sections contain: Newsletter, Classifieds, and Discussion Forum.

13981 ■ MedHealthJobs.com
URL: http://medhealthjobs.com

Description: Covers online healthcare career resource and job search tools. Includes non-clinical jobs in the healthcare field.

13982 ■ MediaJobMarket.com
URL: http://jobs.adweek.com

Description: Exists as a job search resource for finding advertising and media jobs.

13983 ■ MediaRecruiter.com
E-mail: art@mediarecruiter.com
URL: http://www.mediarecruiter.com

Description: Provides a listing of media positions nationwide, serving the advertising and communications industry. Specializes in the areas of employment that are associated with the media, including management, marketing, news, talent, research, promotion, co-op, traffic, engineering, production, technical, and sales support.

13984 ■ Medical Fitness Association
1905 Huguenot Rd.
Richmond, VA 23235-8026
Ph: (804)897-5701
E-mail: info@medicalfitness.org
URL: http://medicalfitness.org

Description: Serves as a resource to the medical fitness industry as it informs, promotes, and provides networking and educational opportunities to expand knowledge about the industry. Fosters professional development by sponsoring conferences, seminars, and educational programs. Provides career listings and internships while pursuing growth and success for the medical fitness industry.

13985 ■ MedicalHealthServicesManager.com
URL: http://www.medicalhealthservicesmanager.com

Description: Covers career opportunities and training information for aspiring medical health managers. Offers links, job listings, resumes and more.

13986 ■ MedicalTechnologistsCentral.com
URL: http://www.medicaltechnologistscentral.com

Description: Offers medical technologist jobs and products in the healthcare industry.

13987 ■ MedicalWorkers.com
URL: http://www.medicalworkers.com

Description: Provides a forum where employers and job seekers in the healthcare field can find each other.

13988 ■ MedSourceConsultants.com
300 Main St., 7th Fl.
Stamford, CT 06901
Fax: (203)324-0555
Fr: 800-575-2880
E-mail: dpascale@medsourceconsultants.com
URL: http://www.medsourceconsultants.com

Description: Site houses a physician search and consulting company for psychiatrists. Consultants attempt to match job seekers to positions according to the individual's personal and professional needs. This page also aids institutions looking to recruit psychiatrists.

13989 ■ MedTechJobsite.com
URL: http://www.medtechjobsite.com

Description: Provides new job openings for medical techs, in addition to insightful research into the healthcare and medical employment market, and a career articles section, written and frequented by industry professionals.

13990 ■ Medzilla.com
URL: http://www.medzilla.com

Description: General medical website which matches employers and job hunters to their ideal employees and jobs through search capabilities. Main files include: Post Jobs, Search Resumes, Post Resumes, Search Jobs, Head Hunters, Articles, Salary Survey.

13991 ■ MeteorologyCareers.com
URL: http://www.meteorologycareers.com

Description: Provides information and resources for job seekers searching for meteorology job openings. Includes job title, company, location, job type, salaries, employers, and recruiters.

13992 ■ Michigan Wines
E-mail: mda-michigan-wines@michigan.gov
URL: http://www.michiganwines.com

Online resource provides a directory of Michigan wineries, listings of meetings and events, articles, newsletters, and additional resources concerning the wine industry in Michigan.

13993 ■ MinistryJobs.com
URL: http://www.ministryjobs.com

Description: Provides listing of job openings for ministers.

13994 ■ MinistrySearch.com
URL: http://www.ministrysearch.com

Description: Provides listings of available Christian ministry jobs. Includes senior pastors, worship leaders, youth pastors, and other church leadership positions.

13995 ■ Mobile Marketing Joblist
URL: http://www.mobilemarketingjoblist.com

Description: Focuses on the mobile marketing, special event, seasonal marketing, experiential marketing and promotional marketing industries.

13996 ■ Monster Healthcare
URL: http://healthcare.monster.com

Description: Delivers nationwide access to healthcare recruiting. Employers can post job listings or ads. Job seekers can post and code resumes, and search over 150,000 healthcare job listings, healthcare career advice columns, career resources information, and member employer profiles and services.

13997 ■ Monster.com
E-mail: sales@monster.com.ph
URL: http://www.monster.com.ph

Description: An interactive, continually expanding database of current job openings, including an online career fair, career search help, employer profiles, and a resume posting service. Searching is available by industry, location, company, discipline and keyword. Users can search over 50,000 of position openings, advertise openings, or submit resumes. Employers pay a fee for posting position openings and company profiles. An online form allows for contact with the producers of the database. Main files include: Press Box, Career Center, Job Search Agent, Recruiters' Center. Fee: Free to job seekers; fees for job advertisers.

13998 ■ MonsterTRAK
URL: http://college.monster.com/?wt.mc_n=monster trak

Description: College-targeted job hunting and recruiting site. Students and alumni may enter a user profile or resume to be reviewed by potential employers, or search job listings without doing so. Employers may enter full-time, part-time, temporary, and internship opportunities into the database to be reviewed by students and recent graduates, and may review resumes.

13999 ■ Motion Control Online
URL: http://www.motioncontrolonline.org
Description: Features available positions by location, specialty and other criteria. Serves automation companies involved in robotics, machine vision, motion control and related technologies.

14000 ■ MyMusicJob.com
URL: http://www.mymusicjob.com
Description: Provides international music industry jobs, employment, and internships.

14001 ■ NannyJobs.com
URL: http://www.nannyjobs.com
Description: Provides free access to nanny jobs available across the nation. Offers resources and tools, including career information, conferences and event dates for nannies, and more.

14002 ■ NannyLocators.com
E-mail: nannylocators@gmail.com
URL: http://www.nannylocators.com
Description: Allows posting of nanny availabilities and job-wanted ads. Includes key points on evaluating salary offers and other nanny job information.

14003 ■ NannyNeeded.com
URL: http://www.nannyneeded.com
Description: Provides a database of nanny jobs and nanny services. Offers listings and specific requirements of the jobs.

14004 ■ National Auction List
URL: http://www.nationalauctionlist.com
Description: Provides a list of professional auctioneers, a list of upcoming auctions, and current auction news.

14005 ■ National Insurance Recruiters Association
URL: http://www.insurancerecruiters.com
Description: Contains lists of recruiters (listed by department and line of business) and available insurance positions.

14006 ■ National Society of Genetic Counselors E-Blast
E-mail: nsgc@nsgc.org
URL: http://www.nsgc.org
Allows members to email announcements and messages to the desktops of other members.

14007 ■ National Society of Genetic Counselors Job Connection Service
E-mail: nsgc@nsgc.org
URL: http://jobconnection.nsgc.org
Services include a three-month posting on the Society's website as well as a one-time posting on its Listserv, reaching more than 85 percent of the society's full and associated members. The Listserv

allows users to target a select audience of members in the following specialties: cancer, prenatal, pediatric, cardiovascular, industry, psychiatric disorders, and general.

14008 ■ NationJob Network
E-mail: customerservice@nationjob.com
URL: http://www.nationjob.com
Description: Online job database containing job listings and company profiles. Main files include: Specialty Pages; Custom Jobs Pages; Community Pages; Customer Success Stories.

14009 ■ Net Temps
URL: http://www.net-temps.com
Description: Site specializing in the Staffing industry serving direct placement and temporary (contract) professionals. Net-Temps provides a convenient and free method to post resumes, inquire about available positions and apply for jobs online. Recruiters utilize Net-Temps to publicize available employment opportunities and search the Resume Bank to identify qualified job candidates.

14010 ■ NetJobs.com
E-mail: info@atsnetjobs.com
URL: http://www.netjobs.com
Description: Source for Canadian job hunters and employers. Job seekers may post resumes online and search through job openings. Searches can be performed by job category, company name, or location, or on listings posted within the last ten days.

14011 ■ NetShare.com
83 Hamilton Dr., Ste. 202
Novato, CA 94949
Fr: 800-241-5642
E-mail: netshare@netshare.com
URL: http://www.netshare.com
Description: Members-only resource for $100,000+ executives who are actively searching for new positions or passively tracking the job market. Listings that match posted profile will be e-mailed. Fee: Fees vary by level of service; annual basic level dues are $360.

14012 ■ New Executive Jobs
URL: http://www.newexecutivejobs.com
Description: Provides a listing of companies with available executive jobs in all specialties.

14013 ■ NSBE Online
URL: http://www.nsbe.org
Description: A section of the website of the National Society of Black Engineers. Main files include: Job Search (includes full-time, co-ops, internships, and student jobs), Post a Job, Post a Resume. Fee: $250 to post a job for 60 days.

14014 ■ NuclearMarket.com
E-mail: info@nuclearmarket.com
URL: http://www.nuclearmarket.com
Description: Nuclear Market's Career Center allows seekers to search a database of nuclear jobs in the United States, Europe and beyond. Candidates also have the option of registering their profile in database in order to receive email notification of any relevant vacancies.

14015 ■ NutritionJobs.com
URL: http://www.nutritionjobs.com
Description: Advances the career opportunities for professionals in the fields of nutrition and dietetics. Allows searching or recruiting for jobs online, including timely access to opportunities.

14016 ■ O&P Digital Technologies: OandP.com
E-mail: info@oandp.com
URL: http://www.oandp.com
Online resource provides comprehensive information and services to the orthotics and prosthetics profes-

sion including news, articles, job listings, a calendar of events and a directory of products and services.

14017 ■ OccupationalHealthSafetyTechnician.com
URL: http:// www.occupationalhealthsafetytechnician.com
Description: Provides job and career opportunities for aspiring occupational health safety technicians. Offers links, job listings, sample resumes and more.

14018 ■ OccupationalTherapistAssistant.com
URL: http://www.occupationaltherapistassistant.com
Description: Provides career and employment information for aspiring occupational therapist assistants. Offers links, job listings, sample resumes and more.

14019 ■ OccupationalTherapistJobs.com
E-mail: jobs@healthcarejobstore.com
URL: http://www.occupationaltherapistjobs.com
Description: Includes occupational therapy job listings from all over the United States.

14020 ■ OccupationalTherapyCrossing.com
URL: http://www.occupationaltherapycrossing.com
Description: Provides instant access to job listings based on a job hunter's area of focus. Lists occupational therapy jobs from all Fortune 500 and Fortune 1,000 companies.

14021 ■ Online Sports Career Center
Fr: 800-856-2638
E-mail: comments@atsonlinesports.com
URL: http://www.onlinesports.com/pages/careercenter.html
Description: Resource for sports-related career opportunities, as well as a resume bank for the perusal of potential employers within the sports and recreation industries. Main files include: Job Bank, Resume Bank, Newsletter, Work With Online Sports, Other Internet Resources.

14022 ■ OnlineOrganizing.com
URL: http://www.onlineorganizing.com
Description: Serves as an online source for organizing advice, products, and other information related to professional organizing. Maintains an online listing of professional organizers.

14023 ■ Optometry.com
URL: http://optometry.com/index.php
Description: Features a job board which allows employers and job seekers to quickly and efficiently find one another. Connects thousands of applicants with potential employers for a wide variety of ophthalmic jobs.

14024 ■ OregonWines.com
URL: http://www.oregonwines.com
Online resource provides job postings, a directory of Oregon wineries, an events calendar, news concerning the wine industry and editorials.

14025 ■ Organizing Network
PO Box 12312
Ogden, UT 84414-2312
Ph: (801)668-2410
Fax: (801)782-9832
E-mail: contact.info@organizingnetwork.com
URL: http://www.myorganizedlife.com
Description: Provides a searchable online list of professional organizers based on geographic location for those seeking professional organizing services.

14026 ■ ParalegalJobFinder.com
URL: http://www.paralegaljobfinder.com
Description: Serves as an online career site that provides paralegal jobs, careers and employment. Caters to both job seekers and employers with its free job database where companies that are seeking to hire paralegals, paralegal positions, law assistants

and other industry related positions post jobs daily on the network.

14027 ■ ParalegalJobs.com
URL: http://www.paralegaljobs.com
Description: Offers paralegal job postings and resumes.

14028 ■ PastorFinder.com
URL: http://www.pastorfinder.com
Description: Serves as a job site where churches leaders come to find or fill a job.

14029 ■ PATHcareer.com
URL: http://www.pathcareer.com
Description: Exists as a job board designed to meet the career needs of pathologists.

14030 ■ PayScale, Inc.
E-mail: service@payscale.com
URL: http://www.payscale.com
Online resource provides detailed information concerning salary, vacation time, bonuses and commute time. Also gives tips for salary negotiation and career planning.

14031 ■ Pedorthic Footwear Association
2025 M St. NW, Ste. 800
Washington, DC 20036
Ph: (202)367-1145
Fax: (202)367-2145
Fr: 800-673-8447
E-mail: info@pedorthics.org
URL: http://www.pedorthics.org
Represents the interests of certified and/or licensed pedorthists, the design, manufacture, modification, and fit of shoes and foot orthoses to alleviate problems caused by disease, congenital condition, overuse or injury. Website provides listings of help wanted classified for individuals in the pedorthic industry.

14032 ■ PharmaceuticalCrossing.com
URL: http://www.pharmaceuticalcrossing.com
Description: Consolidates pharmaceutical job openings from various Internet sites.

14033 ■ PharmacyCareerCentral.com
URL: http://www.pharmacycareercentral.com
Description: Features pharmacy jobs and products to the healthcare industry.

14034 ■ PharmacyPostings.com
E-mail: info@pharmacypostings.com
URL: http://www.pharmacypostings.com
Description: Offers pharmacy jobs including pharmacist jobs and other traditional and non-traditional positions. Provides a job search database by category, state or type of position.

14035 ■ PhysEmp.com
URL: http://www.physemp.com
Description: Provides listings of physician jobs for all specialties. Features online physician jobs, job search, and physician employment opportunities and recruitment.

14036 ■ PhysicalSecurityCrossing.com
URL: http://www.physicalsecuritycrossing.com
Description: Offers a comprehensive collection of researched job openings in the physical security field. Lists security jobs from Fortune 500 and Fortune 1,000 companies.

14037 ■ PhysicalTherapist.com
URL: http://www.physicaltherapist.com
Description: Exists as a collaborative informational website designed for the physical therapy community. Provides listings of job opportunities and features physical therapy resources, associations, school search, library search and more.

14038 ■ PhysicalTherapyCrossing.com
URL: http://www.physicaltherapycrossing.com
Description: Provides a collection of researched job openings in the physical therapy field.

14039 ■ Physician-Employments.com
URL: http://www.physician-employments.com
Description: Exists as an employment opportunities resource center for physicians and others in the healthcare industry.

14040 ■ PhysicianCrossroads.com
E-mail: info@physiciancrossroads.com
URL: http://physiciancrossroads.com
Description: Consists of physicians within their professional specialties and a multitude of physician advocate professionals who are intent and passionate about helping colleagues be more successful in their medical practices.

14041 ■ PhysicianRecruiting.com
Fr: 800-880-2028
E-mail: info@physicianrecruiting.com
URL: http://www.physicianrecruiting.com
Description: Provides listings of job opportunities for physicians. Lists jobs according to specialty and state.

14042 ■ PhysiciansCentral.com
URL: http://www.physicianscentral.com
Description: Provides physician jobs and products in the healthcare industry.

14043 ■ Plus50Lifestyles.com
URL: http://plus50lifestyles.com
Description: Serves as a resource of information and materials that are intended to encourage boomers and seniors to live an inspiring life. Provides listings and other resources for individuals involved in coaching such as retirement coaching, life coaching, wellness coaching and others.

14044 ■ PoliceEmployment.com
URL: http://www.policeemployment.com
Description: Online job information center for a variety of careers in federal, state, and local law enforcement. Offers career information and answers questions about obtaining a law enforcement job.

14045 ■ PoliceOne.com
URL: http://www.policeone.com
Description: Provides police officers and law enforcement professionals information and resources. Includes news, videos, products, training, jobs and career resources, awards and grants.

14046 ■ PracticeLink.com
E-mail: physicianhelpdesk@practicelink.com
URL: http://www.practicelink.com
Description: Provides listings of job opportunities for physicians.

14047 ■ PRCrossing.com
URL: http://www.prcrossing.com
Description: Provides a collection of public relations job openings from Fortune 500 and Fortune 1,000 companies.

14048 ■ Premier Careers, Inc.
913 Dogwood Dr.
Fayetteville, TN 37334
Ph: (931)227-8496
E-mail: jim@premiercareers.com
URL: http://www.premiercareers.com
Description: Contains a database with information on candidates searching for jobs in the property and casualty insurance industry and with national sales organizations. Houses resumes and letters of reference. Candidate searches may be run by industry, geography, job title, years of experience, compensation, education, and/or accreditation. Also

offers resume writing and interviewing tips to job hunters.

14049 ■ Premier Health and Fitness Resources
URL: http://phfr.com
Description: Health and fitness professionals. Offers a broad spectrum of health promotion services, networking opportunities, and resource sharing materials. Features resources for finding quality fitness jobs, health promotion job postings, corporate wellness employment opportunities, or other fitness staff positions.

14050 ■ PrintCareers.com
URL: http://www.printcareers.com
Description: Provides job opportunities for marketing, advertising and creative professionals.

14051 ■ PrintingMVP.com
URL: http://www.printingmvp.com
Description: Provides job opportunities for marketing, advertising and creative professionals.

14052 ■ PrintJobs.com
E-mail: printjobs@roadrunner.com
URL: http://www.printjobs.com
Description: Aims to find suitable graphic arts jobs for qualified candidates. Over a hundred jobs are maintained and updated on the site. Fee: Must be paid by employers using the site; no registration charge for job hunters.

14053 ■ PRMVP.com
URL: http://www.prmvp.com
Description: Provides job opportunities for public relations professionals.

14054 ■ Professional Friends of Wine
E-mail: jimlamar@winepros.org
URL: http://winepros.org
Online resource providing wine education, wine information and wine training as well as a directory of wineries and an events calendar.

14055 ■ Professional Organizers Web Ring
E-mail: ringmasters@organizerswebring.com
URL: http://www.organizerswebring.com
Description: Maintains a searchable member directory, as well as information on upcoming organizing events, seminars, workshops, and conferences. Provides an online collection of featured articles written by professional organizers and a section on frequently asked questions in the field of professional organizing.

14056 ■ ProjectManagementCareers.net
URL: http://www.projectmanagementcareers.net
Description: Provides new job openings in addition to research into the management and business employment market. Also contains a career articles section which is written and frequented by industry professionals.

14057 ■ ProjectManagementCrossing.com
URL: http://www.projectmanagementcrossing.com
Description: Lists new job openings for project managers. Shows jobs from employer career pages, job websites, association websites, newspaper classifieds and recruiter sites.

14058 ■ ProjectManager.com
E-mail: support@projectmanager.com
URL: http://www.projectmanager.com
Description: Allows job seekers to create an online resume, browse available jobs, and use a career alert tool linking them with potential employers. Also maintains a knowledge section containing employment information and resources for project managers.

14059 ■ Projects@Work
E-mail: aaron@projectsatwork.com
URL: http://www.projectsatwork.com

Description: Online newsletter for project management professionals. Provides a forum for networking and examines trends in project management.

14060 ■ PromotionsCareers.com
URL: http://www.promotionscareers.com

Description: Provides job opportunities for marketing professionals.

14061 ■ PRRecruiter.com
URL: http://www.prrecruiter.com

Description: Provides online job search for marketing, advertising jobs and resources for both job seekers and employers.

14062 ■ Publish.com
Ziff Davis Enterprise
28 E 28th St.
New York, NY 10016
Ph: (212)503-5900
E-mail: customerservice@ziffdavisenterprise.com
URL: http://www.publish.com

Description: Offers a variety of resources for desktop publishers.

14063 ■ PurchasingCrossing.com
URL: http://www.purchasingcrossing.com

Description: Lists purchasing jobs from Fortune 500 and Fortune 1,000 companies.

14064 ■ RadiologistCareer.com
URL: http://www.radiologistcareer.com

Description: Job board for radiologists and job listings for those who work in radiology. Includes career resources, equipment, product and services.

14065 ■ RadWorking.com
E-mail: service@atsradworking.com
URL: http://www.radworking.com

Description: Employment resource dedicated to the profession of radiology. Site is divided into various job-search sections based on job type or nature of support position.

14066 ■ Recruiters Online Network
E-mail: recruitersonline@earthlink.net
URL: http://www.recruitersonline.com

Description: Site is used by over 8,000 recruiters, search firms, employment agencies, and employment professionals. Job seekers may read the Careers Online magazine, post resumes, and search jobs. Fee: Free to job seekers; fee for recruiters.

14067 ■ RehabJobs Online
E-mail: support@atsrehabjobs.com
URL: http://www.rehabjobsonline.com

Description: Resource center for the professional therapist. Main files include: Therapists Only, Therapy Forums, Nationwide Job Search (database), Therapy Job Outlook, Therapy Job Search Utilities, Therapy Links, Information for Employers and Recruiters.

14068 ■ RehabWorld.com
URL: http://www.rehabworld.com

Description: Site for rehabilitation professionals to learn about the profession and locate jobs. Includes user groups, salary surveys, and chat capabilities. Main files include: Physical Therapy, Occupational Therapy, Speech Therapy, Mental Health, Employer World, Student World, International World, Forum.

14069 ■ RestaurantManager.net
URL: http://www.restaurantmanager.net

Description: Exists as a job site for professional restaurant managers.

14070 ■ RetailSalesManager.net
URL: http://www.retailsalesmanager.net

Description: Provides career opportunities and professional networking community for aspiring retail sales managers. Offers a database of jobs and resumes for both candidates and employers.

14071 ■ Robot Report
URL: http://www.therobotreport.com

Description: Online site that tracks the business of robotics. Maintains a comprehensive worldwide database of public and private companies that are participants in the robotics industry. Gathers and reports industry news, tracks the business of robotics and develops proprietary methods to compare and report industry stock performance to the NASDAQ Composite Index. Also features startup companies.

14072 ■ RTstudents.com
URL: http://www.rtstudents.com

Description: Features medical imaging job listings and career information to help radiology students find jobs upon graduation.

14073 ■ Rx Career Center
URL: http://www.rxcareercenter.com

Description: Serves as a job board on the internet for the pharmacist, pharmacy technician and pharmaceutical industry professional. Provides candidates with current opportunities in a variety of settings that include retail, hospital, clinical, and industry positions.

14074 ■ Ryze Business Networking
E-mail: press@ryze.com
URL: http://www.ryze.com

Description: Provides an online classifieds section as well as networking services.

14075 ■ Sales Classifieds
URL: http://www.salesclassifieds.com

Description: Serves as career site for sales professionals. Provides resources such as job search agents, resume creation and postings.

14076 ■ SalesManagementCentral.com
URL: http://www.salesmanagementcentral.com

Description: Provides resources for sales managers. Offers sales management jobs and products.

14077 ■ Saludos.com
Ph: (323)726-2188
Fax: 800-730-3560
Fr: 800-748-6426
E-mail: info@atssaludos.com
URL: http://www.saludos.com

Description: Supported by Saludos Hispanos magazine, this site is devoted to promoting Hispanic careers and education. It is a prime resource for employers to gain access to the resumes of bilingual college graduates. Online job listings and a resume pool are offered, as well as a career center, links to Hispanic resources, career links, and access to Saludos Magazine.

14078 ■ SelectLeaders.com
E-mail: support@selectleaders.com
URL: http://www.selectleaders.com

Description: Exists as a real estate job site focused on the real estate and finance industries. Serves as a source of information for real estate professionals and executives in managing their careers and networking.

14079 ■ SellingCareers.com
URL: http://www.sellingcareers.com

Provides job opportunities for sales professionals.

14080 ■ SellingCrossing.com
URL: http://www.sellingcrossing.com

Description: Provides collection of sales jobs, including sales manager, sales director, sales consultant,

and media sales positions. Also features industry-specific articles relating to job searches and developments in the professional field.

14081 ■ SLPJob.com
URL: http://www.slpjob.com

Description: Focuses on speech language pathologist-pathology speech therapy jobs.

14082 ■ SmileJobs.com
URL: http://www.smilejobs.com

Description: Features job opportunities, resume search and postings for dental professionals.

14083 ■ Social Work and Social Services Jobs Online
George Warren Brown School of Social Work
Washington University
Campus Box 1196
1 Brookings Dr.
St. Louis, MO 63130-4899
Ph: (314)935-6600
Fax: (314)935-4859
Fr: 800-321-2426
URL: http://gwbweb.wustl.edu/CareerDevelopment/JobsOnline/Pages/Overview.aspx

Description: Specialized database of social work and social services jobs gives a large list of openings sorted by location (both within and outside the United States). Employers may submit job openings. Site also contains career resources and links to related internet job sites.

14084 ■ SocialService.com
E-mail: info@socialservice.com
URL: http://www.socialservice.com

Description: Offers social service or social work jobs, whether in mental health, substance abuse, children and youth, medical social work, criminal justice, domestic violence, counseling, community organizing an outreach, EAP, mentoring homelessness or a variety of other human service areas.

14085 ■ SocialWorkJobBank.com
URL: http://www.socialworkjobbank.com

Description: Serves as an online job board and career center devoted to helping match professional social workers with employers. Allows finding and posting of jobs in all areas of professional social work.

14086 ■ Society of Broadcast Engineers Job Line
Ph: (317)846-9000
Fax: (317)846-9120
E-mail: kjones@sbe.org
URL: http://www.sbe.org/career_jobsonline.php

Description: Job Line is one benefit of membership in the Society of Broadcast Engineers. Includes a resume service to distribute resumes to employers, job contact information, and descriptions of job openings. Also accessible via telephone.

14087 ■ SoftwareEngineer.com
URL: http://www.softwareengineer.com

Description: Provides lists of job and career opportunities for software engineering professionals.

14088 ■ Spedex.com
E-mail: spedex.com@gmail.com
URL: http://www.spedex.com

Description: Provides resources for educators, professionals, parents, consumers, students and other individuals interested in special education. Offers links, online documents, listings of professionals, job listings, school and university listings and more.

14089 ■ Speech-LanguagePathologist.org
URL: http://www.speech-languagepathologist.org

Description: Serves as a community organization and website portal dedicated to the sharing of resources and information about the field of speech-language pathology. Offers resources for clinicians, students, caregivers, educators, and all who are interested in the study and practice of speech-language pathology.

14090 ■ SpeechPathology.com
URL: http://www.speechpathology.com

Description: Provides speech-language pathologists and other interested professionals with opportunities for continuing education, professional news and information, and career opportunities throughout the world.

14091 ■ SportsCareerFinder.com
E-mail: admin@sportscareerfinder.com
URL: http://www.sportscareerfinder.com

Description: Serves as a source of sports job and sports careers. Includes job listings, industry information, and company lists.

14092 ■ Squire Partners LLC:
   WineSquire.com
URL: http://www.winesquire.com/users/scott-miller

Online resource provides job listings for the wine industry as well as directories, links, event listings and articles.

14093 ■ StarChefs.com
E-mail: liz@starchefs.com
URL: http://www.starchefs.com

Description: Contains job board, resume writing service and career advice for job seekers in the culinary arts. Seekers can sign up for free e-mail account and receive job notifications through this service.

14094 ■ StartWright.com
URL: http://www.startwright.com

Description: Provides a comprehensive list of links to various sites on project management, project management methodology, and the project management profession.

14095 ■ StyleCareers.com
E-mail: info@stylecareers.com
URL: http://www.stylecareers.com

Description: Provides a job board for people in the fashion industry.

14096 ■ SummerJobs.com
URL: http://www.summerjobs.com

Description: Database listing seasonal and part-time job opportunities. Job listings are organized by country, state, region, and city. Primary focus is on summer jobs for students and education professionals.

14097 ■ Sunoasis Jobs
E-mail: sunoasisjobs@earthlink.net
URL: http://www.sunoasis.com

Description: Provides job leads for individuals intending to work in the writing, editing and copyediting industry while also providing a resource base for individuals looking for writers, editors, and copywriters.

14098 ■ TalentNetworks.com
E-mail: info@talentnetworks.com
URL: http://www.talentnetworks.com/index.html

Description: A business-to-business portal for the fashion, arts, and entertainment industries. Online site contains industry listings, portfolios and news items.

14099 ■ TaxTalent.com
URL: http://www.taxtalent.com

Description: Provides career management information and access to other career enhancing tools.

14100 ■ Tech-Engine.com
URL: http://techengine.com

Description: Features employment listings concern-

ing the IT and engineering fields. Features employers and recruiters information, resume posting and career resources.

14101 ■ TechRepublic
URL: http://www.techrepublic.com

Description: Online community for IT professionals. Provides a forum where IT professionals can interact, exchange advise and discuss IT topics of interest. Lists employment opportunities by date of posting, job title, company and location.

14102 ■ TechWritingJobs.com
URL: http://www.techwritingjobs.com

Description: Offers up-to-the-minute job listings and job advice for tech writers. Includes other vital career information for tech writers such as writing a tech writing resume, jobs with tech writing agencies, marketing oneself as a freelance technical writer, training for tech writers and more.

14103 ■ TedJob.com
E-mail: contact@tedjob.com
URL: http://www.tedjob.com

Description: Serves as a higher-education job marketplace designed to meet the unique, recruitment requirements for universities, colleges, and other academic organizations.

14104 ■ Telecommuting Jobs
URL: http://www.tjobs.com

Description: Job hunters may enter a resume or post a job-wanted listing. Employers may search talent available and post job availabilities. Site also includes tools to connect telecommuters with employers and job news about telecommuting.

14105 ■ Therapeutic Recreation Directory
URL: http://www.recreationtherapy.com

Description: Provides resources and interworking opportunities for recreation therapists and activity directors. Includes a job bulletin, internship directory, activity and treatment resources, articles and news, chatroom, bulletin boards, and surveys.

14106 ■ TMP/Hudson Global Resources
URL: http://jobs.us.hudson.com

Description: Professional staffing firm website. Job seekers can search job databank and submit their resume to the firm for posting to employers.

14107 ■ Today's Military
URL: http://www.todaysmilitary.com/military-careers

Description: Site provides details on many enlisted and officer occupations and describes training, advancement, and educational services within each of the major services. Includes browsing capabilities to match positions with interests.

14108 ■ TopEchelon.com
PO Box 21390
Canton, OH 44701-1390
Ph: (330)455-1433
E-mail: info@topechelon.com
URL: http://www.topechelon.com

Description: Online placement recruiter network. Job seekers may search job board compiled by network member recruiters, create an online profile for recruiters' reviews, and contact specific member recruiters in their field of business.

14109 ■ Transearch.com
E-mail: contact@transearch.com
URL: http://www.transearch.com

Description: International executive search firm concentrating in searches for executives in retail, real estate, information technology, industry, life sciences and financial services. Seekers may search job board and submit their resume for recruiter review.

14110 ■ TranslationDirectory.com
E-mail: ceo@translationdirectory.com
URL: http://www.translationdirectory.com

Description: Offers a directory of a wide variety of resources, including groups and mailing lists for translators, tools for language professionals, glossaries and dictionaries, translation organizations, payment collection agencies, translation blogs, freelance translators and translation agencies, language education companies and other related resources.

14111 ■ TravelingCrossing.com
URL: http://www.travelingcrossing.com

Description: Provides collection of travel job listings. Offers travel industry insights, including travel news briefs, articles, and e-resources to keep members up to date on the latest happenings in the travel world.

14112 ■ Trovix
URL: http://www.trovix.com

Description: Provides products and services that bridge the gulf between employers and people in search of the best career opportunities. Focuses on key attributes such as skills, work history and education to provide meaningful search results.

14113 ■ UnderwritingCrossing.com
URL: http://www.underwritingcrossing.com

Description: Provides a collection of top underwriting job openings. Includes Fortune 500 and Fortune 1,000 companies.

14114 ■ UnderwritingJobs.com
Ph: (972)679-4542
E-mail: admin@underwritingjobs.com
URL: http://www.underwritingjobs.com

Description: Job search website for underwriters. Seekers may search databank by field of interest or geography, post their resume or visit career-related links.

14115 ■ United Search Associates: Health
   Network USA
PO Box 342
Vinita, OK 74301
Ph: (918)323-4165
E-mail: jobs@hnusa.com
URL: http://homepage.mac.com/hnusa

Description: Visitors may explore healthcare positions, submit an electronic resume, or advertise with the site.

14116 ■ UrbanPlanningNow.com
URL: http://www.urbanplanningnow.com

Description: Provides employment services in urban planning. Offers a general search service, a private list of job openings found throughout the internet and a location for employers to post their jobs.

14117 ■ US Army Recruiting Command:
   GoArmy.com
URL: http://www.goarmy.com

Online resource lists jobs, particularly those in the field of counterintelligence.

14118 ■ USADefenseIndustryJobs.com
E-mail: resumes@defensecareers.com
URL: http://usadefenseindustryjobs.com

Provides an online job search for intelligence positions with the American defense industry.

14119 ■ USAJOBS - United States Office of
   Personnel Management
URL: http://www.usajobs.gov

Description: Provides information about jobs that are available in the Federal government. The online search program allows users to search job announcements on the bulletin board by either series number or job title. Also has resume builder and e-mail alert services. Free.

14120 ■ USJobNetwork.com
URL: http://www.usjobnetwork.com

Description: Provides users with access to career search related resources. Serves as a career opportunity resource and job search engine for all industries.

14121 ■ USPilot.com
URL: http://www.uspilot.com

Description: Provides information on pilot job openings, interview gouge, forums, and evaluation of pilot resumes.

14122 ■ Vault Inc.
URL: http://www.vault.com

Online resource provides job listings, particularly for the food and wine industry.

14123 ■ Vault.com
132 W 31st St., 15th Fl.
New York, NY 10001
Ph: (212)366-4212
Fax: (212)366-6117
E-mail: publicity@vault.com
URL: http://www.vault.com

Description: Job board website with searches emphasizing jobs in legal, business, consulting and finance fields of practice. Contains online profile posting, resume review, company research, salary calculators and relocation tools.

14124 ■ VeterinaryCrossing.com
URL: http://www.veterinarycrossing.com

Description: Offers employment opportunities for veterinarians and veterinary technicians. Includes lists of employer career pages, job websites, newspaper classifieds and recruitment sites.

14125 ■ VeterinaryLife.com
URL: http://www.veterinarylife.com

Description: Posts classified ads for veterinarian and clinic jobs available worldwide.

14126 ■ VetRelief.com
URL: http://www.vetrelief.com

Description: Serves as a career network that caters to the needs of individuals searching for work as a veterinarian as well as for individuals seeking to hire a veterinarian.

14127 ■ Voice of the Vine
E-mail: schwenso@wsu.edu
URL: http://wine.wsu.edu/vinevoice

Biweekly. Free. Provides current news concerning Washington's wine industry as well as profiles of researchers, students and alumni working in the field.

14128 ■ Wall Street Journal Executive Career Site
URL: http://online.wsj.com/public/page/news-career-jobs.html

Description: Contains numerous job-related resources, search engines and resume databases for job-seekers, employers and executive recruiters. Contains career columnists, salary negotiating instruments, discussion forums and e-mail alerting system. Fee: Must be subscribers to WSJ.com in order to fully utilize resources; year's subscription is $99.

14129 ■ WashingtonPost.com
URL: http://www.washingtonpost.com

Description: Allows resume posting, company research, per industry job searching, and networking. Offers expert advise on job hunting, resume writing, and interviews.

14130 ■ WellnessCoachCareers.com
URL: http://www.exercisecareers.com/index.cfm?page=wellnesscoachcareers

Description: Serves as a job board for wellness

coaches. Also features a resume writing tool for coaches seeking employment.

14131 ■ WellnessJobs.com
URL: http://www.wellnessjobs.com

Description: Features employment listings across the United States. Includes review of salary information, free resume posting and healthcare recruiters.

14132 ■ WetFeet.com
URL: http://www.wetfeet.com

Description: Job board website with free membership for job seekers. Contains job board, resume listing, self assessment guides, company and city research, discussion forums, e-guides and online bookstore, salary calculators and listings of internship opportunities.

14133 ■ What Color Is Your Parachute? Job Hunters Bible
URL: http://www.jobhuntersbible.com

Description: Companion internet guide to the job-hunting book, What Color is Your Parachute? Includes lists of helpful links to other resources on the internet. Main files include: Jobs, Resumes, Counseling, Contacts, Research, Dealing With Depression.

14134 ■ WildlandFire.com
E-mail: abercrombie@wildlandfire.com
URL: http://www.wildlandfire.com

Description: Provides career services for fire fighters through features that includes issues, news, forum, and a classifieds page.

14135 ■ Wine Business Daily News
E-mail: info@winebusiness.com
URL: http://www.winebusiness.com/news

Daily. Free. Emailed newsletter covers the top stories concerning the winemaking industry.

14136 ■ Wine Events Calendar
E-mail: events@wineevents-calendar.com
URL: http://www.wineevents-calendar.com

Online directory of regional wine events, classes, wine tastings, and other networking opportunities and resources also includes ratings, reviews and editorials concerning the wine industry.

14137 ■ Wine and Spirits Jobs
PO Box 22
Mokena, IL 60448
Fr: (866)975-4473
E-mail: info@wineandspiritsjobs.com
URL: http://www.wineandspiritsjobs.com

Online resource lists jobs in the wine industry. Also encourages job seekers to post their resumes.

14138 ■ WineAndHospitalityJobs.com
URL: http://www.wineandhospitalityjobs.com

Online resource for both job seekers looking for work in the wine industry and employers from the wine industry in need of help. Website also includes articles, industry news, forums and other information concerning the industry and encourages job seekers to post their resumes.

14139 ■ WineBusiness.com
E-mail: info@winebusiness.com
URL: http://www.winebusiness.com

Resource includes information about the business and technology of winemaking as well as classified ads and listings of jobs in the wine industry.

14140 ■ WineCountry.com
URL: http://www.winecountry.com

Online resource provides interviews and profiles of leading winemakers and wine professionals across the country as well as information about the business of wine; also includes message boards, an event calendar and a directory of wineries throughout the country.

14141 ■ WineJobs.com
E-mail: info@winebusiness.com
URL: http://www.winebusiness.com/classifieds/winejobs

Online resource for the wine industry includes classified ads for used equipment, real estate, grapes and bulk wine.

14142 ■ WineJobs.com Daily Email Alert
E-mail: info@winebusiness.com
URL: http://www.winebusiness.com/classifieds/winejobs/?go=emailalerts

Provides the latest job listings for all sectors of the winemaking industry including finance, winemaking and production, vineyards, sales and marketing, information systems, hospitality and retail, human resources and general administration.

14143 ■ Women at Work
3871 E Colorado Blvd.
Pasadena, CA 91107
Ph: (626)796-6870
Fax: (626)793-7396
E-mail: jobs@womenatwork1.org
URL: http://womenatwork.org

Description: Site of nonprofit job and career resource center, serving the greater Los Angeles area.

14144 ■ WomenGamers.com
URL: http://www.womengamers.com

Description: Provides employment and networking opportunities for women in the gaming industry.

14145 ■ Work from Home
URL: http://www.jobs-telecommuting.com

Description: Contains a listing of over 700 companies currently looking for telecommuters. Employers may add or remove job listings. Also information on starting a home business available.

14146 ■ WorkforceHRjobs.com
URL: http://www.workforcehrjobs.com/a/all-jobs/list

Description: Provides job opportunities for human resource professionals.

14147 ■ WorkInSports.com
URL: http://www.workinsports.com

Description: Provides listing of current sports jobs and internships.

14148 ■ WorkTree.com
E-mail: support@worktree.com
URL: http://www.worktree.com

Description: Job search engine portal, listing career-related search engines and websites by geography, field of practice, experience level, company and more. Also lists links to career resources such as resume coaching and interviewing tips. Resume broadcast service available. Fee: Membership available in several levels, depending on length of membership desired; three months' unlimited access is $47.

14149 ■ WorldwideWorker.com
URL: http://www.worldwideworker.com

Description: Features energy jobs for engineers and professionals covering all types of energy sectors, including oil and gas, renewables, mining, nuclear, power, marine, and railway. Provides any individual, engineer or professional, graduate or with an extensive experience list of jobs that can be browsed by location, job category, or company name, or can be directly found with search functionality.

14150 ■ WriteJobs.com
URL: http://www.writejobs.com

Description: Provides job listings, career resources and information for journalism, media and publishing professionals.

14151 ■ WritingCareer.com
URL: http://www.writingcareer.com

Description: Offers valuable advice on career training, career education, and changing careers aimed at writers and freelance writers. Includes site features such as career guides, free writing career articles, podcasts, writing career help, writing career jobs and writing events.

14152 ■ WritingCrossing.com
URL: http://www.writingcrossing.com

Description: Features listings of writing jobs worldwide. Offers job listings for writers, freelancers, technical writers, associate writers, marketing writers, copywriters, business writers, web writers, and editors.

14153 ■ WSA Executive Job Search Center
Ph: (251)895-2125
E-mail: info@wsacorp.com
URL: http://www.wsacorp.com

Description: A site intended for $50K-$700K range executives. Offers resume preparation, critiques and distribution, and interview preparation.

14154 ■ Yahoo! Careers
701 1st Ave.
Sunnyvale, CA 94089
URL: http://us.careers.yahoo.com

Description: Contains over 360,000 jobs for job seekers to search and post resumes for, as well as weekly features, relocation resources, a daily column, and links to resume banks and services and temp agencies. Special sections are devoted to industry research, company research, advice, high tech jobs, and first jobs and internships.

14155 ■ You the Designer
URL: http://www.youthedesigner.com

Description: Serves as an online career resource that contains a graphic design blog, graphic design tips and graphic design job openings.

14156 ■ ZDNet Tech Jobs
URL: http://www.zdnet.com

Description: Site houses a listing of national employment opportunities for professionals in high tech fields. Also contains resume building tips and relocation resources.

SOFTWARE

14157 ■ SmartRecruiters
330 Townsend St., Ste. 237
San Francisco, CA 94107
Ph: (415)508-3755
E-mail: contact@smartrecruiters.com
URL: http://www.smartrecruiters.com

Serves as a recruiting software that manages the hiring process into easiest and fastest way.

REFERENCE WORKS

14158 ■ Association of Consulting Foresters—Membership Specialization Directory
Association of Consulting Foresters
312 Montgomery St., Ste. 208
Alexandria, VA 22314
Ph: (703)548-0990
Fax: (703)548-6395
URL: http://www.acf-foresters.org

Annual, August. Free. Covers: Nearly 500 member forestry consulting firms and professional foresters who earn the largest part of their income from consulting. Entries include: Name, address, phone, specialties, background, career data, staff (if a consulting firm), geographic area served, capabilities, including equipment available and foreign language proficiency. Arrangement: Alphabetical. Indexes: Name, office location, language, international capability.

14159 ■ Careers in the Environment
The McGraw-Hill Companies
PO Box 182604
Columbus, OH 43272
Fax: (614)759-3749
Fr: 877-883-5524
E-mail: customer.service@mcgraw-hill.com
URL: http://www.mhprofessional.com/
    product.php?cat=106&isbn=0071476113

Michael Fasulo and Paul Walker. 2007. $15.95 (paper). 192 pages. Comprehensive information on the diverse career opportunities available in environmental services.

14160 ■ Careers for Health Nuts and Others Who Like to Stay Fit
The McGraw-Hill Companies
PO Box 182604
Columbus, OH 43272
Fax: (614)759-3749
Fr: 877-883-5524
E-mail: customer.service@mcgraw-hill.com
URL: http://www.mhprofessional.com

Blythe Camenson. Second edition. $13.95 (paper). 208 pages.

14161 ■ Conservation Directory
National Wildlife Federation
11100 Wildlife Center Dr.
Reston, VA 20190-5362
Ph: (703)638-6000
Fax: (703)438-6061
Fr: 800-822-9919
E-mail: admin@nwf.org
URL: http://www.nwf.org/conservationdirectory/

Annual, latest edition 2010. Covers: Over 4,258 organizations, agencies, colleges and universities with conservation programs and more than 18,000 officials concerned with environmental conservation, education, and natural resource use and management. Entries include: Agency name, address, branch or subsidiary office name and address, names and titles of key personnel, descriptions of program areas, size of membership (where appropriate), telephone, fax, e-mail and URL addresses. Arrangement: Classified by type of organization. Indexes: Personal name, keyword, geographic, organization.

14162 ■ Latinnovating: Green American Jobs and the Latinos Creating Them
Gracefully Global, LLC
22568 Mission Blvd., No. 427
Hayward, CA 94541
Ph: (510)542-9449
URL: http://www.gracefullyglobal.com

Graciela Tiscareno-Sato. 2011. $25.00 (paper). 212 pages. Profiles ten different career paths for Latinos interested in environmental business. Shows the culturally-rooted environmental entrepreneurship in the Latino community.

14163 ■ Managing Green Spaces: Careers in Wilderness and Wildlife Management (Green-Collar Careers)
Crabtree Publishing Company
350 5th Ave., 59th Fl.
PMB 59051
New York, NY 10118
Ph: (212)496-5040
Fax: 800-355-7166
Fr: 800-387-7650
URL: http://www.crabtreebooks.com

Suzy Gazlay. 2010. $31.93. 64 pages (hardcover). Features careers in wilderness and wildlife management.

14164 ■ Paint Your Career Green: Get a Green Job Without Starting Over
JIST Publishing
875 Montreal Way
St. Paul, MN 55102
Fr: 800-648-5478
E-mail: educate@emcp.com
URL: http://www.jist.com

Stan Schatt and Michelle Lobl. 2011. $12.95 (softcover). 208 pages. Provides an overview of green certificate programs and shows how and where to search for green jobs and prospective employers. Includes practical advice on career transition plans, finance management and use of social networking sites in finding green opportunities.

14165 ■ Tailoring the Green Suit: Empowering Yourself for an Executive Career in the New Green Economy
AuthorHouse
1663 Liberty Dr.
Bloomington, IN 47403
Fr: 888-519-5121
E-mail: authorsupport@authorhouse.com
URL: http://www.authorhouse.com

Dan Smolen. 2011. $9.99. 136 pages. Helps jobseekers land a successful executive career in the green business.

NEWSPAPERS, MAGAZINES, AND JOURNALS

14166 ■ Climate Alert
The Climate Institute
900 17th St. NW, Ste. 700
Washington, DC 20006
Ph: (202)552-4723
Fax: (202)737-6410
E-mail: info@climate.org
URL: http://www.climate.org/publications/climate-alert.html

Description: Quarterly. Addresses global climate issues in terms of science and policy.

14167 ■ Environmental Business Journal
Environmental Business International Inc.
4452 Park Blvd., Ste. 306
San Diego, CA 92116
URL: http://www.ebiusa.com

Description: Twelve issues/year. $995/year. Provides research and articles on various segments of the environmental business industry. Recurring features include news of research.

14168 ■ The Job Seeker
PO Box 451
Fruita, CO 81521
Fax: (267)295-2004
E-mail: sarah@thejobseeker.net
URL: http://www.thejobseeker.net

Description: Semimonthly. Specializes in environmental and natural resource vacancies nationwide. Lists current vacancies from federal, state, local, private, and non-profit employers. Also available via e-mail.

14169 ■ Journal of Forestry
Society of American Foresters
5400 Grosvenor Ln.
Bethesda, MD 20814-2198
Ph: (301)897-3691
Fax: (301)897-3690
Fr: (866)897-8720
E-mail: journal@safnet.org
URL: http://www.safnet.org/publications/jof/index.cfm

$123.00/year for nonmembers, U.S./Canada, print only; $270.00/year for institutions, U.S./Canada, print only; $224.00/year for nonmembers, online only; $333.00/year for institutions, online only; $253.00/year for nonmembers, U.S./Canada, print and online; $386.00/year for institutions, U.S./Canada, print and online; $168.00/year for nonmembers, foreign, print only; $315.00/year for institutions, foreign, print only; $298.00/year for nonmembers, foreign, print and online; $431.00/year for institutions, other countries, print and online. Peer-reviewed journal of forestry serves to advance the profession by keeping professionals informed about significant developments and ideas in forest science, natural resource management, and forest policy.

14170 ■ *Nature International Weekly Journal of Science*
Nature Publishing Group
75 Varick St., 9th Fl.
New York, NY 10013-1917
Ph: (212)726-9200
Fax: (212)696-9006
Fr: 888-331-6288
E-mail: nature@natureny.com
URL: http://www.nature.com/nature/index.html

Weekly. $199.00/year for individuals, print and online; $338.00/year for two years, print and online. Magazine covering science and technology, including the fields of biology, biochemistry, genetics, medicine, earth sciences, physics, pharmacology, and behavioral sciences.

14171 ■ *NRPA Career Center*
National Recreation and Park Association, Professional Services Div.
22377 Belmont Ridge Rd.
Ashburn, VA 20148
Ph: (703)858-0784
Fax: (703)858-0794
Fr: 800-626-6772
E-mail: customerservice@nrpa.org
URL: http://www.nrpa.org

Description: Provides listings of employment opportunities in the park, recreation, and leisure services field.

14172 ■ *Recycling Today*
G.I.E. Media, MC
4020 Kinross Lakes Pkwy., Ste. 201
Richfield, OH 44286
Ph: (330)523-5400
Fax: (330)659-0823
Fr: 800-456-0707
URL: http://www.recyclingtoday.com

Monthly. Magazine covering recycling of secondary raw materials and solid-waste management.

14173 ■ *Resource Recycling*
Resource Recycling
PO Box 42270
Portland, OR 97242-0270
Ph: (503)233-1305
Fax: (503)233-1356
URL: http://www.resource-recycling.com/

Monthly. $52.00/year for individuals. Journal reporting on all aspects of recycling and composting of solid waste, from collection and materials processing to markets and governmental policies.

14174 ■ *Water Environment Research*
Water Environment Federation
601 Wythe St.
Alexandria, VA 22314-1994
Ph: (703)684-2400
Fax: (703)684-2492
Fr: 800-666-0206
URL: http://www.wef.org/Publications/page_detail.aspx?id=796

Monthly. $125.00/year for individuals, WEF Member, print plus online; $350.00/year for individuals, print plus online; $850.00/year for institutions, print plus online; $200.00/year for other countries, WEF Member, print plus online; $350.00/year for other countries, print plus online; $905.00/year for institutions, other countries, print plus online; $100.00/year for members, print only; $324.00/year for individuals, print only; $770.00/year for institutions, print only; $125.00/year for other countries, members, print only. Technical journal covering municipal and industrial water

pollution control, water quality, and hazardous wastes.

ONLINE AND DATABASE SERVICES

14175 ■ AirPollutionSpecialistJobs.com
URL: http://www.airpollutionspecialistjobs.com

Description: Serves as a clearinghouse for air pollution specialist jobs. Features job videos, search agents, salary information, salary surveys, resume tips, news, educational programs, and other career resources.

14176 ■ AirQualityEngineerJobs.com
URL: http://airqualityengineerjobs.com

Description: Features air quality engineer jobs, resume postings, blogs, job videos, salary calculation, resume writing tips, educational programs, and other resources.

14177 ■ Environmental Career Center
URL: http://www.environmentalcareer.info

Description: Acts as an employment search engine devoted to providing the connection between environmental jobs and job seekers.

14178 ■ Environmental Career Opportunities
URL: http://www.ecojobs.com

Description: Lists environmental jobs in conservation, education, policy, science and engineering.

14179 ■ Environmental Expert
URL: http://www.environmental-expert.com

Description: Connects environmental industry professionals from around the globe to companies that provide the products, services and information they need to do their job successfully.

14180 ■ Environmental Jobs Finder
URL: http://www.environmentaljobsfinder.com

Description: Provides an online listing of environment related jobs.

14181 ■ GoingGreenJobs.com
URL: http://www.goinggreenjobs.com

Description: Features a searchable database of green-collar jobs. Provides relevant career resources pertaining to green jobs.

14182 ■ Green Zone
URL: http://greenzone.org

Description: Provides green job postings from different sectors.

14183 ■ greenjobsearch.org
URL: http://www.greenjobsearch.org

Description: Serves as a search engine for finding green jobs.

14184 ■ JobsinGeothermal.com
E-mail: info@jobsingeothermal.com
URL: http://www.jobsingeothermal.com

Description: Lists geothermal jobs across the United States. Dedicated to connecting geothermal energy suppliers with people who want to apply their skills toward helping the planet.

14185 ■ USAGreenJobsNow.org
URL: http://www.usagreenjobsnow.org

Description: Connects job seekers to employers in renewable energy industries. Works in collaboration with businesses, government, and green organizations to promote quality careers and opportunities in the green industry.

OTHER SOURCES

14186 ■ Aerotek Environmental
7301 Parkway Dr.
Hanover, MD 21076
Ph: (410)694-5100
Fr: 800-237-6835
URL: http://environmental.aerotek.com

Description: Provides environmental employment and staffing services. Offers environmental jobs for individuals with experience in engineering, project management, health and safety, remediation and inspection.

14187 ■ Air and Waste Management Association (A&WMA)
1 Gateway Ctr., 3rd Fl.
420 Ft. Duquesne Blvd.
Pittsburgh, PA 15222-1435
Ph: (412)232-3444
Fax: (412)232-3450
Fr: 800-270-3444
E-mail: info@awma.org
URL: http://www.awma.org

Description: Serves as environmental, educational, and technical organization. **Purpose:** Seeks to provide a neutral forum for the exchange of technical information on a wide variety of environmental topics.

14188 ■ Alliance for Global Conservation
PO Box 1200
Washington, DC 20013-1200
Ph: (202)739-8155
E-mail: jwise@pewtrusts.org
URL: http://www.actforconservation.org

Description: Aims to protect life on earth through conservation of wildlife, natural areas and human communities around the world. Supports global policies that will prevent the destruction of the world's remaining natural ecosystems for the species and human communities that depend on them.

14189 ■ Alliance for Water Efficiency (AWE)
300 W Adams St., Ste. 601
Chicago, IL 60606
Ph: (773)360-5100
Fax: (773)345-3636
Fr: (866)730-A4WE
E-mail: jeffrey@a4we.org
URL: http://www.a4we.org

Description: Promotes efficient and sustainable use of water. Serves as an advocate for water-efficient products and programs. Provides information and assistance on water conservation efforts.

14190 ■ American Academy of Environmental Engineers (AAEE)
130 Holiday Ct., Ste. 100
Annapolis, MD 21401
Ph: (410)266-3311
Fax: (410)266-7653
E-mail: info@aaee.net
URL: http://www.aaee.net

Description: Environmentally oriented registered professional engineers certified by examination as Diplomates of the Academy. Seeks to improve the standards of environmental engineering. Certifies those with special knowledge of environmental engineering. Furnishes lists of those certified to the public. Maintains speakers' bureau. Recognizes areas of specialization: Air Pollution Control; General Environmental; Hazardous Waste Management; Industrial Hygiene; Radiation Protection; Solid Waste Management; Water Supply and Wastewater. Requires written and oral examinations for certification. Works with other professional organizations on environmentally oriented activities. Identifies potential employment candidates through Talent Search Service.

14191 ■ American Public Health Association (APHA)
800 I St. NW
Washington, DC 20001
Ph: (202)777-2742
Fax: (202)777-2534
E-mail: comments@apha.org
URL: http://www.apha.org

Description: Professional organization of physicians, nurses, educators, academicians, environmentalists, epidemiologists, new professionals, social workers, health administrators, optometrists, podiatrists, pharmacists, dentists, nutritionists, health planners, other community and mental health specialists, and interested consumers. Seeks to protect and promote personal, mental, and environmental health. Services include: promulgation of standards; establishment of uniform practices and procedures; development of the etiology of communicable diseases; research in public health; exploration of medical care programs and their relationships to public health. Sponsors job placement service.

14192 ■ American Reef Coalition (ARC)
PO Box 844
Kihei, HI 96753
Ph: (808)870-5817
E-mail: info@americanreef.org
URL: http://www.americanreef.org

Description: To protect coral reef ecosystems, ocean resources and wilderness through a variety of proven methods and by providing support to other nonprofit organizations and government agencies engaged in marine, wilderness and natural area research, conservation and education.

14193 ■ Audubon International
46 Rarick Rd.
Selkirk, NY 12158
Ph: (518)767-9051
Fax: (518)767-9076
E-mail: kfletcher@auduboninternational.org
URL: http://www.auduboninternational.org

Description: Promotes sustainable communities through good stewardship of the natural environment where people live, work and recreate. Collaborates with nonprofits, governments, businesses and the public to ensure better environmental decision-making and improve the quality of human and natural communities. Provides people with the assistance needed to practice responsible management of land, water, wildlife and natural resources.

14194 ■ Center for Environmental Science Advocacy and Reliability (CESAR)
1990 3rd St., Ste. 400
Sacramento, CA 95811
Ph: (916)341-7407
Fax: (916)341-7410
E-mail: info@bestscience.org
URL: http://bestscience.org

Description: Seeks to ensure the efficient and effective enforcement of the Endangered Species Act (ESA). Provides members and the public with educational information about ESA and its applications. Encourages scientific rigor in implementing environmental statutes.

14195 ■ Conservation through Poverty Alleviation International (CPALI)
221 Lincoln Rd.
Lincoln, MA 01773
E-mail: ccraig@cpali.org
URL: http://www.cpali.org/CPALI_Home.html

Description: Works to identify, develop and implement new means of income generation for poor farmers living in areas of high biodiversity or conservation value. Promotes natural resource conservation by developing integrated, small enterprise systems that link the livelihood of farm families and communities to the maintenance of natural ecosystems.

14196 ■ Environmental Paper Network (EPN)
16 Eagle St., Ste. 200
Asheville, NC 28801
Ph: (828)251-8558
E-mail: info@environmentalpaper.org
URL: http://www.environmentalpaper.org

Description: Works to accelerate social and environmental transformation in the pulp and paper industry. Aims to protect the world's last endangered forests, to safeguard the global climate and ensure abundant, clean drinking water and respect for community and indigenous rights.

14197 ■ Forest Planters International
3120 228th St. SW
Brier, WA 98036
E-mail: brendac@forestplanters.org
URL: http://www.forestplanters.org

Description: Seeks to improve the quality of life of farmers in the Brazilian Atlantic Rainforest. Funds the replanting of deforested areas to combat environmental problems. Teaches small scale farmers to collect and raise seeds and reforest waterways.

14198 ■ GAIA Movement USA
8918 S Green St.
Chicago, IL 60620
Ph: (773)651-7870
Fax: (773)651-7890
Fr: 877-651-7870
E-mail: eva@gaia-movement.org
URL: http://www.gaia-movement-usa.org

Description: Educates young and old people on environmental issues including recycling, renewable energy, conservation and wildlife preservation. Develops and preserves natural areas and virgin lands as nature reserves. Promotes the use of renewable energies such as solar, wind and geothermal.

14199 ■ Gray is Green: The National Senior Conservation Corps
26 Broadway
North Haven, CT 06473
Fr: 800-684-5889
E-mail: rosikerr@grayisgreen.org
URL: http://www.grayisgreen.org

Description: Enables people over 65 to actively participate in creating a positive environmental change. Provides resources to seniors in three distinct areas: greening, advocacy and learning and teaching. Serves as a clearinghouse for senior citizens interested in greening their lives, learning about sustainability, developing second careers in conservation, advocating for sound climate change policy and in serving as resources for younger people involved in sustainability.

14200 ■ Green Parent Association
2601 Westhall Ln.
Maitland, FL 32751
Ph: (407)493-1372
E-mail: joy@greenparentassociation.org
URL: http://www.greenparentassociation.org

Description: Strives to empower families, teachers and businesses to live greener lifestyles through education and awareness. Seeks to share information about clean, healthy living that benefits families and the communities in which they live. Aims to inspire parents to continue to improve their children's lives through the food that they eat and the world in which they live.

14201 ■ National Association of Conservation Districts (NACD)
509 Capitol Ct. NE
Washington, DC 20002-4937
Ph: (202)547-6223
Fax: (202)547-6450
Fr: 888-695-2433
E-mail: jeff-eisenberg@nacdnet.org
URL: http://www.nacdnet.org

Description: Soil and water conservation districts organized by the citizens of watersheds, counties, or communities under provisions of state laws. Directs and coordinates, through local self-government efforts, the conservation and development of soil, water, and related natural resources. Includes districts over 90% of the nation's privately owned land. Conducts educational programs and children's services.

14202 ■ National Association of Environmental Professionals
PO Box 460
Collingswood, NJ 08108
Ph: (856)283-7816
Fax: (856)210-1619
E-mail: naep@bowermanagementservices.com
URL: http://www.naep.org

Description: Promotes advancement in environmental education through the formation and operation of colleagues in industry, government, academia and the private sectors. Aims to develop the highest standards of ethics and proficiency in the environmental professions.

14203 ■ National Environmental Health Association (NEHA)
720 S Colorado Blvd., Ste. 1000-N
Denver, CO 80246-1926
Ph: (303)756-9090
Fax: (303)691-9490
Fr: (866)956-2258
E-mail: staff@neha.org
URL: http://www.neha.org

Description: Represents all professionals in environmental health and protection, including Registered Sanitarians, Registered Environmental Health Specialists, Registered Environmental Technicians, Certified Environmental Health Technicians, Registered Hazardous Substances Professionals and Registered Hazardous Substances Specialists. Advances the environmental health and protection profession for the purpose of providing a healthful environment for all. Provides educational materials, publications, credentials and meetings to members and non-member professionals who strive to improve the environment.

14204 ■ National Registry of Environmental Professionals
PO Box 2099
Glenview, IL 60025
Ph: (847)724-6631
Fax: (847)724-4223
E-mail: nrep@nrep.org
URL: http://www.nrep.org

Description: Represents individuals working and serving the environmental field. Offers professional certification and proficiency examinations.

14205 ■ Nature's Voice Our Choice (NVOC)
1940 Duke St. Ste. 200
Alexandria, VA 22314
Ph: (202)360-8373
E-mail: brandy@nv-oc.org
URL: http://www.naturesvoice-ourchoice.org

Description: Aims to preserve, conserve and restore the world's water resources through education and public awareness. Empowers people to become stewards of their natural resources and implements projects that make environmental protection economically feasible. Supports ecologically engineered natural waste water treatment systems.

14206 ■ Neotropical Grassland Conservancy (NGC)
6274 Heathcliff Dr.
Carmichael, CA 95608
Ph: (916)967-3223
URL: http://www.conservegrassland.org

Description: Promotes the conservation of savannas, gallery forests, wetlands and associated ecosystems in Central and South America. Collaborates with North American, Central and South American scientists and institutions by providing shared scientific and educational opportunities. Offers equipment and grants to students and scientists from Central and South America working in grassland habitats.

14207 ■ Reverb

386 Fore St., No. 202
Portland, ME 04101
Ph: (207)221-6553
E-mail: info@reverb.org
URL: http://www.reverb.org

Description: Seeks to educate and engage musicians and their fans to participate in protecting the environment. Conducts outreach programs and engages music fans online and in concerts while greening musicians' tours. Conducts presentations at music shows to promote carbon offset programs and to encourage fans to participate in eco-village activities.

14208 ■ Save the Frogs!

303 Potrero St., No. 51
Santa Cruz, CA 95060
Ph: (831)621-6215
E-mail: contact@savethefrogs.com
URL: http://www.savethefrogs.com

Description: Seeks to protect amphibian populations and promote a society that respects and appreciates nature and wildlife. Educates the public about the necessity of protecting the world's amphibians and provides them with information and capabilities to protect amphibian populations. Conducts scientific research to stop amphibian extinction.

14209 ■ Society for Ecological Restoration International

1017 O St. NW
Washington, DC 20001
Ph: (202)299-9518
Fax: (270)626-5485
URL: http://www.ser.org

Description: Promotes ecological restoration as a means of sustaining the diversity of life and re-establishing a healthy relationship between nature and culture. Helps connect members with new employment opportunities.

14210 ■ Student Conservation Association (SCA)

PO Box 550
Charlestown, NH 03603-0550
Ph: (603)543-1700
Fax: (603)543-1828
E-mail: dfitzgerald@thesca.org
URL: http://www.thesca.org

Description: Works to build the next generation of conservation leaders and inspire lifelong stewardship of the environment and communities by engaging young people in hands-on service to the land. Provides conservation service opportunities, outdoor education and leadership development for young people. Offers college and graduate students, as well as older adults expense-paid conservation internships, these positions includes wildlife research, wilderness patrols and interpretive opportunities and provide participants with valuable hands-on career experience. Places 15-19 year old high school students in four-week volunteer conservation crews in national parks forests and refuges across the country each summer to accomplish a range of trail building and habitat conservation projects. Offers year-round diversity conservation programs for young women and young persons of color in leading metropolitan areas of U.S.

14211 ■ United Nations Environment Program/Global Resource Information Database (UNEP/GRID)

USGS National Center of EROS
47914 252nd St.
Sioux Falls, SD 57198-0001
Ph: (605)594-6117
Fax: (605)594-6119
E-mail: geas@unep.org
URL: http://www.unep.org

Description: Individuals interested in raising public awareness of the importance of a global environmental effort. Encourages activism in support of the United Nations Environment Program. Acts as a liaison between the UNEP and the public. Sponsors educational programs and children's services. Offers placement services to job seekers in international environmental work. Maintains speakers' bureau.

14212 ■ Water Environment Federation (WEF)

601 Wythe St.
Alexandria, VA 22314-1994
Ph: (703)684-2400
Fax: (703)684-2492
Fr: 800-666-0206
E-mail: jeger@wef.org
URL: http://www.wef.org

Description: Technical societies representing chemists, biologists, ecologists, geologists, operators, educational and research personnel, industrial wastewater engineers, consultant engineers, municipal officials, equipment manufacturers, and university professors and students dedicated to the enhancement and preservation of water quality and resources. Seeks to advance fundamental and practical knowledge concerning the nature, collection, treatment, and disposal of domestic and industrial wastewaters, and the design, construction, operation, and management of facilities for these purposes. Disseminates technical information; and promotes good public relations and regulations that improve water quality and the status of individuals working in this field. Conducts educational and research programs.

14213 ■ World Federation for Coral Reef Conservation

PO Box 942
Safety Harbor, FL 34695
E-mail: vic.ferguson@wfcrc.org
URL: http://wfcrc.org/default.aspx

Description: Works to stop the destruction of coral reefs by involving local citizens, scientists and recreational divers. Collaborates with like-minded organizations in implementing programs for coral reef decline management. Supports conservation efforts on coral reefs.

14214 ■ Equal Employment Opportunity Commission
131 M St., NE
Washington, DC 20507
Ph: (202)663-4900
Fax: (202)663-4494
Fr: 800-669-4000
E-mail: info@eeoc.gov
URL: http://www.eeoc.gov

The Equal Employment Opportunity Commission enforces laws which prohibit discrimination based on race, color, religion, sex, national origin, disability, or age in hiring, promoting, firing, setting wages, testing, training, apprenticeship, and all other terms and conditions of employment. The Commission conducts investigations of alleged discrimination; makes determinations based on gathered evidence; attempts conciliation when discrimination has taken place; files lawsuits; and conducts voluntary assistance programs for employers, unions, and community organizations. The Commission also has adjudicatory and oversight responsibility for all compliance and enforcement activities relating to equal employment opportunity among Federal employees and applicants, including discrimination against individuals with disabilities.

14215 ■ Federal Labor Relations Authority
1400 K St. NW
Washington, DC 20424-0001
Ph: (202)218-7770
URL: http://www.flra.gov

The Federal Labor Relations Authority oversees the Federal service labor-management relations program. It administers the law that protects the right of employees of the Federal Government to organize, bargain collectively, and participate through labor organizations of their own choosing in decisions affecting them. The Authority also ensures compliance with the statutory rights and obligations of Federal employees and the labor organizations that represent them in their dealings with Federal agencies.

14216 ■ Merit Systems Protection Board
1615 M St. NW
Washington, DC 20036
Ph: (202)653-7200
Fax: (202)653-7130
Fr: 800-209-8960
E-mail: mspb@mspb.gov
URL: http://www.mspb.gov

The Merit Systems Protection Board protects the integrity of Federal merit systems and the rights of Federal employees working in the systems. In overseeing the personnel practices of the Federal Government, the Board conducts special studies of the merit systems, hears and decides charges of wrongdoing and employee appeals of adverse agency actions, and orders corrective and disciplinary actions when appropriate.

14217 ■ National Labor Relations Board
1099 Fourteenth St., NW
Washington, DC 20570

Ph: (202)273-1000
Fr: (866)667-6572
URL: http://www.nlrb.gov

The National Labor Relations Board is vested with the power to prevent and remedy unfair labor practices committed by private sector employers and unions and to safeguard employees' rights to organize and determine whether to have unions as their bargaining representative.

14218 ■ Occupational Safety and Health Review Commission
1120 20th St., NW, 9th Fl.
Washington, DC 20036-3457
Ph: (202)606-5383
E-mail: it_gpo@oshrc.gov
URL: http://www.oshrc.gov

The Occupational Safety and Health Review Commission works to ensure the timely and fair resolution of cases involving the alleged exposure of American workers to unsafe or unhealthy working conditions.

14219 ■ Office of Personnel Management
1900 E St., NW
Washington, DC 20415
Ph: (202)606-2532
E-mail: general@opm.gov
URL: http://www.opm.gov

The Office of Personnel Management (OPM) administers a merit system to ensure compliance with personnel laws and regulations and assists agencies in recruiting, examining, and promoting people on the basis of their knowledge and skills, regardless of their race, religion, sex, political influence, or other non-merit factors. OPM's role is to provide guidance to agencies in operating human resources programs which effectively support their missions and to provide an array of personnel services to applicants and employees. OPM supports Government program managers in their human resources management responsibilities and provide benefits to employees, retired employees, and their survivors.

14220 ■ U.S. Commission on Civil Rights
624 Ninth St. NW
Washington, DC 20425
Ph: (202)376-7700
URL: http://www.usccr.gov

The Commission on Civil Rights collects and studies information on discrimination or denials of equal protection of the laws because of race, color, religion, sex, age, disability, national origin, or in the administration of justice in such areas as voting rights, enforcement of Federal civil rights laws, and equal opportunity in education, employment, and housing.

14221 ■ U.S. Department of Justice, Civil Rights Division
950 Pennsylvania Ave., NW
Washington, DC 20530
Ph: (202)514-4609

Fax: (202)514-0293
URL: http://www.justice.gov/crt

The Division is the primary institution within the Federal Government responsible for enforcing Federal statutes prohibiting discrimination on the basis of race, sex, disability, religion, and national origin.

14222 ■ U.S. Department of Labor
200 Constitution Ave., NW
Washington, DC 20210
Ph: 877-889-5627
Fr: (866)487-2365
URL: http://www.dol.gov

Seeks to foster, promote, and develop the welfare of the wage earners of the United States, to improve their working conditions, and to advance their opportunities for profitable employment. In carrying out this mission, the Department administers a variety of Federal labor laws guaranteeing workers' rights to safe and healthful working conditions, a minimum hourly wage and overtime pay, freedom from employment discrimination, unemployment insurance, and workers' compensation. The Department also protects workers' pension rights; provides for job training programs; helps workers find jobs; works to strengthen free collective bargaining; and keeps track of changes in employment, prices, and other national economic measurements. As the Department seeks to assist all Americans who need and want to work, special efforts are made to meet the unique job market problems of older workers, youths, minority group members, women, the handicapped, and other groups.

14223 ■ U.S. Department of Labor, Adult Services Administration
200 Constitution Ave., NW
Washington, DC 20210
Fax: (202)693-2726
Fr: 877-889-5627
E-mail: etapagemaster@dol.gov
URL: http://www.doleta.gov/Programs

The Adult Services Administration is responsible for planning and developing policies, legislative proposals, goals, strategies, budgets, and resource allocation for the operation of comprehensive services to adults in the work force investment system; designing, developing, and administering employment and training services for welfare recipients, Native Americans, migrant and seasonal farm workers, older workers, individuals with disabilities, and individuals dislocated due to mass layoffs and emergencies; and providing direction for the investigation of worker petitions and the preparation of industry impact studies relating to trade adjustment assistance.

14224 ■ U.S. Department of Labor, Bureau of International Labor Affairs
200 Constitution Ave., NW
Washington, DC 20210
Ph: (202)693-4770
Fax: (202)693-4780

Fr: (866)487-2365
E-mail: contact-ilab@dol.gov
URL: http://www.dol.gov/ilab

The Bureau of International Labor Affairs assists in formulating international economic, social, trade, and immigration policies affecting American workers, with a view to maximizing higher wage and higher value U.S. jobs derived from global economic integration; gathers and disseminates information on child labor practices worldwide; promotes respect for international labor standards to protect the economic and physical well-being of workers in the United States and around the world; gathers and disseminates information on foreign labor markets and programs so that U.S. employment policy formulation might benefit from international experiences; carries out overseas technical assistance projects; and conducts research on the labor market consequences of immigration proposals and legislation.

14225 ■ U.S. Department of Labor, Bureau of Labor Statistics
Postal Square Bldg.
2 Massachusetts Ave. NW
Washington, DC 20212-0001
Ph: (202)691-5200
URL: http://www.bls.gov

The Bureau of Labor Statistics (BLS) is the principal fact-finding agency of the Federal Government in the broad field of labor economics and statistics. The Bureau is an independent national statistical agency that collects, processes, analyzes, and disseminates essential statistical data to the American public, Congress, other Federal agencies, State and local governments, businesses, and labor.

14226 ■ U.S. Department of Labor, Employee Benefits Security Administration
200 Constitution Ave., NW
Washington, DC 20210
Fr: (866)444-3272
URL: http://www.dol.gov/ebsa

The Employee Benefits Security Administration (EBSA) is responsible for promoting and protecting the pension, health, and other benefits of the over 150 million participants and beneficiaries in over 6 million private sector employee benefit plans. In administering its responsibilities, PWBA assists workers in understanding their rights and protecting their benefits; facilitates compliance by plan sponsors, plan officials, service providers, and other members of the regulated community; encourages the growth of employment-based benefits; and deters and corrects violations of the relevant statutes. ERISA is enforced through 15 PWBA field offices nationwide and the national office in Washington, DC.

14227 ■ U.S. Department of Labor, Employment and Training Administration
200 Constitution Ave., NW
Washington, DC 20210
Fax: (202)693-2726
Fr: 877-872-5625
E-mail: etapagemaster@dol.gov
URL: http://www.doleta.gov

The Employment and Training Administration fulfills responsibilities assigned to the Secretary of Labor that relate to employment services, job training, and unemployment insurance. Component offices and services administer a Federal/State employment security system; fund and oversee programs to provide work experience and training for groups having difficulty entering or returning to the work force; formulate and promote apprenticeship standards and programs; and conduct continuing programs of research, development, and evaluation.

14228 ■ U.S. Department of Labor, Employment and Training Administration
200 Constitution Ave., NW
Washington, DC 20210
Fax: (202)693-7888
Fr: 877-872-5627
URL: http://www.doleta.gov/usworkforce

The Administration is responsible for interpreting Federal legislative requirements for State unemployment compensation and employment service programs and one-stop systems; guiding and assisting States in adopting laws, regulations, and policies that conform with and support Federal law; developing, negotiating, and monitoring reimbursable agreements with States to administer the Targeted Jobs Tax Credit Program; providing policy guidance for the Immigration and Nationality Act concerning aliens seeking admission into the United States in order to work; and overseeing the development and implementation of the Nation's labor market information system.

14229 ■ U.S. Department of Labor, Mine Safety and Health Administration
1100 Wilson Blvd., 21st Fl.
Arlington, VA 22209-3939
Ph: (202)693-9400
Fax: (202)693-9401
E-mail: mshahelpdesk@dol.gov
URL: http://www.msha.gov

The Mine Safety and Health Administration is responsible for safety and health in the Nation's mines. The Administration develops and promulgates mandatory safety and health standards, ensures compliance with such standards, assesses civil penalties for violations, and investigates accidents. It cooperates with and provides assistance to the States in the development of effective State mine safety and health programs; improves and expands training programs in cooperation with the States and the mining industry; and contributes to the improvement and expansion of mine safety and health research and development. All of these activities are aimed at preventing and reducing mine accidents and occupational diseases in the mining industry.

14230 ■ U.S. Department of Labor, Occupational Safety and Health Administration
200 Constitution Ave., NW
Washington, DC 20210
Fr: 800-321-6742
URL: http://www.osha.gov

The Occupational Safety and Health Administration (OSHA) sets and enforces workplace safety and health standards and assists employers in complying with those standards.

14231 ■ U.S. Department of Labor, Office of Apprenticeship
200 Constitution Ave., NW
Washington, DC 20210
Ph: (202)693-2796
Fax: (202)693-2808
Fr: 877-872-5627
URL: http://www.doleta.gov/OA

The Administration is responsible for developing materials and conducting a program of public awareness to secure the adoption of training in skilled occupations and related training policies and practices used by employers, unions, and other organizations; developing policies and plans to enhance opportunities for minority and female participation in skilled training; and coordinating the effective use of Federal, labor, and employer resources to create a clear training-to-employment corridor for customers of the work force development system.

14232 ■ U.S. Department of Labor, Office of Federal Contract Compliance Programs
200 Constitution Ave., NW
Washington, DC 20210
Fr: 800-397-6251
E-mail: ofccp-public@dol.gov
URL: http://www.dol.gov/ofccp/index.htm

The Office of Federal Contract Compliance Programs (OFCCP) ensures that companies that do business with the Government promote affirmative action and equal employment opportunity on behalf of minorities, women, the disabled, and Vietnam veterans.

14233 ■ U.S. Department of Labor, Office of Labor-Management Standards
200 Constitution Ave., NW
Washington, DC 20210
Ph: (202)693-0123
Fr: (866)487-2365
E-mail: olms-public@dol.gov
URL: http://www.dol.gov/olms/index.htm

The Office of Labor-Management Standards conducts criminal and civil investigations to safeguard the financial integrity of unions and to ensure union democracy, and conducts investigative audits of labor unions to uncover and remedy criminal and civil violations of the Labor-Management Reporting and Disclosure Act and related statutes.

14234 ■ U.S. Department of Labor, Office of Small Business Programs
200 Constitution Ave., NW
Washington, DC 20210
Ph: 877-889-5627
Fr: (866)487-2365
URL: http://www.dol.gov

The Office of Small Business Programs administers the Department's efforts to ensure procurement opportunities for small businesses, disadvantaged businesses, women-owned businesses, HUBZone businesses, and businesses owned by service-disabled veterans.

14235 ■ U.S. Department of Labor, Office of Workers' Compensation Programs
200 Constitution Ave. NW
Washington, DC 20210
Ph: (202)693-0031
Fr: (866)487-2365
URL: http://www.dol.gov/owcp

The Office of Workers' Compensation Programs is responsible for programs providing workers' compensation for Federal employees; benefits to employees in private enterprise while engaged in maritime employment on navigable waters in the United States; benefits to coal miners who are totally disabled due to pneumoconiosis, a respiratory disease contracted after prolonged inhalation of coal mine dust, and to their survivors when the miner's death is due to pneumoconiosis; and to energy employees who contract occupational illnesses.

14236 ■ U.S. Department of Labor, Veterans' Employment and Training Service
200 Constitution Ave., NW
Washington, DC 20210
Fr: (866)487-2365
E-mail: vets-public@dol.gov
URL: http://www.dol.gov/VETS

The Veterans' Employment and Training Service (VETS) is responsible for administering veterans' employment and training programs and activities to ensure that legislative and regulatory mandates are accomplished.

14237 ■ U.S. Department of Labor, Wage and Hour Division
200 Constitution Ave. NW
Washington, DC 20210
Fr: (866)487-9243
E-mail: ofccp-public@dol.gov
URL: http://www.dol.gov/whd/index.htm

The Wage and Hour Division is responsible for planning, directing, and administering programs dealing with a variety of Federal labor legislation. These programs are designed to protect low-wage incomes; safeguard the health and welfare of workers by discouraging excessively long hours of work; safeguard the health and well-being of minors; prevent curtailment of employment and earnings for students, trainees, and handicapped workers; minimize losses of income and job rights caused by indebtedness; and direct a program of farm labor contractor registration designed to protect the health, safety, and welfare of migrant and seasonal agricultural workers.

14238 ■ U.S. Department of Labor, Women's Bureau
200 Constitution Ave., NW
Washington, DC 20210
Ph: (202)693-6710
Fr: 800-827-5335
E-mail: women'sbureaunetwork@dol.gov
URL: http://www.dol.gov/wb

The Women's Bureau is responsible for formulating standards and policies that promote the welfare of wage-earning women, improve their working conditions, increase their efficiency, and advance their opportunities for profitable employment.

14239 ■ U.S. Department of Labor, Youth Services Administration
200 Constitution Ave., NW
Washington, DC 20210
Fax: (202)693-2726
Fr: 877-872-5627
E-mail: etapagemaster@dol.gov
URL: http://www.doleta.gov/Youth_services

The Administration is responsible for planning, developing, and recommending objectives, policies, and strategies for operations of a comprehensive youth employment and training system; and providing policy guidance and program performance oversight for Job Corps youth employment and training services and youth services grant programs authorized under the Workforce Investment Act and the school-to-work system.

REFERENCE WORKS

14240 ■ 9 Steps to a Great Federal Job
LearningExpress, LLC
Two Rector St., 26th Fl.
New York, NY 10006
Ph: (212)995-2566
Fax: (212)995-5512
Fr: 800-295-9556
E-mail: customerservice@learningexpressllc.com
URL: http://www.learningexpressllc.com

Lee Wherry Brainerd, C. Roebuck Reed. February 2004. $19.95. Illustrated. 176 pages.

14241 ■ 150 Best Federal Jobs
JIST Publishing
875 Montreal Way
St. Paul, MN 55102
Fax: 800-547-8329
Fr: 800-648-5478
E-mail: info@jist.com
URL: http://www.jist.com

Laurence Shatkin. 2012. $17.95. 480 pages. Helps jobseekers target the federal job of their choice. Includes descriptions of 150 jobs detailing pay, growth and openings, comparative data, required education and training, skills needed, and work environment. Covers additional material on the federal hiring process, pay systems, opportunities for veterans and jobseekers with disabilities and college majors that connect to federal jobs.

14242 ■ The Book of U.S. Government Jobs
Bookhaven Press L.L.C.
249 Field Club Cir.
McKees Rocks, PA 15136
Ph: (412)494-6926
Fax: (412)494-5749
Fr: 800-782-7424
URL: http://www.bookhavenpress.com

Annual, Latest edition 11th, June 2011. $27.95 for individuals. Publication includes: Lists of Washington, D.C., departments and agencies, Web sites, and job centers nationwide. Indexes: Alphabetical.

14243 ■ Career Ideas for Teens in Government and Public Service
Facts On File Inc.
132 W 31st St., 17th Fl.
New York, NY 10001
Ph: (212)967-8800
Fax: 800-678-3633
Fr: 800-322-8755
URL: http://www.infobasepublishing.com

Published August, 2005. Covers: A multitude of career possibilities based on a teenager's specific interests and skills and links his/her talents to a wide variety of actual professions.

14244 ■ Careers in Focus: Government
Ferguson Publishing
132 W 31st St., 17th Fl.
New York, NY 10001
Fr: 800-322-8755
E-mail: custserv@factsonfile.com
URL: http://factsonfile.infobasepublishing.com

2007. $32.95. 208 pages. Covers an overview of governmental jobs, followed by a selection of jobs profiled in detail, including the nature of the job, earnings, prospects for employment, what kind of training and skills it requires and sources for further information.

14245 ■ Careers in Horticulture and Botany
The McGraw-Hill Companies
PO Box 182604
Columbus, OH 43272
Fax: (614)759-3749
Fr: 877-883-5524
E-mail: customer.service@mcgraw-hill.com
URL: http://www.mhprofessional.com/
    product.php?isbn=0071467734

Jerry Garner. 2006. 16.95 (paper). 192 pages. Includes bibliographical references.

14246 ■ Careers in Public Works
American Public Works Association
1275 K St. NW, Ste. 750
Washington, DC 20005
Ph: (202)408-9541
Fax: (202)408-9542
URL: http://www.apwa.net/bookstore/
    detail.asp?PC=PB.A512

Jan Goldberg. 2005. 152 pages. $3 for members; $14 for non-members. Provides an overview of the world of public works for students and job seekers. Includes design, construction, maintenance and operation of roads, water and sewer services, power and communication systems, building and bridges.

14247 ■ Carroll's Federal Directory
Carroll Publishing
4701 Sangamore Rd., Ste. S-155
Bethesda, MD 20816
Ph: (301)263-9800
Fax: (301)263-9801
Fr: 800-336-4240
URL: http://www.carrollpub.com

4x/yr. $450.00 for single issue. Covers: About 38,000 executive managers in federal government offices in Washington, DC, including executive, congressional and judicial branches; members of Congress and Congressional committees and staff. Entries include: Agency names, titles, office address (including room numbers), e-mail addresses, and telephone and fax numbers. Also available as part of a "library edition" titled "Federal Directory Annual". Arrangement: By cabinet department or administrative agency. Indexes: Keyword, personal name (with phone) and e-mail addresses.

14248 ■ Carroll's State Directory
Carroll Publishing
4701 Sangamore Rd., Ste. S-155
Bethesda, MD 20816
Ph: (301)263-9800
Fax: (301)263-9801
Fr: 800-336-4240
URL: http://www.carrollpub.com/stateprint.asp

3x/yr. $425.00 for individuals. Covers: About 70,000 state government officials in all branches of government; officers, committees and members of state legislatures; managers of boards and authorities. Entries include: Name, address, phone, fax, title. Arrangement: Geographical; separate sections for state offices and legislatures. Indexes: Personal name (with phone and e-mail address), organizational, keyword.

14249 ■ The Complete Idiot's Guide to Getting Government Jobs
Alpha Books
375 Hudson St.
New York, NY 10014
Fr: 800-631-8571
E-mail: ecommerce@us.penguingroup.com
URL: http://us.penguingroup.com

The Partnership for Public Service. 2010. $18.95 (paper). 352 pages. Teaches readers the effective government application process to find stable employment opportunities available from county municipalities and state and federal agencies.

14250 ■ Congressional Directory
Capitol Advantage
2751 Prosperity Ave., Ste. 600
Fairfax, VA 22031
Ph: (703)289-4670
Fax: (703)289-4678
Fr: 800-659-8708
URL: http://capitoladvantage.com/publishing/
    products.html

Annual. $17.95 for individuals. Covers: 100 current senators and 440 House of Representative members. Entries include: Name, district office address, phone, fax; names and titles of key staff; committee and subcommittee assignments; biographical data, percentage of votes won, photo. Arrangement: Available in separate alphabetical, geographical, or condensed editions. Indexes: Name.

14251 ■ Encyclopedia of Governmental Advisory Organizations
Gale
PO Box 6904
Florence, KY 41022-6904
Fr: 800-354-9706
URL: http://www.gale.cengage.com

Annual, Latest edition 26th; June, 2011. $1,073.00 for individuals. Covers: More than 7,300 boards, panels, commissions, committees, presidential conferences, and other groups that advise the President, Congress, and departments and agencies of federal government; includes interagency committees and federally sponsored conferences. Also includes historically significant organizations. Entries include: Unit name, address, phone, URL and email (if active), name of principal executive, legal basis for the unit, purpose, reports and publications, findings and recommendations, description of activities, members. Arrangement: Classified by general subject. Indexes: Alphabetical/keyword, personnel, publication, federal department/agency, presidential administration.

14252 ■ The Everything Guide to Government Jobs
Adams Media
57 Littlefield St.
Avon, MA 02322
Ph: (508)427-7100
Fax: 800-872-5628
Fr: 800-872-5627
URL: http://www.adamsmedia.com

James Mannion. 2007. $14.95. 304 pages. Provides a comprehensive and unique guidebook to the ins and outs of finding government jobs.

14253 ■ FBI Careers, Third Edition
JIST Publishing
875 Montreal Way
St. Paul, MN 55102
Fax: 800-547-8329
Fr: 800-648-5478
E-mail: info@jist.com
URL: http://www.jist.com

Thomas H. Ackerman. 2010. $19.95. 368 pages. Guide to handling the FBI's rigorous selection process; reveals what it takes to succeed in landing a job. Useful for special agents as well as professional support personnel.

14254 ■ Federal Career Opportunities
Federal Research Service Inc.
PO Box 1708
Annandale, VA 22003
Ph: (703)914-5627
Fax: (703)281-7639
Fr: 800-822-5027
URL: http://www.fedjobs.com/index.html

Biweekly, Latest edition 2010. $19.97 for members; $59.95 for members; $99.95 for members; $39.95 for members. Covers: more than 3,000 current federal job vacancies in the United States and overseas; includes permanent, part-time, and temporary positions. Entries include: Position title, location, series and grade, job requirements, special forms, announcement number, closing date, application address. Arrangement: Classified by occupation.

14255 ■ Federal Jobs Digest
Federal Jobs Digest
326 Main St.
Emmaus, PA 18049
Fr: 800-824-5000
URL: http://www.jobsfed.com

25x/yr. $125.00 for U.S.; $152.75 for Canada; $183.75 for individuals; $112.50 for libraries; $140.25 for libraries; $171.25 for libraries. Covers: Over 10,000 specific job openings in the federal government in each issue. Vacancies from over 300 Federal Agencies are covered. Entries include: Position name, title, General Schedule (GS) grade, and Wage Grade (WG), closing date for applications, announcement number, application address, phone, and name of contact. Arrangement: By federal department or agency, then geographical.

14256 ■ Federal Law Enforcement Careers, Second Edition: Profiles of 250 High-Powered Positions and Tactics for Getting Hired
JIST Publishing
875 Montreal Way
St. Paul, MN 55102
Fax: 800-547-8329

Fr: 800-648-5478
E-mail: info@jist.com
URL: http://www.jist.com

Thomas H. Ackerman. 2006. $19.95. 464 pages. Provides information about federal law enforcement jobs with detailed profiles of 250 careers with more than 130 agencies, plus qualification requirements and training program descriptions.

14257 ■ Federal Resume Guidebook
JIST Publishing
875 Montreal Way
St. Paul, MN 55102
Fr: 800-648-5478
E-mail: educate@emcp.com
URL: http://www.jist.com

Kathryn Kraemer Troutman. 2011. $21.95 (softcover). 448 pages. Teaches readers how to develop resumes online and how to write KSAs, ECQs, essays, and short answers that will impress employers. Features sample resumes in actual online builder format. Contains tips for writing KSAs (knowledge, skills and abilities statements) and tips on security clearance requirements.

14258 ■ Federal Staff Directory
CQ Press
2300 North St. NW, Ste. 800
Washington, DC 20037
Ph: (202)729-1900
Fax: 800-380-3810
Fr: (866)427-7737
URL: http://www.cqpress.com/product/Federal-Staff-Directory-Winte

Latest edition Winter 2010. $348.00 for individuals. Covers: Approximately 45,000 persons in federal government offices and independent agencies, with biographies of 2,600 key executives; includes officials at policy level in agencies of the Office of the President, Cabinet-level departments, independent and regulatory agencies, military commands, federal information centers, and libraries, and United States attorneys, marshals, and ambassadors. Entries include: Name, title, location (indicating building, address, and/or room), phone, fax, e-mail address, website, symbols indicating whether position is a presidential appointment and whether senate approval is required. Arrangement: Classified by department/ agency. Indexes: Office locator page; extensive subject/keyword; individual name.

14259 ■ Federal Yellow Book
Leadership Directories Inc.
104 5th Ave.
New York, NY 10011
Ph: (212)627-4140
Fax: (212)645-0931
URL: http://www.leadershipdirectories.com/ Products.aspx

Quarterly, Latest edition 2011. $550.00 for individuals; $385.00 for individuals; $523.00 for individuals; $366.00 for individuals. Covers: Federal departments, including the Executive Office of the President, the Office of the Vice President, the Office of Management and Budget, the Cabinet, and the National Security Council, and over 40,000 key personnel; over 85 independent federal agencies. Entries include: For personnel—Name, address, phone, fax, e-mails, titles. For departments and agencies—Office, or branch name and address; names and titles of principal personnel, with their room numbers, direct-dial phone numbers, and E-mails. Arrangement: Classified by department or agency. Indexes: Subject, organization, individuals' names.

14260 ■ Find Your Federal Job Fit
JIST Publishing
875 Montreal Way
St. Paul, MN 55102
Fr: 800-648-5478
E-mail: educate@emcp.com
URL: http://www.jist.com

Janet Ruck and Karol Taylor. 2012. $14.95 (softcover). 256 pages. Gives a valuable insight about

government job seeking. Provides tips on how to find the right occupation, develop a vision for one's career, develop essential skills, and create a career plan.

14261 ■ Government Job Finder
Planning Communications
7215 Oak Ave.
River Forest, IL 60305-1935
Ph: (708)366-5200
Fax: (708)366-5280
Fr: 888-366-5200
E-mail: info@planningcommunications.com
URL: http://www.planningcommunications.com

Daniel Lauber and Deborah Verlench. Fourth edition, 2008. 348 pages. $19.95. Covers 2,002 sources. Discusses how to use sources of local, state, and federal government job vacancies in a number of specialties and state-bystate, including job-matching services, job hotlines, specialty periodicals with job ads, salary surveys, and directories. Explains how local, state, and federal hiring systems work. Includes chapters on resume and cover letter preparation and interviewing.

14262 ■ Guide to America's Federal Jobs, Fourth Edition
JIST Publishing
875 Montreal Way
St. Paul, MN 55102
Fax: 800-547-8329
Fr: 800-648-5478
E-mail: info@jist.com
URL: http://www.jist.com

Bruce Maxwell. 2009. $19.95. 448 pages. Provides summaries of all federal agencies plus guidance on creating federal resumes; applying online; interviewing for federal jobs; and special programs for students, veterans, and people with disabilities.

14263 ■ How to Land a Top-Paying Federal Job
AMACOM Publishing
c/o American Management Association
1601 Broadway
New York, NY 10019-7434
Ph: (212)586-8100
Fr: 800-714-6395
E-mail: pubs_cust_serv@amanet.org
URL: http://www.amacombooks.org

Lily Whiteman. 2008. $24.95 (paper). 304 pages. Provides readers advice on how to land a federal job, internship, or fellowship and how to land federal promotions.

14264 ■ Jobseeker's Guide
The Resume Place, Inc.
89 Mellor Ave.
Baltimore, MD 21228
Ph: (410)744-4324
Fax: (410)744-0112
Fr: 888-480-8265
E-mail: resume@resume-place.com
URL: http://www.resume-place.com

Kathryn Troutman. 2010. $14.95 (paper). 150 pages. Contains essential information for military and family members who are seeking federal employment. Includes resume and cover letter samples.

14265 ■ Managing Your Government Career
AMACOM Publishing
c/o American Management Association
1601 Broadway
New York, NY 10019-7434
Ph: (212)586-8100
Fax: (518)891-0368
Fr: 800-714-6395
E-mail: pubs_cust_serv@amanet.org
URL: http://www.amacombooks.org

Stewart Liff. 2009. $19.95 (paper). 272 pages. Provides current and future government employees advice for starting out and maneuvering through their entire career. Helps readers decide whether working for the government is right for them; understand the differences between federal, state, and local levels; apply, interview for, and get the job that they want; take advantage of the training offered; understand the culture; become familiar with local politics; make themselves valuable; develop the right mentors; and fluidly transition up the ladder.

14266 ■ Nonprofits and Government: Field Guides to Finding a New Career

Facts On File
132 W 31st St., 17th Fl.
New York, NY 10001
Fax: 800-678-3633
Fr: 800-322-8755
E-mail: custserv@factsonfile.com
URL: http://factsonfile.infobasepublishing.com

Amanda Kirk. 2009. $39.95 (hardcover). 176 pages. Guides career changers in exploring career possibilities in the nonprofits and government fields. Contains tips and advice from professionals. Provides readers with an overview of nonprofits and government, ways to map out career goals for the future, and self-assessment questions.

14267 ■ Opportunities in Government Careers

The McGraw-Hill Companies
PO Box 182604
Columbus, OH 43272
Fax: (614)759-3749
Fr: 877-883-5524
E-mail: customer.service@mcgraw-hill.com
URL: http://www.mhprofessional.com/
   product.php?isbn=0658010492

Neale J. Baxter. $12.95. 160 pages. VGM Opportunities Series.

14268 ■ Opportunities in Overseas Careers

The McGraw-Hill Companies
PO Box 182604
Columbus, OH 43272
Fax: (614)759-3749
Fr: 877-883-5524
E-mail: customer.service@mcgraw-hill.com
URL: http://www.mhprofessional.com/
   product.php?isbn=0071454470

Blythe Camenson. 2004. $13.95 (paper). 173 pages.

14269 ■ The Student's Federal Career Guide

JIST Publishing
875 Montreal Way
St. Paul, MN 55102
Fax: 800-547-8329
Fr: 800-648-5478
E-mail: info@jist.com
URL: http://www.jist.com

Kathryn Kramer and Emily K. Troutman. $21.95. 184 pages. Comprehensive guide to federal government jobs for young adults.

14270 ■ Take Charge of Your Federal Career

Bookhaven Press LLC
249 Field Club Cir.
McKees Rocks, PA 15136
Ph: (412)494-6926
E-mail: info@bookhavenpress.com
URL: http://www.bookhavenpress.com

Dennis V. Damp. 2010. $29.95. 224 pages. Provides federal workers with practical career management and guidance they need to qualify for new and better federal jobs.

14271 ■ Ten Steps to a Federal Job: Navigating the Federal Job System

JIST Publishing
875 Montreal Way
St. Paul, MN 55102
Fax: 800-547-8329
Fr: 800-648-5478
E-mail: info@jist.com
URL: http://www.jist.com/shop/
   product.php?productid=1490&printable=Y

Kathryn Kraemer Troutman. 2009. $28.95. 360 pages. Provides information for developing resumes and cover letters that will get noticed in the federal system, as well as guidance to landing a federal job.

14272 ■ United States Government Manual

Office of the Federal Register
c/o The National Archives & Records Administration
8601 Adelphi Rd.
College Park, MD 20740-6001
Ph: (301)837-0482
Fax: (301)837-0483
Fr: (866)272-6272
URL: http://www.archives.gov/federal-register/
   publications/govern

Annual, latest edition 2009-2010. $29.00 for individuals. Provides information on the agencies of the executive, judicial, and legislative branches of the Federal government. Contains a section on terminated or transferred agencies. Arrangement: Classified by department and agency. Indexes: Personal name, agency/subject.

14273 ■ Washington Information Directory

CQ Press
2300 North St. NW, Ste. 800
Washington, DC 20037
Ph: (202)729-1900
Fax: 800-380-3810
Fr: (866)427-7737
URL: http://www.cqpress.com

Annual, Latest edition 2010-2011. $155.00 for individuals. Covers: 10,000 governmental agencies, congressional committees, and non-governmental associations considered competent sources of specialized information. Entries include: Name of agency, committee, or association; address, phone, fax, and Internet; annotation concerning function or activities of the office; and name of contact. Arrangement: Classified by activity or competence (economics and business, housing and urban affairs, etc.). Indexes: Subject, agency/organization name, contact name.

14274 ■ Who's Who in Local Government Management

International City/County Management Association
777 N Capitol St. NE, Ste. 500
Washington, DC 20002-4201
Ph: (202)289-4262
Fax: (202)962-3500
Fr: 800-745-8780
E-mail: membership@icma.org
URL: http://www.icma.org

Annual, September. Covers: 8,000 appointed administrators of cities, counties, and councils of governments. Entries include: Name, position, office address, educational history, career data, offices held in ICMA. Arrangement: Alphabetical by individual name.

14275 ■ Writing your NSPS Self-Assessment, Second Edition

The Resume Place, Inc.
89 Mellor Ave.
Baltimore, MD 21228
Ph: (410)744-4324
Fax: (410)744-0112
Fr: 888-480-8265
E-mail: resume@resume-place.com
URL: http://www.resume-place.com

Kathryn K. Troutman and Nancy H. Segal. 2009. $28.95 (softcover). 186 pages. Serves as a guide to writing accomplishments for the Department of Defense employees and supervisors. Includes an appendix that details four complete NSPS self-assessment samples.

NEWSPAPERS, MAGAZINES, AND JOURNALS

14276 ■ Federal Acquisition Report

Management Concepts Inc.
8230 Leesburg Pike
Vienna, VA 22182

Fax: (703)790-1371
Fr: 800-506-4450
E-mail: customerservice1@
   managementconcepts.com
URL: http://www.managementconcepts.com

Description: Monthly. $329 for print version; $269/year for online version. Focuses on developments in federal contracting, legislation, changes in rules and regulations, and recent decisions by the board of contract appeals and by the courts. Features job listings and guest essays.

14277 ■ The Federal Physician

Federal Physicians Association
12427 Hedges Run Dr., Ste. 104
Lake Ridge, VA 22192
Fax: (703)426-8400
Fr: 800-528-3492
E-mail: info@fedphy.com
URL: http://www.fedphy.org

Description: Bimonthly. Covers issues affecting physicians in the federal government. Recurring features include news of research, reports of meetings, and job listings.

14278 ■ Federal Times

Gannett Government Media Corporation
6883 Commercial Dr.
Springfield, VA 22159-0500
Ph: (703)750-7400
Fr: 800-368-5718
URL: http://www.federaltimes.com/

Weekly (Mon.). Federal bureaucracy; technology in government.

14279 ■ FEW's News and Views

Federally Employed Women Inc.
700 N Fairfax St., No. 510
Alexandria, VA 22314
Ph: (202)898-0994
Fax: (202)898-1535
E-mail: few@few.org
URL: http://www.few.org/publications.asp

Description: Bimonthly. Concerned with women's issues, particularly those involving women in the federal government. Reports on administration actions affecting the status of women and analyzes significant legislation. Recurring features include letters to the editor, news of members, a calendar of events, book reviews, and notices of career development and training opportunities.

14280 ■ Government Finance Officers Association Newsletter

Government Finance Officers Association
203 N LaSalle St., Ste. 2700
Chicago, IL 60601-1210
Ph: (312)977-9700
Fax: (312)977-4806
URL: http://www.gfoa.org/

Description: Semimonthly. Provides updates on current events, innovations, and federal legislation affecting public finance management for state and local government finance officers. Covers cash management, budgeting, accounting, auditing, and financial reporting, public employee retirement administration, and related issues. Recurring features include news of research, news of members, a calendar of events, and columns titled Career Notes and Employment Opportunities. Subscription includes the bimonthly magazine Government Finance Review.

14281 ■ The Municipality

League of Wisconsin Municipalities
122 W Washington Ave., Ste. 300
Madison, WI 53703-2715
Ph: (608)267-2380
Fax: (608)267-0645
Fr: 800-991-5502
URL: http://www.lwm-info.org/

Monthly. Magazine for officials of Wisconsin's local municipal governments.

14282 ■ Postal Record
National Association of Letter Carriers
100 Indiana Ave. NW
Washington, DC 20001-2144
Ph: (202)393-4695
E-mail: postalrecord@nalc.org
URL: http://www.nalc.org/news/precord/index.html

Monthly. Magazine for active and retired letter carriers.

ONLINE AND DATABASE SERVICES

14283 ■ ExecSearches.com
E-mail: info@execsearches.com
URL: http://www.execsearches.com

Description: Job site specializing in matching seekers with non-profit, public sector, academic and "socially conscious" positions. Contains job board, resume databank, e-mail alert system and reference articles. Employers may also post jobs and check resume references.

14284 ■ FedWorld Federal Job Search
National Technical Information Service
5301 Shawnee Rd.
Alexandria, VA 22312
Ph: (703)605-6000
Fr: 800-553-6847
E-mail: helpdesk@fedworld.gov
URL: http://www.fedworld.gov

Description: Database containing employment information in the public sector. Listings include address, job title and information, contact information, geographic location, and data of availability, among others. Main files include: NTIS Federal Job Opportunities; Atlanta Regional Federal Jobs; Chicago Regional Federal Jobs; Dallas Regional Federal Jobs; Philadelphia Regional Federal Jobs; San Francisco Regional Federal Jobs; Washington DC Regional Federal Jobs; National Federal Jobs; S&S Federal Positions Available; Public Health Service Positions; Federal Jobs Listed by State; Atlantic Overseas; Pacific Overseas; Puerto Rico; Virgin Islands; Information on Downloading Files; Federal Jobs EMail Forum; Exit to Main Menu; and Enter Jobs File Library. Free.

14285 ■ Government and Military Jobs
URL: http://www.governmentandmilitaryjobs.com

Description: Provides information on available government and military jobs in all specialties.

14286 ■ GovJobs.com
URL: http://www.govjobs.com

Description: Provides cost-efficient, user-friendly ways of sharing employment information to worldwide job seekers and all government and commercial employers.

14287 ■ GovtJobs.com
URL: http://www.govtjobs.com

Description: Devoted to helping individuals find jobs in the public sector. Each listing includes a description of the position title, job requirements (education, special skills), duties/responsibilities, salary, closing date, name of agency, and any other information pertinent to the position and job applicant.

14288 ■ Local Government Talent
URL: http://www.lgcareers.com

Description: Serves as a one-stop resource for information about working in local government. Caters to individuals looking for career information, searching for job vacancies or seeking new talent for organizations.

14289 ■ Search Fed Jobs
URL: http://searchfedjobs.com

Description: Features federal job listings in metropolitan areas across the United States.

OTHER SOURCES

14290 ■ African Studies Association (ASA)
Rutgers University, Livingston Campus
54 Joyce Kilmer Ave.
Piscataway, NJ 08854-8045
Ph: (848)445-8173
Fax: (732)445-1366
E-mail: karen.jenkins@africanstudies.org
URL: http://www.africanstudies.org

Description: Persons specializing in teaching, writing, or research on Africa including political scientists, historians, geographers, anthropologists, economists, librarians, linguists, and government officials; persons who are studying African subjects; institutional members are universities, libraries, government agencies, and others interested in receiving information about Africa. Seeks to foster communication and to stimulate research among scholars on Africa. Sponsors placement service; conducts panels and discussion groups; presents exhibits and films.

14291 ■ Celia D. Crossley & Associates Ltd.
3011 Bethel Rd., Ste. 201
Columbus, OH 43220
Ph: (614)538-2808
Fax: (614)442-8886
E-mail: info@crosworks.com
URL: http://www.crosworks.com

Firm specializes in career planning and development, executive and organizational career coaching, assessment, key employee selection and team integration. Also offers career transition services, including in-placement, outplacement, and career coaching. Serves government, nonprofit, health-care, higher education and service industries.

14292 ■ Civil Service Employees Association (CSEA)
143 Washington Ave.
Albany, NY 12210
Ph: (518)257-1000
Fr: 800-342-4146
URL: http://www.csealocal1000.org

Description: AFL-CIO. Represents state and local government employees from all public employee classifications. Negotiates work contracts; represents members in grievances; provides legal assistance for on-the-job problems; provides advice and assistance on federal, state, and local laws affecting public employees. Conducts research, training and education programs. Compiles statistics.

14293 ■ Federally Employed Women (FEW)
700 N Fairfax St., No. 510
Alexandria, VA 22314
Ph: (202)898-0994
Fax: (202)898-1535
E-mail: few@few.org
URL: http://www.few.org

Description: Represents men and women employed by the federal government. Seeks to end sexual discrimination in government service; to increase job opportunities for women in government service and to further the potential of all women in the government; to improve the merit system in government employment; to assist present and potential government employees who are discriminated against because of sex; to work with other organizations and individuals concerned with equal employment opportunity in the government. Provides speakers and sponsors seminars to publicize the Federal Women's Program; furnishes members with information on pending legislation designed to end discrimination against working women; informs and provides members opportunities for training to improve their job potential; issuesfact sheets interpreting civil service rules and regulations and other legislative issues; provides annual training conference for over 3,000 women and men

14294 ■ Focus Learning Corp.
173 Cross St., Ste. 200
San Luis Obispo, CA 93401
Ph: (805)543-4895
Fax: (805)543-4897
Fr: 800-458-5116
E-mail: info@focuslearning.com
URL: http://www.focuslearning.com

Provides professional services to corporations for the development and implementation of training programs. Assists clients with needs assessment related to training and professional development, goals definition, and development of training materials. Industries served include: government, utility, aerospace, business, and computer.

14295 ■ National Alliance of Postal and Federal Employees (NAPFE)
1628 11th St. NW
Washington, DC 20001
Ph: (202)939-6325
Fax: (202)939-6330
E-mail: headquarters@napfe.org
URL: http://www.napfe.com

Description: Independent. Works to eliminate employment discrimination.

14296 ■ National Association of Government Communicators (NAGC)
201 Park Washington Ct.
Falls Church, VA 22046-4527
Ph: (703)538-1787
Fax: (703)241-5603
E-mail: info@nagconline.org
URL: http://www.nagc.com

Description: Government employees, retired persons, non-government affiliates, and students. Seeks to advance communications as an essential professional resource at every level of national, state, and local government by: disseminating information; encouraging professional development, public awareness, and exchange of ideas and experience; improving internal communications. Maintains placement service.

14297 ■ National Association of Government Employees (NAGE)
159 Burgin Pkwy.
Quincy, MA 02169
Ph: (617)376-0220
Fax: (617)376-0285
Fr: (866)412-7762
E-mail: membership@nage.org
URL: http://www.nage.org

Description: Union of civilian federal government employees with locals and members in military agencies, Internal Revenue Service, Post Office, Veterans Administration, General Services Administration, Federal Aviation Administration, and other federal agencies, as well as state and local agencies. Activities include direct legal assistance, information service, legislative lobbying and representation, trained leadership in contract negotiations, employment protection, and insurance. Offers seminars; sponsors competitions.

14298 ■ National Association of Hispanic Federal Executives (NAHFE)
PO Box 23270
Washington, DC 20026
Ph: (202)315-3942
E-mail: president@nahfe.org
URL: http://www.nahfe.org

Description: Hispanic and other federal employees ranked GS-12 and above; individuals in the private sector whose positions are equivalent to rank GS-12. Purpose: Promotes the federal government as a model employer by encouraging qualified individuals to apply for federal government positions. Activities: Offers increased productivity training to federal employees. Maintains speakers' bureau and placement service. Offers educational programs; compiles statistics; conducts research.

14299 ■ Voorhees Associates, LLC
500 Lake Cook Rd., Ste. 350
Deerfield, IL 60015
Ph: (847)580-4246

Fax: (866)401-6100
E-mail: info@varesume.com
URL: http://www.voorheesassociates.com

Description: Specializes in executive recruitment of candidates for governmental entities of all sizes throughout the United States.

REFERENCE WORKS

14300 ■ Federal Career Opportunities
Federal Research Service Inc.
PO Box 1708
Annandale, VA 22003
Ph: (703)914-5627
Fax: (703)281-7639
Fr: 800-822-5027
URL: http://www.fedjobs.com/index.html

Biweekly. Latest edition 2010. $19.97 for members; $59.95 for members; $99.95 for members; $39.95 for members. Covers: more than 3,000 current federal job vacancies in the United States and overseas; includes permanent, part-time, and temporary positions. Entries include: Position title, location, series and grade, job requirements, special forms, announcement number, closing date, application address. Arrangement: Classified by occupation.

14301 ■ Federal Jobs Digest
Federal Jobs Digest
326 Main St.
Emmaus, PA 18049
Fr: 800-824-5000
URL: http://www.jobsfed.com

25x/yr. $125.00 for U.S.; $152.75 for Canada; $183.75 for individuals; $112.50 for libraries; $140.25 for libraries; $171.25 for libraries. Covers: Over 10,000 specific job openings in the federal government in each issue. Vacancies from over 300 Federal Agencies are covered. Entries include: Position name, title, General Schedule (GS) grade, and Wage Grade (WG), closing date for applications, announcement number, application address, phone, and name of contact. Arrangement: By federal department or agency, then geographical.

14302 ■ INSIGHT Into Diversity
INSIGHT Into Diversity
c/o Potomac Publishing, Inc.
225 Meramec Ave., Ste. 400
St. Louis, MO 63105
Ph: (314)863-2900
Fax: (314)863-2905
Fr: 800-537-0655
URL: http://www.aarjobs.com

Monthly. $15.00 for individuals; $8.00 for individuals. Covers: In each issue, about 300 positions at a professional level (most requiring advanced study) available to women, minorities, veterans, and the handicapped; listings are advertisements placed by employers with affirmative action programs. Entries include: Company or organization name, address, contact name; description of position including title, requirements, duties, application procedure, salary, etc. Arrangement: Classified by profession.

14303 ■ International Employment Hotline
International Employment Hotline
PO Box 6729
Charlottesville, VA 22906-6729

Ph: (434)970-5033
Fax: (434)295-7989
E-mail: ieo@mindspring.com
URL: http://www.internationaljobs.org/monthly.html

Monthly. $69.00 for individuals; $21.00 for individuals; $39.00 for individuals; $129.00 for individuals. Covers: Temporary and career job openings overseas and advice for international job hunters. Entries include: Company name, address, job title, description of job, requirements, geographic location of job. Arrangement: Geographical.

NEWSPAPERS, MAGAZINES, AND JOURNALS

14304 ■ Employment & the Economy: Northern Region
New Jersey Department of Labor and Workforce Development
1 John Fitch Plaza
PO Box 110
Trenton, NJ 08625-0110
Ph: (609)292-2515
Fax: (609)984-2515
E-mail: dwc@dol.state.nj.us
URL: http://lwd.dol.state.nj.us

Description: Quarterly. Covers economic trends and developments in 11 northern New Jersey counties, including employment conditions and construction project updates. Recurring features include list of job opportunities.

14305 ■ Employment & the Economy: Southern Region
New Jersey Department of Labor and Workforce Development
1 John Fitch Plaza
PO Box 110
Trenton, NJ 08625-0110
Ph: (609)292-2515
Fax: (609)984-2515
E-mail: dwc@dol.state.nj.us
URL: http://lwd.dol.state.nj.us

Description: Quarterly. Covers economic developments in six counties in southern New Jersey, including employment conditions and construction project updates. Recurring features include a list of job opportunities.

14306 ■ Item-Interference Technology Engineers Master
Robar Industries Inc.
3 Union Hill Rd.
West Conshohocken, PA 19428-2788
Fax: (610)834-7337
E-mail: item@rbitem.com
URL: http://www.interferencetechnology.com/rebrand_redirect.asp

Design magazine about measurement and control of electromagnetic interference.

14307 ■ The NonProfit Times
NPT Publishing Group Inc.
201 Littleton Rd., 2nd Fl.
Morris Plains, NJ 07950
Ph: (973)401-0202
Fax: (973)401-0404
E-mail: ednchief@nptimes.com
URL: http://www.nptimes.com/

$49.95/year for individuals, print; $19.95/year for individuals, digital only; $59.95/year for individuals, digital & print. Trade journal serving nonprofit organizations.

14308 ■ RFID Journal
RFID Journal, LLC
38 Kings Hwy., Ste. 1
Hauppauge, NY 11788
Ph: (631)249-4960
Fax: (631)980-4314
E-mail: admin@rfidjournal.com
URL: http://www.rfidjournal.com

Bimonthly. $189/year. Covers strategic issues to help senior executives develop and execute an intelligent RFID strategy. Includes a career center section designed to connect employers who need to hire skilled RFID professionals with those seeking new opportunities.

ONLINE AND DATABASE SERVICES

14309 ■ Beyond.com
URL: http://www.beyond.com

Description: Website providing free tools to job seekers including job database, career test, magazines, career evaluation, job alerts, personal portfolio, and career videos.

14310 ■ Criagslist.org
URL: http://manila.en.craigslist.com.ph

Description: Provides a forum for online help-wanted ads.

14311 ■ FindItClassifieds.com
URL: http://www.finditclassifieds.com

Description: Online help-wanted ads.

14312 ■ HelpWantedSite.com
URL: http://www.helpwantedsite.com

Description: Online help-wanted site. Features job postings.

14313 ■ Simply Hired, Inc.
URL: http://www.simplyhired.com

Description: A vertical search engine company providing an online database of jobs.

14314 ■ USfreeads.com
URL: http://www.usfreeads.com/_wanted-ads

Description: Provides online help-wanted ads.

REFERENCE WORKS

14315 ■ *The Career Guide—Dun's Employment Opportunities Directory*
Dun & Bradstreet Corp.
103 JFK Pky.
Short Hills, NJ 07078
Ph: (973)921-5500
Fr: 800-234-3867
URL: http://dnb.com/us

Annual. Covers: More than 10,000 companies on leading employers throughout the U.S. that provide career opportunities in sales, marketing, management, engineering, life and physical sciences, computer science, mathematics, statistics planning, accounting and finance, liberal arts fields, and other technical and professional areas; based on data supplied on questionnaires and through personal interviews. Also covers personnel consultants; includes some public sector employers (governments, schools, etc.) usually not found in similar lists. Entries include: Company name, location of headquarters and other offices or plants; entries may also include name, title, address, and phone of employment contact; disciplines or occupational groups hired; brief overview of company, discussion of types of positions that may be available, training and career development programs, benefits offered, internship and work-study programs. Arrangement: Employers are alphabetical; geographically by industry, employer branch offices geographically, disciplines hired geographically, employees offering work-study or internship programs and personnel consultants. Indexes: Geographical, SIC code.

14316 ■ *Corporate Affiliations Library*
LexisNexis Group
9443 Springboro Pike
Dayton, OH 45342
Fr: 888-285-3947
URL: http://www.corporateaffiliations.com

Annual, Latest edition 2008. A 8-volume set listing public and private companies worldwide. Comprises the following: Master Index (volumes 1 and 2); U.S. Public Companies (volume 3 and 4), listing 6,200 parent companies and 52,000 subsidiaries, affiliates, and divisions worldwide; U.S. Private Companies (volume 5), listing 15,000 privately held companies and 70,000 U.S. and international subsidiaries; and International Public and Private Companies (volume 7 and 8), listing 4,800 parent companies and 69,000 subsidiaries worldwide. Entries include: Parent company name, address, phone, fax, telex, e-mail addresses, names and titles of key personnel, financial data, fiscal period, type and line of business, SIC codes; names and locations of subsidiaries, divisions, and affiliates, outside service firms (accountants, legal counsel, etc.). Arrangement: Alphabetical within each volume. Indexes: Each volume includes company name index; separate Master Index volumes list all company names in the set in one alphabetic sequence in five indexes includ-

ing private, public, international, alphabetical, geographical, brand name, SIC, and corporate responsibilities.

14317 ■ *Courting Your Career*
JIST Publishing
875 Montreal Way
St. Paul, MN 55102
Fr: 800-648-5478
E-mail: educate@emcp.com
URL: http://www.jist.com

Shawn Graham. 2008. $6.47 (softcover). 208 pages. Contains anecdotes and advice appropriate for every stage of a typical job search - from what initially attracts job seekers to a potential employer to strategies for landing that dream job.

14318 ■ *D & B Million Dollar Directory*
Dun & Bradstreet Corp.
103 JFK Pky.
Short Hills, NJ 07078
Ph: (973)921-5500
Fr: 800-234-3867
URL: http://www.dnblearn.com/
  index.php?page=million-dollar-direct

Annual, Latest edition 2008. Covers: 1,600,000 public and private businesses with either a net worth of $500,000 or more, 250 or more employees at that location, or $25,000,000 or more in sales volume; includes industrial corporations, utilities, transportation companies, bank and trust companies, stock brokers, mutual and stock insurance companies, wholesalers, retailers, and domestic subsidiaries of foreign corporations. Entries include: Company name, address, phone, state of incorporation; annual sales; number of employees, company ticker symbol on stock exchange, Standard Industrial Classification (SIC) number, line of business; principal bank, accounting firm; parent company name, current ownership date, division names and functions, directors or trustees; names, titles, functions of principal executives, number of employees, import/export designation. Arrangement: Alphabetical, cross referenced geographically and by industry classification. Indexes: Geographical (with address and SIC), product by SIC (with address).

14319 ■ *Forbes—Up-and-Comers 200*
Forbes Magazine
60 5th Ave.
New York, NY 10011
Ph: (212)366-8900
Fr: 800-295-0893
URL: http://www.forbes.com

Weekly, Latest edition October, 2007. Publication includes: List of 200 small companies judged to be high quality and fast-growing on the basis of 5-year return on equity and other qualitative measurements. Also includes a list of the 100 best small companies outside the U.S. Note: Issue does not carry address or CEO information for the foreign companies.

14320 ■ *Headquarters USA*
Omnigraphics Inc.
PO Box 31-1640
Detroit, MI 48231
Fr: 800-234-1340
URL: http://www.omnigraphics.com

Annual, latest edition 34th. $195.00 for individuals; $216.00. Covers: Approximately 113,000 U.S. Businesses, federal, state, and local government offices, banks, colleges and universities, associations, labor unions, political organizations, newspapers, magazines, TV and radio stations, foundations, postal and shipping services, hospitals, office equipment suppliers, airlines, hotels and motels, profiles of top cities, accountants, law firms, computer firms, foreign corporations, overseas trade contacts, and other professional services. Also covers Internet access providers; Internet mailing lists, publications, and sources; freenets. Personal names now included. Entries include: Company, organization, agency, or firm name, address, phone, fax, website addresses as available, and toll-free phone. Arrangement: Arranged alphabetically by name (white pages) and in a classified subject arrangement (yellow pages). Indexes: Classified headings.

14321 ■ *International Directory of Company Histories*
St. James Press
PO Box 9187
Farmington Hills, MI 48333-9187
Ph: (248)699-4253
Fax: (248)699-8035
Fr: 800-877-4253
URL: http://www.gale.cengage.com

Approximately 10 volumes per year. $286.00 for individuals. Covers: 55 volumes, over 5,700 leading companies world-wide. Entries include: Company name, address, phone, names of subsidiaries, dates of founding, sales data, SICs or NAICS, products or services, company history, key dates, principal subsidiaries, principal competitors, sources for further reading. Arrangement: Alphabetical. Indexes: Company, industry, geographical.

14322 ■ *National Directory of Minority-Owned Business Firms*
Business Research Services Inc.
7720 Wisconsin Ave., Ste. 213
Bethesda, MD 20814
Ph: (301)229-5561
Fax: (301)229-6133
Fr: 800-845-8420
URL: http://www.sba8a.com

Annual, latest edition 15th; June 2010. $295.00 for individuals. Covers: Over 30,000 minority-owned businesses. Entries include: Company name, address, phone, name and title of contact, minority group, certification status, date founded, number of employees, description of products or services, sales volume, government contracting experience, references. Arrangement: Standard Industrial Classification (SIC) code, geographical. Indexes: Alphabetical by company name, SIC by name.

14323 ■ National Directory of Nonprofit Organizations
Taft Group
27500 Drake Rd.
Farmington Hills, MI 48331-3535
Ph: (248)699-4253
Fax: (248)699-8061
Fr: 800-877-4253
URL: http://www.gale.cengage.com

Annual, latest edition 27th; February 2012. $718.00 for individuals; $484.00 for individuals. Covers: Over 265,000 nonprofit organizations; volume 1 covers organizations with annual incomes of over $100,000; volume 2 covers organizations with incomes between $25,000 and $99,999. Entries include: Organization name, address, phone, annual income, IRS filing status, employer identification number, tax deductible status, activity description. Arrangement: Alphabetical. Indexes: Area of activity, geographical.

14324 ■ National Directory of Woman-Owned Business Firms
Business Research Services Inc.
7720 Wisconsin Ave., Ste. 213
Bethesda, MD 20814
Ph: (301)229-5561
Fax: (301)229-6133
Fr: 800-845-8420
URL: http://www.sba8a.com

Annual, latest edition 13th. $295.00 for individuals. Covers: 30,000 woman-owned businesses. Entries

include: Company name, address, phone, name and title of contact, minority group, certification status, date founded, number of employees, description of products or services, sales volume, government contracting experience, references. Arrangement: Standard Industrial Classification (SIC) code, geographical. Indexes: Alphabetical by company.

14325 ■ Plunkett's Employers' Internet Sites with Careers Information: The Only Complete Guide to Careers Websites Operated by Major Employers
Plunkett Research, Ltd.
PO Box 541737
Houston, TX 77254-1737
Ph: (713)932-0000
Fax: (713)932-7080
E-mail: customersupport@plunkettresearch.com
URL: http://www.plunkettresearch.com

Jack W. Plunkett. Revised, 2004. $229.99 (includes CD-ROM). Provides profiles of Internet sites for major employers. Job hunters can use the profiles or indexes to locate the Internet job sites that best fit their needs. 681 pages.

14326 ■ Standard & Poor's Register of Corporations, Directors and Executives
Standard & Poor's
55 Water St.
New York, NY 10041-0004
Ph: (212)438-2000
Fr: 800-852-1641
URL: http://www2.standardandpoors.com

Annual, January; supplements in April, July, and

October. Covers: over 55,000 public and privately held corporations in the United States, including names and titles of over 400,000 officials (Volume 1); 70,000 biographies of directors and executives (Volume 2). Entries include: For companies—Name, address, phone, names of principal executives and accountants; primary bank, primary law firm, number of employees, estimated annual sales, outside directors, Standard Industrial Classification (SIC) code, product or service provided. For directors and executives—Name, home and principal business addresses, date and place of birth, fraternal organization memberships, business affiliations. Arrangement: Alphabetical. Indexes: Volume 3 indexes companies geographically, by Standard Industrial Classification (SIC) code, and by corporate family groups.

14327 ■ Thomas Register of American Manufacturers
Thomas Publishing Co.
5 Penn Plz.
New York, NY 10001
Ph: (212)695-0500
Fax: (212)290-7362
URL: http://www.thomasregister.com

Annual, January. More than 168,000 manufacturing firms are listed in this 34 volume set. Volumes 1-23 list the firms under 68,000 product headings. Thomas Register is enhanced with over 8,000 manufacturers' catalogs and is available in print, CD-ROM, DVD or online. Logistics Guide, a reference manual for freight and shipping sourcing. Arrangement: Volumes 1-23, classified by product or service; Volumes 24-26 alphabetical by company; Volumes 27-34 company catalogs alphabetical by company. Indexes: Product/service, brand/trade name (volume 22).

REFERENCE WORKS

14328 ■ Alternative Travel Directory
Transitions Abroad Publishing
18 Hulst Rd.
Amherst, MA 01002
Ph: (413)253-4924
URL: http://www.transitionsabroad.com

Annual, January; latest edition 7th. $19.95 for individuals. Covers: Over 2,000 sources of information on international employment, education, and specialty travel opportunities. Entries include: Source name, address, phone, description, cost dates. Arrangement: Classified by subject and country. Indexes: Geographical.

14329 ■ Careers in International Affairs
Georgetown University Press
3240 Prospect St., NW
Washington, DC 20007
Ph: (202)687-5889
Fax: (202)687-6340
Fr: 800-537-5487
E-mail: gupress@georgetown.edu
URL: http://www.press.georgetown.edu

Maria Carland and Candace Faber (editors). Eighth edition, 2008. $24.95 (paper). 432 pages. Includes index and bibliography.

14330 ■ The Corporate Guide to Expatriate Employment
Kogan Page Publishers
1518 Walnut St., Ste. 1100
Philadelphia, PA 19102
Ph: (215)928-9112
Fax: (215)928-9113
E-mail: info@koganpage.com
URL: http://www.koganpageusa.com

Jonathan Reuvid. 2009. $99.00 (hardcover). 288 pages. Provides guidelines on deploying staff in short- to medium-term assignments working overseas, managing the integration of overseas staff into a home business unit, and placing staff in permanent employment outside their home country.

14331 ■ Directory of American Firms Operating in Foreign Countries
Uniworld Business Publications Inc.
6 Seward Ave.
Beverly, MA 01915
Ph: (978)927-0219
Fax: (978)927-0219
URL: http://www.uniworldbp.com

Biennial, latest edition 20th, March 2009. $435.00 for individuals; $975.00 for individuals. Covers: About 4,300 American corporations with 125,000 subsidiaries or affiliates outside the United States. Entries include: Company name, address, phone; names and titles of key personnel; number of employees, annual sales, NAICS code, web address, locations and types of facilities in foreign countries, number of employees,

product/service. Separate country editions also available. Arrangement: Alphabetical. Indexes: Foreign operation by country.

14332 ■ Directory of International Internships
Dean's Office of International Studies and Programs
Michigan State University
209 International Ctr.
East Lansing, MI 48824-1035
Ph: (517)355-2350
Fax: (517)353-7254
E-mail: infonew@isp.msu.edu
URL: http://www.isp.msu.edu/students/internships/intlguide

Irregular, latest edition 5th. $34.00 for individuals; $27.00 for students; $30.00 for students; $37.00 for individuals. Covers: International internships sponsored by academic institutions, private sector, and the federal government. Entries include: Institution name, address, phone, names and titles of key personnel, subject areas in which internships are available, number available, location, duration, financial data, academic credit available, evaluation procedures, application deadline, requirements of participation. Arrangement: Classified by type of sponsor, then alphabetical. Indexes: Sponsor, subject, geographical.

14333 ■ Federal Career Opportunities
Federal Research Service Inc.
PO Box 1708
Annandale, VA 22003
Ph: (703)914-5627
Fax: (703)281-7639
Fr: 800-822-5027
URL: http://www.fedjobs.com/index.html

Biweekly, Latest edition 2010. $19.97 for members; $59.95 for members; $99.95 for members; $39.95 for members. Covers: more than 3,000 current federal job vacancies in the United States and overseas; includes permanent, part-time, and temporary positions. Entries include: Position title, location, series and grade, job requirements, special forms, announcement number, closing date, application address. Arrangement: Classified by occupation.

14334 ■ Get Ahead by Going Abroad: A Woman's Guide to Fast-Track Career Success
Collins Living
10 E 53rd St.
New York, NY 10022
Ph: (212)207-7000
Fr: 800-242-7737
E-mail: orders@harpercollins.com
URL: http://www.harpercollins.com

C. Perry Yeatman, Stacie Nevadomski Berdan. 2007. $24.95 (hardcover). 256 pages. Provides information for women pursuing career opportunities overseas.

14335 ■ Great Jobs for Foreign Language Majors
The McGraw-Hill Companies
PO Box 182604
Columbus, OH 43272
Fax: (614)759-3749
Fr: 877-883-5524
E-mail: customer.service@mcgraw-hill.com
URL: http://www.mhprofessional.com/product.php?isbn=0071476148

Julie DeGalan and Stephen Lambert. Third edition, 2007. $15.95 (paper). 192 pages. Part of "Great Jobs for...Majors" series.

14336 ■ Guide to Employment Web Sites
Kennedy Information
1 Phoenix Mill Ln., 3rd Fl.
Peterborough, NH 03458
Ph: (603)924-1006
Fax: (603)924-4460
Fr: 800-531-0007
URL: http://www.kennedyinfo.com/hr/hrbookstore.html

Annual, Latest edition 2007-2008. $39.95 for individuals. Covers: Over 40,000 sites for locating high caliber job candidates. Entries include: Website address, duration of the site, visits per month, profile of frequent visitors, candidate visits, fees, number of records, resume acquisition, site features such as automatic notification of resume-job matches.

14337 ■ International Employment Hotline
International Employment Hotline
PO Box 6729
Charlottesville, VA 22906-6729
Ph: (434)970-5033
Fax: (434)295-7989
E-mail: ieo@mindspring.com
URL: http://www.internationaljobs.org/monthly.html

Monthly. $69.00 for individuals; $21.00 for individuals; $39.00 for individuals; $129.00 for individuals. Covers: Temporary and career job openings overseas and advice for international job hunters. Entries include: Company name, address, job title, description of job, requirements, geographic location of job. Arrangement: Geographical.

14338 ■ Opportunities in Overseas Careers
The McGraw-Hill Companies
PO Box 182604
Columbus, OH 43272
Fax: (614)759-3749
Fr: 877-883-5524
E-mail: customer.service@mcgraw-hill.com
URL: http://www.mhprofessional.com/product.php?isbn=0071454470

Blythe Camenson. 2004. $13.95 (paper). 173 pages.

14339 ■ Overseas Employment Opportunities for Educators: Department of Defense Dependents Schools
DIANE Publishing Co.
PO Box 617
Darby, PA 19023-0617

Fr: 800-782-3833
URL: http://www.dianepublishing.net

Barry Leonard, editor. $20.00. 52 pages. An introduction to teachings positions in the Dept. of Defense Dependents Schools (DoDDS), a worldwide school system, operated by the DoD in 14 countries.

14340 ■ Part Time Prospects: International Comparison of Part Time Work in Europe, North America and the Pacific Rim
Taylor & Francis
325 Chestnut St., 8th Fl.
Philadelphia, PA 19106
Ph: (215)625-8900
Fax: (215)269-0363
Fr: 800-821-8312
URL: http://www.taylorandfrancis.com

Jacqueline O'Reilly and Colette Fagan. $55.95 (paper). 304 pages. Presents for the first time a systematically comparative analysis of the common and divergent patterns in the use of part-time work in Europe, America and the Pacific Rim.

14341 ■ Weddle's Recruiter's and Job Seeker's Guide to Association Web Sites
Paul & Co.
814 N Franklin St.
Chicago, IL 60610
Ph: (312)337-0747
Fax: (312)337-5985
Fr: 800-888-4741
URL: http://www.ipgbook.com

$49.95 for individuals; $54.95 for individuals. Covers: More than 2,000 associations from around the world. Entries include: resume database, discussion forum, and association who offers a job board. Indexes: By career field, industry, and Geographical location.

NEWSPAPERS, MAGAZINES, AND JOURNALS

14342 ■ AATSEEL Newsletter
American Association of Teachers of Slavic and East European Languages (AATSEEL)
PO Box 1116
San Juan Bautista, CA 95045-1116
Ph: (831)578-0290
Fax: (831)886-2486
URL: http://www.aatseel.org

Description: 4/academic year. Carries articles of interest to teachers of Slavic languages. Reports on study programs, teaching innovations, and Association news. Recurring features include news of members, notices of employment opportunities, a calendar of events, reviews of materials, and columns titled Chapter Minutes, Computer Information, Communicative Corner, and Russian Language Features.

14343 ■ ASOR Newsletter
American Schools of Oriental Research
656 Beacon St., 5th Fl.
Boston, MA 02215
Ph: (617)353-6570
Fax: (617)353-6575
E-mail: asor@bu.edu
URL: http://www.asor.org

Description: Quarterly. Carries news and reports from archaeological institutes in Amman, Jerusalem, and Cyprus. Recurring features include news of research, a calendar of events, reports of meetings, news of educational opportunities, job listings, and notices of publications available.

14344 ■ Center for European Studies Newsletter
Center for European Studies
FedEx Global Education Center
Univ. of North Carolina
Campus Box 3449
Chapel Hill, NC 27599

Ph: (919)962-6765
E-mail: europe@unc.edu
URL: http://www.unc.edu/depts/europe/

Description: Biweekly. Announces events, visiting scholars, fellowships, scholarships, and grants at the Center. Recurring features include a calendar of events, news of educational opportunities, notes from the director, and job listings.

14345 ■ Current Jobs International
Foster Opportunities, Inc.
1834 Olmstead Dr.
Falls Church, VA 22043
Ph: (703)506-4400
Fr: 888-870-3069
E-mail: admin@graduatejobs.com
URL: http://www.graduatejobs.com/international.htm

Monthly. $49.50/year. Lists entry-level or early career job vacancies in all fields in international organizations, language schools, and companies with significant overseas operations.

14346 ■ International Living
Agora Inc.
PO Box 1936
Baltimore, MD 21203
Ph: (410)783-8499
E-mail: csteam@agorapublishinggroup.com
URL: http://www.agora-inc.com

Description: Monthly. Features articles about international travel, lifestyles, investments, retirement, employment, and real estate. Includes monthly currency reports. Recurring features include news briefs, letters to the editor, book reviews, and a calendar of events.

14347 ■ International Studies Newsletter
International Studies Association
Social Sciences, No. 324
University of Arizona
Tucson, AZ 85721
Ph: (520)621-7715
Fax: (520)621-5780
E-mail: isa@isanet.org
URL: http://www.isanet.org

Description: Monthly. Promotes the Association's interest in a multidisciplinary approach to international affairs and cross-cultural studies. Acts as a forum for discussion among scholars, students, and the general public. Recurring features include Association news; information on publications by members; notices of employment opportunities; calls for papers; and announcements of meetings, conferences, lectures, awards, grants, and fellowships.

14348 ■ NewsNet, the Newsletter of the ASEEES
Association for Slavic, East European, and Eurasian Studies
203C Bellefield Hall
Pittsburgh, PA 15260
Ph: (412)648-9911
Fax: (412)648-9815
E-mail: aseees@pitt.edu
URL: http://www.aseees.org

Description: Bimonthly. Reports on Association activities and on Slavic study research in institutions throughout the world. Alerts readers to research grants, internships, and fellowship opportunities as well as to employment opportunities in universities across the country. Announces awards, upcoming conferences, courses, new scholarly publications, and annual research.

ONLINE AND DATABASE SERVICES

14349 ■ International Career Employment
URL: http://www.internationaljobs.org

Description: Covers temporary and career job openings overseas and offers advice for international job hunters. Includes company name, address, job title,

description of job, requirements, and geographic location of job.

14350 ■ International Jobsites
URL: http://www.internationaljobsites.com

Description: Provides specific career channels with information that is tailored to a job seeker's specific career goals. Provides other career resources such as career consulting and resume writing.

14351 ■ JobsAbroad.com
URL: http://jobs.goabroad.com

Description: Provides access to an international database of jobs abroad. Provides overseas work opportunities worldwide.

14352 ■ OverseasJobs.com
URL: http://www.overseasjobs.com

Description: Features overseas jobs and international employment opportunities for professionals, expatriates, and adventure seekers.

OTHER SOURCES

14353 ■ Association for International Practical Training (AIPT)
10400 Little Patuxent Pkwy., Ste. 250
Columbia, MD 21044-3519
Ph: (410)997-2200
Fax: (410)992-3924
E-mail: aipt@aipt.org
URL: http://www.aipt.org

Description: Providers worldwide of on-the-job training programs for students and professionals seeking international career development and life-changing experiences. Arranges workplace exchanges in hundreds of professional fields, bringing employers and trainees together from around the world. Client list ranges from small farming communities to Fortune 500 companies.

14354 ■ Chinese Christian Mission (CCM)
PO Box 750759
Petaluma, CA 94975-0759
Ph: (707)762-1314
Fax: (707)762-1713
E-mail: ccm@ccmusa.org
URL: http://www.ccmusa.org

Description: Serves as an evangelical faith mission dedicated to reaching Chinese people around the world with the gospel of Jesus Christ. Broadcasts radio programs to foster Christianity in China. Operates placement service providing ministers with churches. Sponsors short-term mission trips to Latin America and East Asia.

14355 ■ The International Educator (TIE)
PO Box 513
Cummaquid, MA 02637
Ph: (508)790-1990
Fax: (508)790-1922
Fr: 877-375-6668
E-mail: tie@tieonline.com
URL: http://www.tieonline.com

Description: Facilitates the placement of teachers and administrators in American, British, and international schools. Seeks to create a network that provides for professional development opportunities and improved financial security of members. Offers advice and information on international school news, recent educational developments, job placement, and investment, consumer, and professional development opportunities. Makes available insurance and travel benefits. Operates International Schools Internship Program.

14356 ■ NAFSA: Association of International Educators (NAFSA)
1307 New York Ave. NW, 8th Fl.
Washington, DC 20005-4701
Ph: (202)737-3699

Fax: (202)737-3657
E-mail: inbox@nafsa.org
URL: http://www.nafsa.org

Description: Individuals, organizations, and institutions dealing with international educational exchange, including foreign student advisers, overseas educational advisers, credentials and admissions officers, administrators and teachers of English as a second language, community support personnel, study-abroad administrators, and embassy cultural or educational personnel. Promotes self-regulation standards and responsibilities in international educational exchange; offers professional development opportunities primarily through publications, workshops, grants, and regional and national conferences. Advocates for increased awareness and support of international education and exchange on campuses, in government, and in communities. Offers services including: a job registry for employers and professionals involved with international education; a consultant referral service. Sponsors joint liaison activities with a variety of other educational and government organizations to conduct a census of foreign student enrollment in the U.S.; conducts workshops about specific subjects and countries.

14357 ■ United Nations Environment Program/Global Resource Information Database (UNEP/GRID)
USGS National Center of EROS
47914 252nd St.
Sioux Falls, SD 57198-0001
Ph: (605)594-6117
Fax: (605)594-6119
E-mail: geas@unep.org
URL: http://www.unep.org

Description: Individuals interested in raising public awareness of the importance of a global environmental effort. Encourages activism in support of the United Nations Environment Program. Acts as a liaison between the UNEP and the public. Sponsors educational programs and children's services. Offers placement services to job seekers in international environmental work. Maintains speakers' bureau.

14358 ■ U.S.-China Education Foundation (USCEF)
4140 Oceanside Blvd., Ste. 159, No. 112
Oceanside, CA 92056-6005
E-mail: info@sage-usa.net
URL: http://www.sage-usa.net

Description: Aims to promote the learning of the Chinese languages (including Mandarin, Cantonese, and minority languages such as Mongolian) by Americans, and the learning of English by Chinese. Conducts short-term travel-study program to prepare Americans and Chinese for stays of four, six, or eight months or one to four years in China or the U.S., respectively. Operates teacher placement service and speakers' bureau. A project of The Society for the Development of Global Education (S.A.G.E. Inc.).

14359 ■ YMCA International Camp Counselor Program (ICCP)
5 W 63rd St., 2nd Fl.
New York, NY 10023
Ph: (212)727-8800
Fax: (212)724-2344
Fr: 888-477-9622
E-mail: ips@ymcanyc.org
URL: http://www.internationalymca.org/ICCP/ymca_international.htm

Description: Serves as a work-travel program designed to introduce international university students and teachers and social workers aged 19-30 to life in America; the students spend 8 to 9 weeks counseling in children's camps across the country, followed by a period of independent or group travel. Sponsors ICCP-Abroad placement service for American university students aged 18-25 wishing to serve as camp counselors in Africa, Asia, Australia, Hungary, New Zealand, and South America.

REFERENCE WORKS

14360 ■ 100 Winning Answers to the Toughest Interview Questions
Barrons Educational Series, Inc.
250 Wireless Blvd.
Hauppauge, NY 11788
Ph: (631)434-3311
Fax: (631)434-3723
Fr: 800-645-3476
E-mail: fbrown@barronseduc.com
URL: http://barronseduc.com

Casey Hawley. 2008. $8.09 (paper). 224 pages. Offers practical advice on career advancement. Helps job interviewees meet the challenges of the employment interview. Presents general tips that apply to all interview questions and gives advice on ways to give answers that are clear, direct, and to the point.

14361 ■ 101 Great Answers to the Toughest Interview Questions
Cengage Learning
PO Box 6904
Florence, KY 41022
Fax: 800-487-8488
Fr: 800-354-9706
E-mail: esales@cengage.com
URL: http://www.cengage.com

Ronald Fry. Sixth edition, 2010. $10.99 (paper). 200 pages. Identifies some of the toughest interview questions and provides proven responses.

14362 ■ 201 Knockout Answers to Tough Interview Questions
AMACOM Publishing
c/o American Management Association
1601 Broadway
New York, NY 10019-7434
Ph: (212)586-8100
Fr: 800-714-6395
E-mail: pubs_cust_serv@amanet.org
URL: http://www.amacombooks.org

Linda Matias. 2009. $13.95 (paper). 195 pages. Features sample questions and answers. Contains fill-in-the-blank exercises that readers can use to prepare themselves to demonstrate sought-after competencies. Includes five core competencies most interviewers are looking for: individual responsibility; managerial skills; motivational skills; analytical skills; and people skills.

14363 ■ 301 Smart Answers to Tough Interview Questions
Sourcebooks, Inc.
1935 Brookdale Rd., Ste. 139
Naperville, IL 60563
Ph: (630)961-3900
Fax: (630)961-2168
Fr: 800-432-7444
URL: http://www.sourcebooks.com

Vicky Oliver. 2005. $10.95. 384 pages. Provides suggestions and advice regarding the interview process.

14364 ■ Acing the Interview: How to Ask and Answer the Questions That Will Get You the Job
AMACOM Publishing
c/o American Management Association
1601 Broadway
New York, NY 10019-7434
Ph: (212)586-8100
Fr: 800-714-6395
E-mail: pubs_cust_serv@amanet.org
URL: http://www.amacombooks.org

Tony Beshara. 2008. $16.95 (paper). 288 pages. Gives job seekers advice on how to answer unexpected questions.

14365 ■ Acing the Interview: Playing Your Best Hand When It Counts!
Outskirts Press, Inc.
10940 S Parker Rd., No. 515
Parker, CO 80134
Fr: 888-672-6657
E-mail: info@outskirtspress.com
URL: http://www.outskirtspress.com

Sandy Scardino. 2009. $24.95 (paper). 79 pages. Guides job seekers through the job interview process. Features exercises on structuring background information into interview answers.

14366 ■ Active Interviewing
Course Technology PTR
20 Channel Center St.
Boston, MA 02210
Fr: 800-354-9706
URL: http://www.courseptr.com

Eric P. Kramer. 2011. $19.99. 320 pages. Focuses on proven higher-level strategies that help job seekers win interviews and secure jobs. Integrates with an online site where readers will find resources to prepare for interviews and develop an interview-winning presentation.

14367 ■ Best Answers to 202 Job Interview Questions
JIST Publishing
875 Montreal Way
St. Paul, MN 55102
Fr: 800-648-5478
E-mail: educate@emcp.com
URL: http://www.jist.com

Daniel Porot and Frances Bolles Haynes. 2007. $17.95 (softcover). 238 pages. Contains interview questions, sample answers, checklists of do's and don'ts, and a mini quiz to help readers understand why some answers are better than others. Help users learn what type of answers interviewers are really looking for when they ask a particular question.

14368 ■ Can I Wear My Nose Ring to the Interview?: A Crash Course in Finding, Landing, and Keeping Your First Real Job
Workman Publishing Company
225 Varick St.
New York, NY 10014-4381
Ph: (212)254-5900
Fax: (212)254-8098
E-mail: info@workman.com
URL: http://www.workman.com

Ellen Gordon Reeves. 2009. $13.95 (paper). 227 pages. Gives a step-by-step guide through the job searching process. Features tips and advice on writing effective resumes and cover letters, networking and winning the interview.

14369 ■ Career Coward's Guide to Job Searching
JIST Publishing
875 Montreal Way
St. Paul, MN 55102
Fr: 800-648-5478
E-mail: educate@emcp.com
URL: http://www.jist.com

Katy Piotrowski. 2008. $10.95 (softcover). 224 pages. Empowers job seekers to step outside their comfort zone by breaking down the job search process into small, attainable goals.

14370 ■ The Complete Idiot's Guide to the Perfect Job Interview
Alpha Books
375 Hudson St.
New York, NY 10014
Fr: 800-631-8571
E-mail: ecommerce@us.penguingroup.com
URL: http://us.penguingroup.com

Marc Dorio. 2009. $16.95 (paper). 352 pages. Contains guidelines on how to ace an interview in today's competitive job market. Presents specific details about each step in the job interview process.

14371 ■ Essential Interviewing: A Programmed Approach to Effective Communication
Wadsworth Publishing
PO Box 6904
Florence, KY 41022
Fax: 800-487-8488
Fr: 800-354-9706
E-mail: esales@cengage.com
URL: http://www.cengage.com

Allen Ivey, Margaret T. Hearn, Max R. Uhlemann and David R. Evans. $84.49. Seventh edition, 2008. 320 pages.

14372 ■ The Essential Phone Interview Handbook
Career Press
220 W Pkwy., Unit 12
Pompton Plains, NJ 07444
Ph: (201)848-0310

Fax: (201)848-1727
URL: http://www.careerpress.com

Paul Bailo. 2011. $13.99 (paper). 192 pages. Provides a guide for jobseekers wanting to perfect their telephone job interviewing skills. Emphasizes the importance of telephone interviews in job hunting.

14373 ■ The Everything Job Interview Book
Adams Media
4700 E Galbraith Rd.
Cincinnati, OH 45236
Ph: (855)278-0402
URL: http://www.adamsmediastore.com

Lin Grensing-Pophal. 2011. $15.95 (paper). 304 pages. Features professional advice on job hunting and networking, pre-interview prep talk, practice questions, and post-interview followup procedure and etiquette.

14374 ■ First 60 Seconds
Sourcebooks, Inc.
1935 Brookdale Rd., Ste. 139
Naperville, IL 60563
Ph: (630)961-3900
Fax: (630)961-2168
Fr: 800-432-7444
E-mail: info@sourcebooks.com
URL: http://www.sourcebooks.com

Daniel Burns. 2009. $12.99 (paper). 288 pages. Prepares job seekers for the first crucial minute of an interview.

14375 ■ Get Hired in a Tough Market: Insider Secrets for Finding and Landing the Job You Need Now
McGraw-Hill Professional
c/o The McGraw-Hill Companies
PO Box 182604
Columbus, OH 43272
Fax: (614)759-3749
Fr: 877-833-5524
URL: http://www.mhprofessional.com

Alan De Back. 2009. $16.95 (paperback). 224 pages. Provides information on how to come up with an effective, concise and customizable presentation in marketing oneself.

14376 ■ The Google Resume: How to Prepare for a Career and Land a Job at Apple, Microsoft, Google, or any Top Tech Company
John Wiley & Sons, Inc.
111 River St.
Hoboken, NJ 07030-5774
Ph: (201)748-6000
Fax: (201)748-6088
E-mail: info@wiley.com
URL: http://www.wiley.com

Gayle Laakmann McDowell. 2011. $22.95 (hardcover). 280 pages. Helps job seekers land a job in top companies such as Google, Apple and Microsoft. Includes tips and advice on resume-writing, interview preparation and other key concerns.

14377 ■ Government Job Finder
Planning Communications
7215 Oak Ave.
River Forest, IL 60305-1935
Ph: (708)366-5200
Fax: (708)366-5280
Fr: 888-366-5200
E-mail: info@planningcommunications.com
URL: http://www.planningcommunications.com

Daniel Lauber and Deborah Verlench. Fourth edition, 2008. 348 pages. $19.95. Covers 2,002 sources. Discusses how to use sources of local, state, and federal government job vacancies in a number of specialties and state-bystate, including job-matching services, job hotlines, specialty periodicals with job ads, salary surveys, and directories. Explains how local, state, and federal hiring systems work. Includes chapters on resume and cover letter preparation and interviewing.

14378 ■ How to Turn an Interview into a Job
Simon & Schuster Inc
1230 Avenue of the Americas
New York, NY 10020
Ph: (212)698-7000
Fr: 800-897-7650
URL: http://www.simonandschuster.com

Jeffrey G. Allen. Rev edition, April 2004. $11.95 (paper). 128 pages. Presents proven advice on the A to Zs of successful interviewing.

14379 ■ Interviewing Principles and Practices
The McGraw-Hill Companies
PO Box 182604
Columbus, OH 43272
Fax: (614)759-3749
Fr: 877-883-5524
E-mail: customer.service@mcgraw-hill.com
URL: http://www.mhprofessional.com/
   product.php?isbn=0073406716

Charles J. Stewart and William B. Cash. 2007. $103 (paper). 448 pages.

14380 ■ The Job Interview Phrase Book
Adams Media
4700 E Galbraith Rd.
Cincinnati, OH 45236
URL: http://www.adamsmediastore.com

Nancy Schuman. 2009. $10.95 (paper). 256 pages. Provides the best ways to answer essential questions during a job interview.

14381 ■ Job Interview Tips for People with Not-So-Hot Backgrounds: How to Put Red Flags Behind You
Impact Publications
9104 Manassas Dr., Ste. N
Manassas Park, VA 20111-5211
Ph: (703)361-7300
Fax: (703)335-9486
Fr: 800-361-1055
E-mail: query@impactpublications.com
URL: http://www.impactpublications.com

Caryl and Ron Krannich. March 2004. $14.95 (paper). 160 pages.

14382 ■ Job Interviews for Dummies
For Dummies
1 Wiley Dr.
Somerset, NJ 08875-1272
Fax: (732)302-2300
Fr: 800-225-5945
URL: http://www.dummies.com/WileyCDA

Joyce L. Kennedy. Third edition, 2008. $16.99 (paper). 336 pages. Covers basic steps of interviewing from preparation to salary negotiation. Part of For Dummies series.

14383 ■ Key Words to Nail Your Job Interview: What to Say to Win Your Dream Job
Impact Publications
9104 Manassas Dr., Ste. N
Manassas Park, VA 20111-5211
Ph: (703)361-7300
Fax: (703)335-9486
Fr: 800-361-1055
E-mail: query@impactpublications.com
URL: http://www.impactpublications.com

Wendy S. Enelow. 2004. $17.95 (paper). 189 pages.

14384 ■ Knock 'Em Dead: The Ultimate Job Seeker's Handbook
Adams Media Corp.
4700 E Galbraith Rd.
Cincinnati, OH 45236
Ph: (513)531-2690
Fax: (513)531-4082
Fr: 800-289-0963
URL: http://www.adamsmediastore.com/product/
   1359/careers

Martin Yate. 2010. $15.95 (paper). 384 pages.

Prepares the job seeker for the interview with advice on dress, manner, how to answer the toughest questions, and how to spot illegal questions. Discusses how to respond to questions of salary to maximize income. Features sections on executive search firms and drug testing.

14385 ■ The Medical Job Interview
Blackwell Science, Incorporated
Commerce Pl.
350 Main St.
Malden, MA 02148-5018
Ph: (781)388-8200
Fax: (781)388-8210
URL: http://www.blackwellpublishing.com

Colin Mumford. Second edition, 2005. $27.95 (paper). 88 pages.

14386 ■ Next-Day Job Interview
JIST Publishing
875 Montreal Way
St. Paul, MN 55102
Fr: 800-648-5478
E-mail: info@jist.com
URL: http://www.jist.com

Michael Farr and Richard Gaither. 2009. $9.95 (softcover). 192 pages. Provides interview advice presented in seven chapters covering self-assessment, company research, key questions, a system for answering any question that might come up, unusual situations, following up after the interview, and salary negotiation.

14387 ■ Online Interviews in Real Time
SAGE Publications
2455 Teller Rd.
Thousand Oaks, CA 91320
Fax: 800-583-2665
Fr: 800-818-7243
URL: http://www.sagepub.com

Janet Salmons. 2009. $53.00 (paper). 256 pages. Provides theoretical background and practical tips to design and conduct online interview research.

14388 ■ Quick Job Interview Guide
JIST Publishing
875 Montreal Way
St. Paul, MN 55102
Fr: 800-648-5478
E-mail: info@jist.com
URL: http://www.jist.com

Michael Farr. 2008. $39.95. 64 pages. Covers interview advice in seven steps.

14389 ■ Resumes, Cover-Letters, Networking, & Interviewing
Wadsworth Publishing
PO Box 6904
Florence, KY 41022
Fax: 800-487-8488
Fr: 800-354-9706
URL: http://www.cengage.com

Clifford W. Eischen and Lynn A. Eischen. 2012. $42.75 (paper). 128 pages. Professional resume using today's business technologies including the Internet and E-mail. Specifically targeted to help individuals with a two-year degree showcase their skills and experiences to get the job they want. Scanable resumes, Internet-based resumes, and etiquette for sending resumes via fax or E-mail are addressed to prepare readers to apply for jobs using today's business technologies. Dedicated chapter on the interview process coaches readers on proper interview attire, preparing for interview questions, introductions, and how to follow up after an interview. Exercises on listing qualifications, producing a first draft, gathering references, and drafting a follow-up letter, all help readers build a finished resume step by step.

14390 ■ Resumes, Cover Letters, Networking and Interviewing
Cengage Learning
PO Box 6904
Florence, KY 41022-6904

Fax: 800-487-8488
Fr: 800-354-9706
URL: http://www.cengage.com

Clifford W. Eischen and Lynn A. Eischen. 2012. $57.95 (paper). 128 pages. Takes job seekers through a step-by-step process of polishing a resume and developing strong interview techniques. Includes topics on using online resources in job hunting, employment databases, cover letters, networking, and job applications.

14391 ■ Sell Yourself in Any Interview

McGraw-Hill Professional
PO Box 182604
Columbus, OH 43272
Fax: (614)759-3749
Fr: 877-833-5524
E-mail: pbg.ecommerce_custserv@mcgraw-hill.com
URL: http://www.mhprofessional.com/product.php?isbn=007164167X

Oscar Adler. 2008. $14.95 (e-book). 200 pages. Teaches readers to translate personal features (skills, experience, education, background) into direct benefits to meet the specific needs of the interviewer.

14392 ■ Tell Me About Yourself: Storytelling to Get Jobs and Propel Your Career

JIST Publishing
875 Montreal Way
St. Paul, MN 55102
Fr: 800-648-5478
E-mail: info@jist.com
URL: http://www.jist.com

Katharine Hansen. 2009. $14.95 (softcover). 208 pages. Introduces storytelling as the key to excelling in job search activities such as writing resumes and cover letters, networking, creating portfolios, and developing a personal brand. Teaches readers how to use storytelling on the job to capitalize on opportunities to advance their career.

14393 ■ Top Answers to Job Interview Questions: Secrets for Interview Success

Rampant TechPress
PO Box 511
Kittrell, NC 27544
Ph: (252)431-0050
URL: http://www.rampant-books.com/book_0401_job_best_answers.htm

Donald K. Burleson. April 2004. $16.95 (paper).

14394 ■ Top Notch Interviews: Tips, Tricks, and Techniques from the First Call to Getting the Job You Want

Career Press
220 W Pkwy., Unit 12
Pompton Plains, NJ 07444
Ph: (201)848-0310
Fax: (201)848-1727
E-mail: sales@careerpress.com
URL: http://www.careerpress.com

Brian Davis. 2010. $13.99 (paper). 224 pages. Teaches job seekers how to ace an interview. Contains tips on answering questions confidently, formulating responses, avoiding common pitfalls and

navigating through the pursuit phase, including thank-you notes, follow-up, negotiations, and acceptance.

AUDIO/VISUAL RESOURCES

14395 ■ The Complete Job Search System

Cambridge Educational
PO Box 2053
Princeton, NJ 08543-2053
Ph: 800-257-5126
Fax: (609)671-0266
Fr: 800-468-4227
E-mail: custserv@films.com
URL: http://cambridge.films.com

VHS and DVD. 2007. $499.75. Individual titles cover career planning, career evaluation, finding a job, interviewing for a job, and succeeding on the job.

14396 ■ Expert Job Search Strategies for the Ex-offender: Interview Techniques

JIST Publishing
875 Montreal Way
St. Paul, MN 55102
Fr: 800-648-5478
E-mail: educate@emcp.com
URL: http://www.jist.com

2007. $149.00. 15 minutes. Offers advice on the different techniques that ex-offenders can use during a job interview. Helps ex-offenders learn what to wear, how to prepare before the interview, and how to handle themselves during the interview.

14397 ■ Expert Job Search Strategies: Interview Techniques

JIST Publishing
875 Montreal Way
St. Paul, MN 55102
Fr: 800-648-5478
E-mail: educate@emcp.com
URL: http://www.jist.com

2007. $149. 15 minutes. Covers techniques that job seekers can use during a job interview.

14398 ■ From Parole to Payroll

Cambridge Educational
PO Box 2053
Princeton, NJ 08543-2053
Ph: 800-257-5126
Fax: (609)671-0266
Fr: 800-468-4227
E-mail: custserv@films.com
URL: http://cambridge.films.com

VHS and DVD. 2008. $311.80. Contains solid, real-world content designed to help job seekers find satisfying work, and features informative interviews, helpful tips, and colorful graphics.

14399 ■ Interviewing for a Job

Cambridge Educational
PO Box 2053
Princeton, NJ 08543-2053
Ph: 800-257-5126
Fax: (609)671-0266

Fr: 800-468-4227
E-mail: custserv@films.com
URL: http://cambridge.films.com

VHS and DVD. 2009. $129.95. 30 minutes. Covers preparing for an interview, dressing for an interview, using body language to good advantage, articulating skills and abilities, answering difficult questions, and handling salary and benefits issues.

14400 ■ The Job Interview

JIST Publishing
875 Montreal Way
St. Paul, MN 55102
Fr: 800-648-5478
E-mail: info@jist.com
URL: http://www.jist.com

2009. $129. 25 minutes. Contains tips and explanations on how to dress, getting prepared, making a good impression, and dealing with interview questions.

14401 ■ The Job Search

JIST Publishing
875 Montreal Way
St. Paul, MN 55102
Fr: 800-648-5478
E-mail: info@jist.com
URL: http://www.jist.com

2009. $129. 25 minutes. Covers ways to find job openings including contacting employers directly, posting resumes online, and using a network of contacts. Provides job search techniques and how to create a job search plan for every situation.

14402 ■ The Public Speaker's Guide to Ace Your Interview: 6 Steps to Get the Job You Want

Macmillan Audio
175 5th Ave.
New York, NY 10010
Ph: (646)600-7856
E-mail: macmillan.audio@macmillanusa.com
URL: http://us.macmillan.com

Lisa B. Marshall. 2009. $5.95 (unabridged digital audio). 1 hour. Serves as a guide for honing one's interviewing skills. Includes tips on how to avoid the most common interviewing mistakes and expert advice on how to acquire specific skills needed to get ahead in a competitive job market.

14403 ■ Quick Interview and Salary Negotiation Video (DVD)

JIST Publishing
875 Montreal Way
St. Paul, MN 55102
Fr: 800-648-5478
E-mail: info@jist.com
URL: http://www.jist.com

2007. $149. 30 minutes. Covers strategies for landing interviews fast, being effective during the interview, and negotiating the salary.

ONLINE AND DATABASE SERVICES

14404 ■ Job-Interview.net

URL: http://www.job-interview.net
Description: Features job interview tips, guides, interview questions and answers, and other interview related resources.

REFERENCE WORKS

14405 ■ *Essential Guide to Federal Employment Laws*
Society for Human Resource Management
1800 Duke St.
Alexandria, VA 22314
Ph: (703)548-3440
Fax: (703)535-6490
Fr: 800-283-SHRM
URL: http://www.shrm.org

Lisa Guerin and Amy DelPo. 2011. $40.99 for members; $49.99 for non-members (paper). 544 pages. Covers topics on all aspects of key federal employment laws. Provides plain-language explanations about each law. Co-published by Nolo.

14406 ■ *Federal Employees Legal Survival Guide: How to Protect and Enforce Your Job Rights*
National Employee Rights Institute
2031 Florida Ave. NW, Ste. 500
Washington, DC 20009
Ph: (202)243-7660
Fax: (202)282-8801
URL: http://www.workplacefairness.org/fedemployees

Second edition, 2004. 615 pages. $49.95.

14407 ■ *The Legal Rights and Responsibilities of Teachers: Issues of Employment and Instruction*
Corwin
2455 Teller Rd.
Thousand Oaks, CA 91320
Ph: (805)499-9734
Fax: (805)499-5323
E-mail: order@corwin.com
URL: http://www.corwin.com

Allan G. Osborne, Jr. and Charles J. Russo. 2011. $43.95 (paper). 352 pages. Serves as a guide book on education law. Provides educators with useful information on legal issues pertaining to employment and teaching. Includes practical suggestions, vignettes and summaries of judicial opinions with real-world applications.

14408 ■ *Mastering Employment Discrimination Law*
Carolina Academic Press
700 Kent St.
Durham, NC 27701
Ph: (919)489-7486
Fax: (919)493-5668
URL: http://www.cap-press.com

Paul M. Secunda and Jeffrey M. Hirsch. 2010. $25.00 (paper). 250 pages. Provides information on coverage and jurisdiction issues surrounding employment discrimination law. Features federal and state procedural topics surrounding the filing of administrative charges of discrimination and civil lawsuits.

14409 ■ *Meeting the Needs of Employees with Disabilities*
Resources for Rehabilitation
22 Bonad Rd.
Winchester, MA 01890-1302
Ph: (781)368-9080
Fax: (781)368-9096
URL: http://www.rfr.org

Biennial, odd years; latest edition 4th, 2004. $46.95 for individuals. Publication includes: Descriptions of organizations and products that assist those involved in the employment of people with disabilities. Entries include: Organization name, address, phone, requirements for membership, admission, or eligibility, description, prices of product. Principal content of publication is information and advice for employers and counselors who recruit and retain employees with disabilities, including coverage of government programs and laws, supported employment, environmental adaptations, mobility impairments, vision impairments, and communication impairments (hearing and speech). Chapters on assistive technology, environmental modification, transition from school to work, and older workers. Arrangement: Alphabetical.

14410 ■ *Your Rights in the Workplace*
Nolo.com
950 Parker St.
Berkeley, CA 94710
Ph: (510)704-2248
Fax: 800-645-0895
Fr: 800-728-3555
URL: http://www.nolo.com/products/your-rights-in-the-workplace-YRW.html

Barbara K. Repa. Ninth edition, 2010. $29.99 (Trade paper). 544 pages. Covers everything from hiring and getting paid through privacy and firing.

NEWSPAPERS, MAGAZINES, AND JOURNALS

14411 ■ *Alabama Employment Law Letter*
M. Lee Smith Publishers L.L.C.
PO Box 5094
Brentwood, TN 37024-5094
Ph: (615)373-7517
Fax: 800-785-9212
Fr: 800-274-6774
E-mail: custserv@mleesmith.com
URL: http://store.hrhero.com/hr-products/newsletters/alemp

Description: Monthly. $247. Covers laws regulating employment activities in Alabama.

14412 ■ *American Academy of Psychiatry and the Law Newsletter*
American Academy of Psychiatry and the Law
1 Regency Dr.
PO Box 30
Bloomfield, CT 06002

Ph: (860)242-5450
Fax: (860)286-0787
Fr: 800-331-1389
E-mail: office@aapl.org
URL: http://www.aapl.org/newsltr.htm

Description: Three issues/year. Discusses psychiatry as it relates to the law. Recurring features include recent legal cases, legislative updates, letters to the editor, notices of publications available, news of educational opportunities, job listings, a calendar of events, and columns.

14413 ■ *Bank Employment Law Report*
A.S. Pratt & Sons
120 Freidrich Ln., Ste. 100
Austin, TX 78744-1003
Ph: (512)472-2244
Fax: (512)305-6575
Fr: 800-456-2340
E-mail: info.pratt@aspratt.com
URL: http://www.aspratt.com

Description: Monthly. $499. Presents legal matters for financial institutions' human resources officers.

14414 ■ *BNA's Corporate Counsel Weekly*
Bureau of National Affairs Inc.
1801 S Bell St.
Arlington, VA 22202
Fax: 800-253-0332
Fr: 800-372-1033
E-mail: customercare@bna.com
URL: http://www.bna.com/corporate-counsel-weekly-p6006

Description: Weekly. Covers law that affects business, including corporate law, securities law, antitrust law, and employment law. Carries brief reports of court cases, looks at government regulation of trade and the environment, and focuses each week on a topic of current importance. Includes texts of regulatory material and practitioner analysis.

14415 ■ *California Employer Advisor*
Employer Resource Institute Inc.
1819 Polk St. No. 290
San Francisco, CA 94109
Fax: 888-321-5066
Fr: 800-695-7178
URL: http://www.employeradvice.com

Description: Monthly. The award-winning guide to California employment law and employee relations.

14416 ■ *California Employment Law Letter*
M. Lee Smith Publishers L.L.C.
PO Box 5094
Brentwood, TN 37024-5094
Ph: (615)373-7517
Fax: 800-785-9212
Fr: 800-274-6774
E-mail: custserv@mleesmith.com
URL: http://store.hrhero.com/hr-products/newsletters/caemp

Description: Monthly. $347. Provides coverage of

court cases and other situations involving employment laws in California.

14417 ■ *California Labor and Employment ALERT Newsletter*

Castle Publications Ltd.
PO Box 580
Van Nuys, CA 91408
Ph: (818)708-3208
Fax: (818)708-9287
E-mail: info@castlepublications.com
URL: http://www.castlepublications.com/alert.htm

Description: Bimonthly. Reports on current developments in California and federal issues concerning personnel and employment issues. Recurring features include notices of publications available.

14418 ■ *California Labor and Employment Law Review*

State Bar of California
180 Howard St.
San Francisco, CA 94105
Ph: (415)538-2000
Fr: 800-843-9053
URL: http://laborlaw.calbar.ca.gov/Publications/LaborLawReview.aspx

Description: Quarterly. Contains information and news on California's labor and employment laws and regulations.

14419 ■ *Colorado Employment Law Letter*

M. Lee Smith Publishers L.L.C.
PO Box 5094
Brentwood, TN 37024-5094
Ph: (615)373-7517
Fax: 800-785-9212
Fr: 800-274-6774
E-mail: custserv@mleesmith.com
URL: http://store.hrhero.com/hr-products/newsletters/coemp

Description: Monthly. $247. Addresses litigation and court decisions affecting employment issues.

14420 ■ *Compensation Planning Journal*

Bureau of National Affairs Inc.
1801 S Bell St.
Arlington, VA 22202
Ph: (703)341-3500
Fax: 800-253-0332
Fr: 800-372-1033
E-mail: customercare@bna.com
URL: http://www.bna.com

Description: Monthly. Offers legal clarification and practical advice on employers' pay and benefit policies. Discusses such topics as health care cost containment, payroll laws and taxes, workers compensation laws, pension law (ERISA), job evaluation, benefit plans, compensation administration, incentive systems, and independent contractors. Compensation is part of the BNA Policy and Practice Series, and can be purchased separately or in any combination with other binder sets entitled Fair Employment Practices, Labor Relations, Personnel Management, or Wages and Hours.

14421 ■ *Connecticut Employment Law Letter*

M. Lee Smith Publishers L.L.C.
PO Box 5094
Brentwood, TN 37024-5094
Ph: (615)373-7517
Fax: 800-785-9212
Fr: 800-274-6774
E-mail: custserv@mleesmith.com
URL: http://store.hrhero.com/hr-products/newsletters/ctemp

Description: Monthly. $247. Addresses legislation and court decisions affecting employment issues.

14422 ■ *Disability Issues*

Information Center for Individuals With Disabilities
2 Boylston St., Ste. 103
Boston, MA 02116
Ph: (617)451-7052

Fr: (866)698-6901
E-mail: contact@disability.net
URL: http://www.disability.net

Description: Quarterly. Addresses persons with disabilities, their relatives and friends, and service providers through articles on education, employment, transportation, housing, legislation, equipment, and entertainment. Recurring features include a calendar of events and columns titled Resources, Sports Scoop, Book Shelf, Support Column, On Screen, To Your Health, and Disability and the law.

14423 ■ *Employee Advocate*

National Employment Lawyers Association
417 Montgomery St., 4th Fl.
San Francisco, CA 94104
Ph: (415)296-7629
Fax: (415)677-9445
E-mail: nelahq@nelahq.org
URL: http://www.nela.org

Description: Quarterly. Contains NELA activities, latest developments in employment law, best practice tips, briefs, and articles of interest to NELA members.

14424 ■ *Florida Employment Law Letter*

M. Lee Smith Publishers L.L.C.
PO Box 5094
Brentwood, TN 37024-5094
Ph: (615)373-7517
Fax: 800-785-9212
Fr: 800-274-6774
E-mail: custserv@mleesmith.com
URL: http://store.hrhero.com/flemp

Description: Monthly. $247. Addresses legal issues in employment and labor relations.

14425 ■ *Georgia Employment Law Letter*

M. Lee Smith Publishers L.L.C.
PO Box 5094
Brentwood, TN 37024-5094
Fax: 800-785-9212
Fr: 800-274-6774
E-mail: custserv@mleesmith.com
URL: http://store.hrhero.com/hr-products/newsletters/gaemp

Description: Monthly. $247. Covers court cases involving employment issues. Outlines employers' legal rights and responsibilities.

14426 ■ *HR Manager's Legal Reporter*

Business & Legal Reports Inc.
141 Mill Rock Rd. E
Old Saybrook, CT 06475
Ph: (860)510-0100
Fr: 800-727-5257
E-mail: service@blr.com
URL: http://catalog.blr.com/product.cfm/product/31510400

Description: Monthly. $249. Provides information, news, and how-to articles on employment law. Recurring features include columns titled Washington Watch, You Be the Judge, From the States, and In Brief.

14427 ■ *Illinois Employment Law Letter*

M. Lee Smith Publishers L.L.C.
PO Box 5094
Brentwood, TN 37024-5094
Ph: (615)373-7517
Fax: 800-785-9212
Fr: 800-274-6774
E-mail: custserv@mleesmith.com
URL: http://store.hrhero.com/hr-products/newsletters/ilemp

Description: Monthly. $247. Addresses Illinois legislation and court decisions affecting employment issues.

14428 ■ *Indiana Employment Law Letter*

M. Lee Smith Publishers L.L.C.
PO Box 5094
Brentwood, TN 37024-5094
Ph: (615)373-7517

Fax: 800-785-9212
Fr: 800-274-6774
E-mail: custserv@mleesmith.com
URL: http://store.hrhero.com/hr-products/newsletters/inemp

Description: Monthly. $247. Contains legal information pertinent to employers in Indiana.

14429 ■ *Kentucky Employment Law Letter*

M. Lee Smith Publishers L.L.C.
PO Box 5094
Brentwood, TN 37024-5094
Ph: (615)373-7517
Fax: 800-785-9212
Fr: 800-274-6774
E-mail: custserv@mleesmith.com
URL: http://store.hrhero.com/hr-products/newsletters/kyemp

Description: Monthly. $247. Addresses the legal rights of employees and obligations of employers as dictated by Kentucky law. Contains case summaries.

14430 ■ *Labor and Employment Law*

Section of Labor and Employment Law
321 N Clark St.
Chicago, IL 60610
Ph: (312)988-5000
Fax: (312)988-5814
Fr: 800-285-2221
E-mail: orders@abanet.org
URL: http://www.americanbar.org/publications/labor_employment_law_news.html

Description: Quarterly. Covers all developments, from recent decisions and new regulations to emerging trends and important people in the profession. Recurring features include a calendar of events, reports of meetings, news of educational opportunities, and notices of publications available.

14431 ■ *Labor & Employment Law Section Journal*

New York State Bar Association
1 Elk St.
Albany, NY 12207
Ph: (518)463-3200
Fr: 800-342-3661
E-mail: newsletters@nysba.org
URL: http://www.nysba.org

Description: Four issues/year. $30 for non-members; $20 for members. Provides topical information about labor and employment law. Recurring features include chair's comments, article from the editor, cartoon, biographical updates, and columns titled Ethics Matters and Legislative Update.

14432 ■ *Louisiana Employment Law Letter*

M. Lee Smith Publishers L.L.C.
PO Box 5094
Brentwood, TN 37024-5094
Ph: (615)373-7517
Fax: 800-785-9212
Fr: 800-274-6774
E-mail: custserv@mleesmith.com
URL: http://store.hrhero.com/hr-products/newsletters/laemp

Description: Monthly. $247. Addresses legislation and court decisions affecting employment issues.

14433 ■ *Managing Today's Federal Employees*

LRP Publications
360 Hiatt Dr.
Palm Beach Gardens, FL 33418
Fr: 800-341-7874
E-mail: custserve@lrp.com
URL: http://www.shoplrp.com/product/p-40351A.html

Description: Monthly. $195. Provides information about federal employment law concerning government employees.

14434 ■ Maryland Employment Law Letter
M. Lee Smith Publishers L.L.C.
PO Box 5094
Brentwood, TN 37024-5094
Ph: (615)373-7517
Fax: 800-785-9212
Fr: 800-274-6774
E-mail: custserv@mleesmith.com
URL: http://store.hrhero.com/hr-products/newsletters/mdemp

Description: Monthly. $247. Covers Maryland laws and court cases involving employment-related issues.

14435 ■ Massachusetts Employment Law Letter
M. Lee Smith Publishers L.L.C.
PO Box 5094
Brentwood, TN 37024-5094
Ph: (615)373-7517
Fax: 800-785-9212
Fr: 800-274-6774
E-mail: custserv@mleesmith.com
URL: http://store.hrhero.com/hr-products/newsletters/maemp

Description: Monthly. $247. Addresses legal issues of interest to employers and employees in Massachusetts.

14436 ■ Michigan Employment Law Letter
M. Lee Smith Publishers L.L.C.
PO Box 5094
Brentwood, TN 37024-5094
Ph: (615)373-7517
Fax: 800-785-9212
Fr: 800-274-6774
E-mail: custserv@mleesmith.com
URL: http://store.hrhero.com/hr-products/newsletters/miemp

Description: Monthly. $247. Addresses employers' legal responsibilities and employee rights as dictated by Michigan law.

14437 ■ Minnesota Employment Law Letter
M. Lee Smith Publishers L.L.C.
PO Box 5094
Brentwood, TN 37024-5094
Ph: (615)373-7517
Fax: 800-785-9212
Fr: 800-274-6774
E-mail: custserv@mleesmith.com
URL: http://store.hrhero.com/hr-products/newsletters/mnemp

Description: Monthly. $247. Contains analysis of issues regarding employment law in Minnesota.

14438 ■ National Partnership News
National Partnership for Women & Families
1875 Connecticut Ave. NW, Ste. 650
Washington, DC 20009
Ph: (202)986-2600
Fax: (202)986-2539
E-mail: info@nationalpartnership.org
URL: http://www.nationalpartnership.org

Description: Four issues/year. Monitors developments in employment discrimination, reproductive health, family leave policies, quality health care issues, and areas of sex discrimination law that affect women's status. Contains updates on the organization's services and activities and discussions of women's rights issues.

14439 ■ New Jersey Employment Law Letter
M. Lee Smith Publishers L.L.C.
PO Box 5094
Brentwood, TN 37024-5094
Ph: (615)373-7517
Fax: 800-785-9212
Fr: 800-274-6774
E-mail: custserv@mleesmith.com
URL: http://store.hrhero.com/hr-products/newsletters/njemp

Description: Monthly. $247. Addresses legislation and court decisions affecting employment issues.

14440 ■ New Jersey Family Lawyer and the Labor and Employment Law Quarterly
New Jersey State Bar Association
New Jersey Law Center
1 Constitution Sq.
New Brunswick, NJ 08901-1520
Ph: (732)249-5000
Fax: (732)249-2815
URL: http://www.njsba.com

Description: Quarterly. Deals with labor and employment legal matters and legislation in New Jersey, including grievances, mediation, and arbitration. Recurring features include Section news and columns titled Editor's Corner and Director's Corner.

14441 ■ North Carolina Employment Law Letter
M. Lee Smith Publishers L.L.C.
PO Box 5094
Brentwood, TN 37024-5094
Ph: (615)373-7517
Fax: 800-785-9212
Fr: 800-274-6774
E-mail: custserv@mleesmith.com
URL: http://store.hrhero.com/hr-products/newsletters/ncemp

Description: Monthly. $247. Contains information on court cases and legislation affecting employment law in North Carolina.

14442 ■ Ohio Employment Law Letter
M. Lee Smith Publishers L.L.C.
PO Box 5094
Brentwood, TN 37024-5094
Ph: (615)373-7517
Fax: 800-785-9212
Fr: 800-274-6774
E-mail: custserv@mleesmith.com
URL: http://store.hrhero.com/hr-products/newsletters/ohemp

Description: Monthly. $247. Addresses legal issues of interest to Ohio employers.

14443 ■ Oklahoma Employment Law Letter
M. Lee Smith Publishers L.L.C.
PO Box 5094
Brentwood, TN 37024-5094
Ph: (615)373-7517
Fax: 800-785-9212
Fr: 800-274-6774
E-mail: custserv@mleesmith.com
URL: http://store.hrhero.com/hr-products/newsletters/okemp

Description: Monthly. $247. Addresses legislation and court decisions affecting employment issues.

14444 ■ Payroll Administration Guide
Bureau of National Affairs Inc.
1801 S Bell St.
Arlington, VA 22202
Fr: 800-372-1033
E-mail: customercare@bna.com
URL: http://www.bna.com

Description: Biweekly. Concerned with federal and state employment tax, and wage-hour and wage-payment laws.

14445 ■ Payroll Legal Alert
Business Management Daily
PO Box 9070
McLean, VA 22102-0070
Fax: (703)905-8040
Fr: 800-543-2055
E-mail: customer@businessmanagementdaily.com
URL: http://www.businessmanagementdaily.com

Description: Monthly. $99. Covers aspects of payroll operations, including key tax and benefits laws, regulations, rulings, and cases. Includes new trends in tax law, ideas on benefits, wage and hour traps, and unemployment issues.

14446 ■ Pennsylvania Employment Law Letter
M. Lee Smith Publishers L.L.C.
PO Box 5094
Brentwood, TN 37024-5094
Ph: (615)373-7517
Fax: 800-785-9212
Fr: 800-274-6774
E-mail: custserv@mleesmith.com
URL: http://store.hrhero.com/hr-products/newsletters/paemp

Description: Monthly. $247. Details court cases and laws affecting employer/employee rights and responsibilities in Pennsylvania.

14447 ■ Personnel Legal Alert
Business Management Daily
PO Box 9070
McLean, VA 22102-0070
Fax: (703)905-8040
Fr: 800-543-2055
URL: http://www.legalworkplace.com/personnel-legal-alert.aspx

Description: Semimonthly. Provides information about employment law. Topics include court opinions and government regulations.

14448 ■ Supervisors Legal Update
Progressive Business Publications
370 Technology Dr.
Malvern, PA 19355
Fax: (610)647-8089
Fr: 800-220-5000
E-mail: customer_service@pbp.com
URL: http://www.pbp.com/SLU.asp

Description: Semimonthly. $94.56/year. Supplies brief updates on employment law for supervisors.

14449 ■ Tennessee Employment Law Letter
M. Lee Smith Publishers L.L.C.
PO Box 5094
Brentwood, TN 37024-5094
Ph: (615)373-7517
Fax: 800-785-9212
Fr: 800-274-6774
E-mail: custserv@mleesmith.com
URL: http://store.hrhero.com/hr-products/newsletters/tnemp

Description: Monthly. $247. Profiles legal issues of interest to employers in Tennessee.

14450 ■ Texas Employment Law Letter
M. Lee Smith Publishers L.L.C.
PO Box 5094
Brentwood, TN 37024-5094
Ph: (615)373-7517
Fax: 800-785-9212
Fr: 800-274-6774
E-mail: custserv@mleesmith.com
URL: http://store.hrhero.com/hr-products/newsletters/txemp

Description: Monthly. $247. Covers laws and legislation affecting Texas employers.

14451 ■ Unemployment Insurance Reports with Social Security
CCH Inc.
4025 W Peterson Ave.
Chicago, IL 60646-6085
Fax: (773)866-3895
Fr: 888-224-7377
URL: http://hr.cch.com/products/ProductID-781.asp

Description: Weekly. Issues of CCH's Unemployment Insurance Reports with Social Security provide timely information on social security and federal/state unemployment insurance taxes, coverage, and benefits. Pertinent federal and state laws are reported promptly and reflected in place in the explanatory guides, as are regulations, judicial and administrative decisions, rulings, releases, and forms. Explanatory guides include examples showing how rules apply and offer practical information regarding the tax management, coverage, and benefit aspects of the social security and unemployment insurance systems. Each issue starts off with an informative Report Letter summarizing recent developments in these areas.

14452 ■ *Virginia Employment Law Letter*
M. Lee Smith Publishers L.L.C.
PO Box 5094
Brentwood, TN 37024-5094
Ph: (615)373-7517
Fax: 800-785-9212

Fr: 800-274-6774
E-mail: custserv@mleesmith.com
URL: http://store.hrhero.com/hr-products/newsletters/vaemp
Description: Monthly. $247. Examines legal issues pertinent to employers in Virginia.

14453 ■ *What's Working in Human Resources*
Progressive Business Publications
370 Technology Dr.
Malvern, PA 19355

Fax: (610)647-8089
Fr: 800-220-5000
E-mail: customer_service@pbp.com
URL: http://www.pbp.com/WHR.asp

Description: Semimonthly. $299. Reports on the latest trends in Human Resources, including the latest employment law rulings. Recurring features include interviews, news of research, a calendar of events, news of educational opportunities, and a column titled Sharpen Your Judgment.

REFERENCE WORKS

14454 ■ Atlanta JobBank
Adams Media Corp.
57 Littlefield St.
Avon, MA 02322-1944
Ph: (508)427-7100
Fax: (508)427-6790
URL: http://www.adamsmedia.com

latest edition 15th. $17.95 for individuals. Covers: 3,900 employers in the state of Georgia, including Albany, Columbus, Macon, and Savannah. Entries include: Firm or organization name, address, local phone, toll-free phone, fax, description of organization, subsidiaries, other locations, recorded jobline, name and title of contact, typical titles for common positions, educational backgrounds desired, number of employees, benefits offered, training programs, internships, parent company, revenues, e-mail and URL address, projected number of hires. Arrangement: Classified by industry. Indexes: Alphabetical.

14455 ■ Boston JobBank
Adams Media Corp.
57 Littlefield St.
Avon, MA 02322-1944
Ph: (508)427-7100
Fax: (508)427-6790
URL: http://www.adamsmedia.com

Annual, latest edition 20th. $17.95 for individuals. Covers: Over 7,000 employers in Massachusetts. Entries include: Firm or organization name, address, local phone, toll-free phone, fax, e-mail, URL, recorded jobline, hours, names of management, name and title of contact, titles of common positions, entry-level positions, fringe benefits offered, stock exchange listing, description of organization, subsidiaries, location of headquarters, educational background desired, projected number of hires, training programs, internships, parent company, number of employees, revenues, other U.S. Locations, and international locations. Arrangement: Classified by industry. Indexes: Alphabetical.

14456 ■ California Job Journal
California Job Journal
3050 Fite Cir., Ste. 100
Sacramento, CA 95827-1818
Ph: (916)925-0800
Fax: (916)366-3436
Fr: 800-655-5627
URL: http://www.jobjournal.com

Weekly, Latest edition 2011. Free. Covers: Employment issues and job openings in California from entry-level to executive positions. Entries include: Company name, address, phone, type of business, name and title of contact; comprehensive description of position and required skills/background, salary and/or benefits offered. Arrangement: Classified by field of employment.

14457 ■ Carolina JobBank
Adams Media Corp.
57 Littlefield St.
Avon, MA 02322-1944
Ph: (508)427-7100
Fax: (508)427-6790
URL: http://www.adamsmediastore.com/product/ 180/6

latest edition 7th. $12.21 for individuals. Covers: 4,600 employers in North Carolina and South Carolina. Entries include: Firm or organization name, address, local phone, toll-free phone, fax, e-mail, URL, recorded jobline, description of organization, subsidiaries, other locations, hours, names of management, name and title of contact, location of headquarters, typical titles for common positions, educational backgrounds desired, projected number of hires, company benefits, stock exchange listing, training programs and internships, parent company, number of employees, revenues. Arrangement: Classified by industry. Indexes: Alphabetical.

14458 ■ Chicago JobBank
Adams Media Corp.
57 Littlefield St.
Avon, MA 02322-1944
Ph: (508)427-7100
Fax: (508)427-6790
URL: http://www.adamsmedia.com

Annual, Latest edition 19th. $17.95 for individuals; $9.00 for individuals. Covers: About 5,500 major employers in northern and central Illinois including Aurora, Peoria, Rockford, and Springfield. Entries include: Firm or organization name, address, local phone, toll-free phone, fax, e-mail, URL, description of organization, hours, recorded jobline, subsidiaries, names of management, name and title of contact, names of management, headquarters locations, typical titles for entry-level and middle-level positions, educational backgrounds desired, company benefits, stock exchange listing, training programs, internships, parent company, number of employees, revenues, other U.S. Locations, international locations. Arrangement: Classified by industry. Indexes: Alphabetical.

14459 ■ The Connecticut JobBank
Adams Media Corp.
57 Littlefield St.
Avon, MA 02322-1944
Ph: (508)427-7100
Fax: (508)427-6790
URL: http://www.adamsmediastore.com/product/ 183/6

Biennial, latest edition 3. $9.00 for individuals. Covers: Approximately 2,000 employers, career resources, industry associations, and employment services in Connecticut. Entries include: Company name, address, phone, fax, e-mail, and web address; names and titles of key personnel; number of employees; geographical area served; financial data; subsidiary names and addresses; description of services; Standard Industrial Classification (SIC) code. Indexes: Alphabetical.

14460 ■ Dallas/Ft. Worth JobBank
Adams Media Corp.
57 Littlefield St.
Avon, MA 02322-1944
Ph: (508)427-7100
Fax: (508)427-6790
URL: http://www.adamsmediastore.com/product/ 732/6

Annual, latest edition 14th. $9.00 for individuals. Covers: 4,000 employers in the Dallas/Ft. Worth, Texas, area including Abilene, Amarillo, Arlington, Garland, Irving, Lubbock, Plano. Entries include: Firm or organization name, address, local phone, toll-free phone, fax, e-mail, URL, recorded jobline, hours, description of organization, subsidiaries, names of management, name and title of contact, location of headquarters, typical titles for common positions, educational backgrounds desired, company benefits, stock exchange listing, training programs, internships, parent company, number of employees, revenues, projected number of hires. Arrangement: Classified by industry. Indexes: Alphabetical.

14461 ■ Denver JobBank
Adams Media Corp.
57 Littlefield St.
Avon, MA 02322-1944
Ph: (508)427-7100
Fax: (508)427-6790
URL: http://www.adamsmedia.com

latest edition 14th. $17.95 for individuals. Covers: 3,500 employers in Denver and the rest of Colorado including Aurora, Boulder, Colorado Springs, Lakewood. Entries include: Firm or organization name, address, local phone, toll-free phone, fax, e-mail, URL, description of organization, subsidiaries, other locations, hours, recorded jobline, names of management, name and title of contact, headquarters location, projected number of hires; listings may also include typical titles for common positions, educational backgrounds desired, company benefits, stock exchange listing, training programs, internships, parent company, number of employees, revenues. Arrangement: Classified by industry. Indexes: Alphabetical.

14462 ■ Florida JobBank
Adams Media Corp.
57 Littlefield St.
Avon, MA 02322-1944
Ph: (508)427-7100
Fax: (508)427-6790
URL: http://www.adamsmediastore.com/product/ 368/6

latest edition 16th. $17.95 for individuals; $9.00 for individuals. Covers: 5,500 employers in Florida including Fort Lauderdale, Jacksonville, Miami, Orlando, Tampa. Entries include: Firm or organization name, address, local phone, toll-free phone, fax, e-mail addresses, web addresses, description of organization, subsidiaries, hours, recorded jobline, name and title of contact, headquarters location, typical titles for common positions, educational backgrounds desired, number of projected hires, company benefits, stock exchange listing, training programs, internships, parent company, number of employees, revenues, other U.S. Locations, international locations. Arrangement: Classified by industry. Indexes: Alphabetical.

14463 ■ *Houston JobBank*
Adams Media Corp.
57 Littlefield St.
Avon, MA 02322-1944
Ph: (508)427-7100
Fax: (508)427-6790
URL: http://www.adamsmedia.com

Annual, latest edition 12th. $17.95 for individuals. Covers: Over 4,000 employers in Houston, Texas and the surrounding areas including Bayton, Beaumont, Galveston, Pasadena. Entries include: Firm or organization name, address, local phone, toll-free phone, fax, recorded jobline, e-mail, URL, hours, name and title of contact; description of organization; headquarters location, subsidiaries, operations at the facility, names of management, typical titles for common positions, educational backgrounds desired, number of projected hires, fringe benefits offered, stock exchange listing, training programs, internships, parent company, number of employees, revenues, other U.S. locations, international locations. Arrangement: Classified by industry. Indexes: Alphabetical.

14464 ■ *Los Angeles JobBank*
Adams Media Corp.
57 Littlefield St.
Avon, MA 02322-1944
Ph: (508)427-7100
Fax: (508)427-6790
URL: http://www.adamsmedia.com

Annual, latest edition 17th. $16.95 for individuals. Covers: Over 7,900 southern California employers including Orange, Riverside, San Bernardino, San Diego, Santa Barbara and Ventura counties. Entries include: Firm or organization name, address, local phone, toll-free phone, fax, e-mail, URL, recorded jobline, hours, subsidiaries, other locations, names of management, name and title of contact, description of organization, number of employees, headquarters location, typical titles for common positions, educational backgrounds desired, fringe benefits offered, stock exchange listing, training programs, internships, parent company, number of employees, revenues, corporate headquarters, and number of projected hires. Projected hires. Arrangement: Classified by industry. Indexes: Alphabetical.

14465 ■ *Metropolitan New York JobBank*
Adams Media Corp.
57 Littlefield St.
Avon, MA 02322-1944
Ph: (508)427-7100
Fax: (508)427-6790
URL: http://www.adamsmedia.com

latest edition 19th. $17.95 for individuals. Covers: Over 7,900 New York City Northern New Jersey, Southwestern Connecticut, Long Island, and Westchester employers. Entries include: Firm or organization name, address, local phone, toll-free phone, fax, e-mail, URL, recorded jobline, hours, name and title of contact; description of organization, subsidiaries, other locations, names of management, headquarters location, typical titles for common positions, educational backgrounds desired, fringe benefits offered, stock exchange listing, training programs, internships, parent company, number of employees, revenues, projected number of hires. Arrangement: Classified by industry. Indexes: Alphabetical.

14466 ■ *Metropolitan Washington DC JobBank*
Adams Media Corp.
57 Littlefield St.
Avon, MA 02322-1944
Ph: (508)427-7100

Fax: (508)427-6790
URL: http://www.adamsmedia.com

Latest edition 17th. $17.95 for individuals. Covers: 6,900 employers in Washington, D.C. , Greater Baltimore, and Northern Virginia. Entries include: Firm or organization name, address, local phone, toll-free phone, fax, recorded jobline, name and title of contact, description of organization, subsidiaries, other locations, names of management, hours, titles for common positions, educational backgrounds desired, company benefits, stock exchange listing, location of headquarters, training programs, internships, parent company, number of employees, revenues, email and URL address, projected number of hires. Arrangement: Classified by industry. Indexes: Alphabetical.

14467 ■ *The New Jersey JobBank*
Adams Media Corp.
57 Littlefield St.
Avon, MA 02322-1944
Ph: (508)427-7100
Fax: (508)427-6790
URL: http://www.adamsmediastore.com/product/ 857/6

Biennial, latest edition 4th. $17.95 for individuals. Covers: Approximately 4,000 employers, career resources, industry associations, and employment services in the Garden State. Entries include: Company name, address, phone, fax, email, and web address; names and titles of key personnel; number of employees; geographical area served; financial data; subsidiary names and addresses; description of services; standard industrial classification (sic) code. Indexes: Alphabetical.

14468 ■ *The Ohio JobBank*
Adams Media Corp.
57 Littlefield St.
Avon, MA 02322-1944
Ph: (508)427-7100
Fax: (508)427-6790
URL: http://www.adamsmediastore.com/product/ 858/6

Biennial, Latest edition 12th. $17.95 for individuals. Covers: 4,800 Employers and employment services in Ohio. Entries include: Firm or organization name, address, phone, name and title of contact; description of organization, headquarters location, typical titles for entry- and middle-level positions, educational backgrounds desired, fringe benefits offered, stock exchange listing, training programs, internships, parent company, number of employees, revenues, e-mail and web address, projected number of hires. Arrangement: Alphabetical.

14469 ■ *San Francisco Bay Area JobBank*
Adams Media Corp.
57 Littlefield St.
Avon, MA 02322-1944
Ph: (508)427-7100
Fax: (508)427-6790
URL: http://www.adamsmedia.com

Latest edition 18th. $17.95 for individuals. Covers: About 5,600 employers in the San Francisco Bay area and the Northern half of California including Oakland, Sacramento, San Jose, and Silicon Valley. Entries include: Firm or organization name, address, local phone, toll-free phone, fax, e-mail, URL, recorded jobline, hours, description of organization, subsidiaries, other locations, number of employees, name and title of contact, headquarters location, typical titles for common positions, educational backgrounds desired, company benefits, stock exchange listing, training programs, internships, parent company, and number of employees, revenues, corporate headquarters, and number of projected hires. Arrangement: Classified by industry. Indexes: Alphabetical.

14470 ■ *Seattle JobBank*
Adams Media Corp.
57 Littlefield St.
Avon, MA 02322-1944

Ph: (508)427-7100
Fax: (508)427-6790
URL: http://www.adamsmediastore.com/product/ 716/6

latest edition 13th. $17.95 for individuals. Covers: About 4,800 employers in Washington state, including Spokane, Tacoma, and Bellevue. Entries include: Firm or organization name, address, local phone, toll-free phone, fax, e-mail, URL, description of organization, subsidiaries, name and title of contact, headquarters location, recorded jobline, typical titles for common positions, educational backgrounds desired, projected number of hires, company benefits, stock exchange listing, training programs, internships, parent company, number of employees, revenues. Arrangement: Classified by industry. Indexes: Alphabetical.

NEWSPAPERS, MAGAZINES, AND JOURNALS

14471 ■ *Arizona Business Gazette*
Phoenix Newspapers Inc.
200 E Van Buren St.
Phoenix, AZ 85004-2238
Ph: (602)444-8000
Fr: 800-331-9303
URL: http://republicmediasolutions.com/product_ detail.aspx?menuld

Weekly (Thurs.). $30.00/year for individuals, 52 weeks; $60.00/year for two years, 104 weeks; $19.50/year for institutions, 26 weeks. Business and legal newspaper.

14472 ■ *Arkansas Business*
Arkansas Business Publishing Group
122 E Second St.
PO Box 3686
Little Rock, AR 72203
Ph: (501)372-1443
Fax: (501)375-7933
Fr: 888-322-6397
URL: http://www.arkansasbusiness.com/weekly_ ab.asp

Weekly. $64.95/year for individuals, in state; $194.95/ year for other countries; $94.95/year for individuals, out of state; $99.95/year for two years, in state; $149.95/year for two years, out of state. Business magazine on the Arkansas business community, covering people and recent news events statewide.

14473 ■ *Atlanta Business Chronicle*
American City Business Journals Inc.
120 W Morehead St.
Charlotte, NC 28202
E-mail: bizchron@mindspring.com
URL: http://www.bizjournals.com/atlanta

Weekly. $99.00/year for individuals; $178.00/year for two years; $227.00/year for individuals, 160 issues. Local business newspaper.

14474 ■ *Austin Business Journal*
American City Business Journals Inc.
120 W Morehead St.
Charlotte, NC 28202
URL: http://www.bizjournals.com/austin

Weekly. $98.00/year for individuals; $150.00/year for two years; $220.00/year for individuals, 3 years. Newspaper (tabloid) serving business and industry in Central Texas.

14475 ■ *Baltimore Business Journal*
American City Business Journals Inc.
120 W Morehead St.
Charlotte, NC 28202
E-mail: baltimore@bizjournals.com
URL: http://www.bizjournals.com/baltimore

Weekly. $92.00/year for individuals; $152.00/year for two years; $182.00/year for individuals, 160 issues. Newspaper reporting Baltimore business news.

14476 ■ Boston Business Journal
American City Business Journals Inc.
120 W Morehead St.
Charlotte, NC 28202
E-mail: boston@bizjournals.com
URL: http://www.bizjournals.com/boston/

Weekly. $120.00/year for individuals; $179.00/year for two years, 108 issues; $234.00/year for individuals, 160 issues. Business newspaper specializing in local and regional business for upper management and CEO's of large and mid-sized businesses.

14477 ■ Business First of Buffalo
American City Business Journals Inc.
120 W Morehead St.
Charlotte, NC 28202
E-mail: buffalo@bizjournals.com
URL: http://www.bizjournals.com/buffalo

Weekly. $100.00/year for individuals; $170.00/year for two years; $216.00/year for individuals, 160 issues. Business Newspaper.

14478 ■ The Business Journal of Charlotte
American City Business Journals Inc.
120 W Morehead St.
Charlotte, NC 28202
E-mail: charlotte@bizjournals.com
URL: http://www.bizjournals.com/charlotte

Weekly. $96.00/year for individuals; $175.00/year for two years; $207.00/year for individuals, 160 issues. Newspaper for the business community of Charlotte and the surrounding thirteen-county area.

14479 ■ Business Times
Choice Media L.L.C.
PO Box 580
New Haven, CT 06513-0580
Ph: (203)782-1420
Fax: (203)782-3793
E-mail: editorial@ctbusinesstimes.com
URL: http://www.ctbusinesstimes.com

Monthly. $36.00/year for individuals. Business journal (tabloid).

14480 ■ Capital District Business Review
American City Business Journals Inc.
120 W Morehead St.
Charlotte, NC 28202
URL: http://www.bizjournals.com/albany

$90.00/year for individuals; $150.00/year for two years; $190.00/year 3 years. Business tabloid providing local business news for Capital Region area.

14481 ■ Crain's Chicago Business
Crain Communications Inc.
360 N Michigan Ave.
Chicago, IL 60601
Ph: (312)649-5200
E-mail: editor@chicagobusiness.com
URL: http://www.chicagobusiness.com

Weekly. $99.00/year for individuals, prin & online; $97.95/year for individuals, print only; $79.00/year for individuals, online. Newspaper covering news stories about various aspects of business and labor activity in the Chicago market.

14482 ■ Crain's Cleveland Business
Crain Communications Inc.
700 W St. Clair Ave., Ste. 310
Cleveland, OH 44113-1230
Ph: (216)522-1383
URL: http://www.crainscleveland.com/

Weekly. $57.00/year for individuals, print; $98.00/year for two years. Metropolitan business newspaper serving seven counties.

14483 ■ Crain's Detroit Business
Crain Communications Inc. (Detroit, Michigan)
1155 Gratiot Ave.
Detroit, MI 48207-2997
Ph: (313)446-6000
Fax: (313)567-7681
URL: http://www.crainsdetroit.com

Weekly (Mon.). $59.00/year for individuals, print edition; $36.00/year for individuals, online edition. Local business tabloid covering Wayne, Macomb, Oakland, Livingston, and Washtenaw counties.

14484 ■ Crain's New York Business
Crain Communications Inc.
1155 Gratiot Ave.
Detroit, MI 48207-2997
Ph: (313)446-6000
URL: http://www.crainsnewyork.com/apps/pbcs.dll/frontpage

Weekly. $29.95/year for individuals, print. Regional business tabloid.

14485 ■ Daily Journal of Commerce
New Orleans Publishing Group Inc.
111 Veterans Blvd., Ste. 1440
Metairie, LA 70005
Ph: (504)834-9292
Fax: (504)832-3550
URL: http://www.djc-gp.com

Daily. $525.00/year for individuals, online; $375.00/year for individuals, 6 months; $225.00/year for individuals, 3 months. Trade newspaper covering construction news in Louisiana and Mississippi.

14486 ■ Des Moines Business Record
Business Publications Corp.
The Depot at Fourth
100 4th St.
Des Moines, IA 50309
Ph: (515)288-3336
Fax: (515)288-0309
URL: http://www.businessrecord.com

Weekly. $69.95/year for individuals. Newspaper covering local business news.

14487 ■ Florida Trend
Trend Magazines Inc.
490 First Ave. S, 8th Fl.
St. Petersburg, FL 33701
Ph: (727)821-5800
Fax: (727)822-5083
E-mail: custrelations@floridatrend.com
URL: http://www.floridatrend.com

Monthly. Business.

14488 ■ Houston Business Journal
American City Business Journals Inc.
120 W Morehead St.
Charlotte, NC 28202
E-mail: houston@bizjournals.com
URL: http://www.bizjournals.com/houston

Weekly. $98.00/year for individuals; $155.00/year for two years; $180.00/year for individuals, 160 issues. Magazine (tabloid) for metropolitan Houston business community.

14489 ■ Long Island
Long Island Association Inc.
300 Broadhollow Rd., Ste. 110W
Melville, NY 11747
Ph: (631)493-3000
Fax: (631)499-2194
URL: http://www.longislandassociation.org/li_magazine.cfm

Monthly. $49.95/year for individuals, special member, for a limited time; $69.95/year for nonmembers. Long Island Association magazine.

14490 ■ Long Island Business News
Long Island Business News
2150 Smithtown Ave., Ste. 7
Ronkonkoma, NY 11779
Ph: (631)737-1700
Fax: (631)737-1890
URL: http://libn.com/

Weekly (Fri.). $119.00/year for individuals; $166.00/year for two years; $59.00/year for individuals, online only. Business tabloid serving Long Island.

14491 ■ The Los Angeles Business Journal
The Los Angeles Business Journal
5700 Wilshire, No. 170
Los Angeles, CA 90036
Ph: (213)549-5225
Fax: (213)549-5255
URL: http://www.labusinessjournal.com

Weekly (Mon.). $99.95/year for individuals; $179.95/year for two years. Newspaper (tabloid) covering local business news, business trends, executive profiles, and information for the Los Angeles area executive.

14492 ■ Miami Today
Today Enterprises Inc.
710 Brickell Ave.
Miami, FL 33131
Ph: (305)358-2663
URL: http://www.miamitodaynews.com

Weekly (Thurs.). $105.00/year for by mail; $155.00/year for two years; $115.00/year for Canada. Newspaper (tabloid) covering business and community information targeted to the upper management levels.

14493 ■ Nashville Business Journal
Nashville Business Journals
1800 Church St., Ste. 300
Nashville, TN 37203
Ph: (615)248-2222
Fax: (615)248-6246
Fr: 800-486-3289
E-mail: nashville@bizjournals.com
URL: http://nashville.bizjournals.com/nashville/

Weekly. $94.00/year for individuals, print and digital; $150.00/year for two years, print and digital; $59.00/year for individuals, digital only. Regional business newspaper.

14494 ■ Northeast Pennsylvania Business Journal
The Scranton Times
149 Penn Ave.
Scranton, PA 18503
Ph: (570)348-9100
Fr: 800-228-4637
URL: http://biz570.com/

Monthly. Business publication serving 19 counties.

14495 ■ Orlando Business Journal
American City Business Journals Inc.
120 W Morehead St.
Charlotte, NC 28202
E-mail: orlando@bizjournals.com
URL: http://www.bizjournals.com/orlando/

Weekly. $92.00/year for individuals; $132.00/year for two years; $184.00/year for individuals, 160 issues. Newspaper (tabloid) covering local business news, trends, and ideas of interest to industry, trade, agribusiness, finance, and commerce.

14496 ■ Pacific Business News
American City Business Journals Inc.
120 W Morehead St.
Charlotte, NC 28202
E-mail: pacific@bizjournals.com
URL: http://www.bizjournals.com/pacific/

Weekly. $88.95/year for individuals; $176.90/year for two years. Business tabloid.

14497 ■ Philadelphia Business Journal
Philadelphia Business Journal
400 Market St., Ste. 1200
Philadelphia, PA 19106
Ph: (215)238-1450
Fax: (215)238-9489
URL: http://www.bizjournals.com/philadelphia

Weekly. $110.00/year for individuals; $183.00/year for two years. Regional and general business newspaper.

14498 ■ *Pittsburgh Business Times*
American City Business Journals Inc.
120 W Morehead St.
Charlotte, NC 28202
E-mail: pittsburgh@bizjournals.com
URL: http://www.bizjournals.com/pittsburgh

Weekly. $114.00/year for individuals; $184.00/year for two years; $228.00/year for individuals, 160 issues. Metropolitan business newspaper (tabloid).

14499 ■ *Providence Business News*
Providence Business News
220 W Exchange St., Ste. 210
Providence, RI 02903
Ph: (401)273-2201
Fax: (401)274-6580
E-mail: circulation@pbn.com
URL: http://www.pbn.com

Weekly. $89.00/year for individuals, print & online; $134.00/year for two years, print & online; $79.00/year for individuals, online. Newspaper (tabloid) covering business news in Southeastern New England. Regular editorial focus sections include banking/finance, computers, boating, industry, real estate and health care.

14500 ■ *Puget Sound Business Journal (Seattle, Washington)*
American City Business Journals Inc.
120 W Morehead St.
Charlotte, NC 28202
E-mail: seattle@bizjournals.com
URL: http://www.bizjournals.com/seattle

Weekly. $94.00/year for individuals; $173.00/year for two years; $184.00/year for individuals, 160 issues. Regional business newspaper (tabloid).

14501 ■ *St. Louis Business Journal*
American City Business Journals Inc.
120 W Morehead St.
Charlotte, NC 28202
E-mail: stlouis@bizjournals.com
URL: http://www.bizjournals.com/stlouis

Weekly. $93.00/year for individuals; $150.00/year for two years; $232.00/year for individuals, 160 issues. Business newspaper.

14502 ■ *St. Louis Countian*
Legal Communications Corp.
319 N 4th St., 5th Fl.
St. Louis, MO 63102
Ph: (314)421-1880
Fr: 800-635-5297
URL: http://www.thedailyrecord.com/

$227.31/year for individuals, standard; $363.69/year for two years, standard. Business and legal newspaper.

14503 ■ *San Antonio Business Journal*
American City Business Journals Inc.
120 W Morehead St.
Charlotte, NC 28202
E-mail: sanantonio@bizjournals.com
URL: http://www.bizjournals.com/sanantonio

Weekly. $99.00/year for individuals; $145.00/year for two years; $191.00/year for individuals, 108 issues. Newspaper featuring news and information about the San Antonio and south Texas business community.

14504 ■ *San Diego Business Journal*
San Diego Business Journal
4909 Murphy Canyon Rd., Ste. 200
San Diego, CA 92123
Ph: (858)277-6359
Fax: (858)277-2149
URL: http://www.sdbj.com

Weekly (Mon.). $99.00/year for individuals; $180.00/year for two years. Metropolitan business newspaper specializing in investigative and enterprise reporting

on San Diego County businesses and related issues.

14505 ■ *San Diego Daily Transcript*
San Diego Daily Transcript
2131 3rd Ave.
San Diego, CA 92101
Ph: (619)232-4381
Fax: (619)239-5716
Fr: 800-697-6397
URL: http://www.sddt.com

Daily (morn.). $229.30/year for individuals, print + online; $366.36/year for two years, print + online. Local business newspaper.

14506 ■ *San Francisco Business Times*
American City Business Journals Inc.
120 W Morehead St.
Charlotte, NC 28202
E-mail: sanfrancisco@bizjournals.com
URL: http://www.bizjournals.com/sanfrancisco

Weekly. $98.00/year for individuals; $176.00/year for two years; $198.00/year for individuals, three years. Local business newspaper (tabloid) serving the San Francisco Bay Area.

14507 ■ *Washington Business Journal*
American City Business Journals Inc.
120 W Morehead St.
Charlotte, NC 28202
E-mail: washington@bizjournals.com
URL: http://www.bizjournals.com/washington

Weekly. $107.00/year for individuals; $162.00/year for two years; $207.00/year for individuals, 160 issues. Metropolitan business newspaper (tabloid).

ONLINE AND DATABASE SERVICES

14508 ■ CareerRelocate.com
URL: http://www.careerrelocate.com

Description: Provides job seekers with data to make decisions about job relocation. Seeks to inform job seekers of historic trends in major markets and cost of living data to assist in relocation decisions. Features a searchable database of categorized jobs that covers all industries.

14509 ■ Corporate Search Consultants, Inc.
PO Box 236
Oakland, FL 34760
Fax: (321)221-1732
Fr: 800-800-7231
E-mail: webmanager@corpsearch.com
URL: http://www.corpsearch.com

Description: Job search consultants. Job board and resume posting for jobs in the healthcare and medical community.

14510 ■ JobBus.com
URL: http://www.jobbus.com

Description: Job search engine portal for those looking to remain in or relocate to Canada. Contains career resources and articles.

OTHER SOURCES

14511 ■ Aberdeen Area Chamber of Commerce
516 S Main St.
Aberdeen, SD 57401
Ph: (605)225-2860
Fax: (605)225-2437
E-mail: info@aberdeen-chamber.com
URL: http://www.aberdeen-chamber.com

Promotes business and community development in the Aberdeen and Brown County, SD area.

14512 ■ Affiliated Chambers of Greater Springfield
1441 Main St., Ste. 136
Springfield, MA 01103-1449
Ph: (413)787-1555
Fax: (413)731-8530
URL: http://www.myonlinechamber.com

Promotes business and community development in the Springfield, MA area.

14513 ■ Alaska State Chamber of Commerce
217 2nd St., Ste. 201
Juneau, AK 99801
Ph: (907)586-2323
Fax: (907)463-5515
URL: http://www.alaskachamber.com

Promotes business and community development in Alaska.

14514 ■ Arizona Chamber of Commerce
3200 N Central Ave., Ste. 1125
Phoenix, AZ 85012
Ph: (602)248-9172
Fax: (602)265-1262
E-mail: info@azchamber.com
URL: http://www.azchamber.com

Promotes business and community development in Arizona.

14515 ■ Arkansas State Chamber of Commerce
1200 W Capitol Ave.
PO Box 3645
Little Rock, AR 72203-3645
Ph: (501)372-2222
E-mail: rzook@arkansasstatechamber.com
URL: http://www.arkansasstatechamber.com

Promotes business and community development in Arkansas.

14516 ■ Arvada Chamber of Commerce
7305 Grandview Ave.
Arvada, CO 80002-9960
Ph: (303)424-0313
Fax: (303)424-5370
E-mail: dot@arvadachamber.org
URL: http://www.arvadachamber.org

Promotes business and community development in the Arvada and Westminster, CO area. Facilitates communication and cooperation among area business people.

14517 ■ Association of Commerce And Industry of New Mexico
2201 Buena Vista Dr. SE, Ste. 410
Albuquerque, NM 87106
Ph: (505)842-0644
Fax: (505)842-0734
E-mail: info@aci-nm.org
URL: http://www.acinm.org

Promotes business and community development in the state of New Mexico.

14518 ■ Association of Washington Business
1414 Cherry St., SE
PO Box 658
Olympia, WA 98501
Ph: (360)943-1600
Fax: (360)943-5811
E-mail: members@awb.org
URL: http://www.awb.org

Promotes business and community development in the state of Washington.

14519 ■ Bellevue Chamber of Commerce
302 Bellevue Sq.
Bellevue, WA 98004
Ph: (425)454-2464
E-mail: staffteam@bellevuechamber.org
URL: http://www.bellevuechamber.org

Promotes business and community development in Bellevue, WA.

14520 ■ Bismarck - Mandan Chamber of Commerce
1640 Burnt Boat Dr.
PO Box 1675
Bismarck, ND 58502-1675
Ph: (701)223-5660
Fax: (701)255-6125
E-mail: info@bismarckmandan.com
URL: http://www.bismarckmandan.com

Promotes business and community development in the Bismarck, ND Area.

14521 ■ Brownsville Chamber of Commerce
1600 University Blvd.
Brownsville, TX 78520
Ph: (956)542-4341
Fax: (956)504-3348
E-mail: info@brownsvillechamber.com
URL: http://www.brownsvillechamber.com

Promotes business and community development in Brownsville, TX.

14522 ■ Burbank Chamber of Commerce
200 W Magnolia Blvd.
Burbank, CA 91502-1724
Ph: (818)846-3111
Fax: (818)846-0109
E-mail: info@burbankchamber.org
URL: http://www.burbankchamber.org

Promotes business and community development in Burbank, CA.

14523 ■ Business Council of Alabama
PO Box 76
2 N Jackson St.
Montgomery, AL 36101
Ph: (334)834-6000
Fax: (334)241-5984
Fr: 800-665-9647
E-mail: kimberly@bcatoday.org
URL: http://www.bcatoday.org

Promotes business and community development in the state of Alabama.

14524 ■ Business Council of New York State, Inc.
The Schuler Bldg.
152 Washington Ave.
Albany, NY 12210-2289
Ph: (518)465-7511
Fax: (518)465-4389
Fr: 800-358-1202
URL: http://www.bcnys.org

Promotes business and community development in the state of New York.

14525 ■ California Chamber of Commerce
1215 K St., Ste. 1400
PO Box 1736
Sacramento, CA 95814
Ph: (916)444-6670
Fax: (916)325-1272
Fr: 800-700-4044
E-mail: techsupport@calchamber.com
URL: http://www.calchamber.com

Acts as legislative advocate for all California business interests. Offers educational seminars.

14526 ■ Cambridge Chamber of Commerce
859 Massachusetts Ave.
Cambridge, MA 02139
Ph: (617)876-4100
Fax: (617)354-9874
E-mail: ccinfo@cambridgechamber.org
URL: http://www.cambridgechamber.org

Promotes business and community development in Cambridge, MA.

14527 ■ Chamber of Commerce of Cape Coral
2051 Cape Coral Pkwy., E
PO Box 100747
Cape Coral, FL 33904
Ph: (239)549-6900
Fax: (239)549-9609
Fr: 800-226-9609
E-mail: info@capecoralchamber.com
URL: http://www.capecoralchamber.com

Promotes business and community development in Cape Coral, FL.

14528 ■ Chamber of Commerce of Southwest Indiana
318 Main St., Ste. 401
Evansville, IN 47708
Ph: (812)425-8147
Fax: (812)421-5883
E-mail: chamberinfo@ccswin.com
URL: http://www.evansvillechamber.com

Promotes business and community development in the Evansville, IN area.

14529 ■ ChamberWest
1241 W Village Main Dr., Ste. B
West Valley City, UT 84119
Ph: (801)977-8755
Fax: (801)977-8329
E-mail: chamber@chamberwest.com
URL: http://www.chamberwest.org/home

The Chamber of Commerce for West Valley City, Taylorsville and Kearns, UT.

14530 ■ Chandler Chamber of Commerce
25 S Arizona Pl., Ste. 201
Chandler, AZ 85225
Ph: (480)963-4571
Fax: (480)963-0188
Fr: 800-963-4571
E-mail: info@chandlerchamber.com
URL: http://www.chandlerchamber.com

Promotes business and community development in Chandler, AZ.

14531 ■ Chula Vista Chamber of Commerce
233 4th Ave.
Chula Vista, CA 91910
Ph: (619)420-6603
Fax: (619)420-1269
E-mail: lisa@chulavistachamber.org
URL: http://www.chulavistachamber.org

Promotes business and community development in Chula Vista, CA.

14532 ■ Clarksville Area Chamber of Commerce
25 Jefferson St., Ste. 300
PO Box 883
Clarksville, TN 37040
Ph: (931)647-2331
Fax: (931)645-1574
Fr: 800-530-2487
E-mail: cmcedc@clarksville.tn.us
URL: http://www.clarksvillechamber.com

Promotes business and community development in the Clarksville, TN area.

14533 ■ Clearwater Regional Chamber of Commerce
401 Cleveland St.
Clearwater, FL 33755
Ph: (727)461-0011
Fax: (727)449-2889
E-mail: info@clearwaterflorida.org
URL: http://www.clearwaterflorida.org

Promotes business and community development in the Clearwater, FL area. Provides networking opportunities and small business assistance.

14534 ■ Connecticut Business and Industry Association
350 Church St.
Hartford, CT 06103-1126
Ph: (860)244-1900
Fax: (860)278-8562
E-mail: jim.bell@cbia.com
URL: http://www.cbia.com/home.php

Promotes business and community development in the state of Connecticut.

14535 ■ Costa Mesa Chamber of Commerce
1700 Adams Ave., Ste. 101
Costa Mesa, CA 92626
Ph: (714)885-9090
Fax: (714)885-9094
E-mail: info@costamesachamber.com
URL: http://www.costamesachamber.com

Promotes business and community development in Costa Mesa, CA.

14536 ■ Daly City - Colma Chamber of Commerce
355 Gellert Blvd., Ste. 138
Daly City, CA 94015
Ph: (650)755-3900
Fax: (650)755-5160
E-mail: gsarles@dalycity-colmachamber.org
URL: http://www.dalycity-colmachamber.org

Promotes business and community development in the Daly City/Colma, CA area.

14537 ■ Delaware State Chamber of Commerce
1201 N Orange St., Ste. 200
PO Box 671
Wilmington, DE 19801
Ph: (302)655-7221
Fax: (302)654-0691
Fr: 800-292-9507
E-mail: publications@dscc.com
URL: http://www.dscc.com

Promotes business and community development in Delaware.

14538 ■ El Monte-South El Monte Chamber of Commerce
10505 Valley Blvd., Ste. 312
PO Box 6008
El Monte, CA 91731
Ph: (626)443-0180
Fax: (626)443-0463
E-mail: chamber@emsem.com
URL: http://www.emsem.com

Promotes business and community development in the El Monte, CA area.

14539 ■ Erie Regional Chamber and Growth Partnership
208 E Bayfront Pkwy., Ste. 100
Erie, PA 16507
Ph: (814)454-7191
Fax: (814)459-0241
URL: http://www.eriepa.com/chamber/

Promotes business and community development in Erie County, PA.

14540 ■ Escondido Chamber of Commerce
720 N Broadway
Escondido, CA 92025
Ph: (760)745-2125
E-mail: info@escondidochamber.org
URL: http://www.escondidochamber.org

Promotes business and community development in Escondido, CA.

14541 ■ Fayetteville-Cumberland County Chamber of Commerce
1019 Hay St.
PO Box 9
Fayetteville, NC 28302
Ph: (910)483-8133

Fax: (910)483-0263
E-mail: info@fayettevillencchamber.org
URL: http://www.fayettevillencchamber.org
Promotes business and community development in the Fayetteville, NC area.

14542 ■ Florida Chamber of Commerce
136 S Bronough St.
PO Box 11309
Tallahassee, FL 32302-3309
Ph: (850)521-1200
URL: http://www.flchamber.com
Promotes business and community development in the state of Florida.

14543 ■ Fontana Chamber of Commerce
8491 Sierra Ave.
Fontana, CA 92335-3860
Ph: (909)822-4433
Fax: (909)822-6238
E-mail: info@fontanachamber.com
URL: http://www.fontanaacc.org
Promotes business and community development in the Fontana, CA area.

14544 ■ Fremont Chamber of Commerce
39488 Stevenson Pl., Ste. 100
Fremont, CA 94539
Ph: (510)795-2244
Fax: (510)795-2240
E-mail: fmtcc@fremontbusiness.com
URL: http://www.fremontbusiness.com
Promotes business and community development in Fremont, CA. Conducts business education and assistance programs.

14545 ■ Fullerton Chamber of Commerce
444 N Harbor Blvd., Ste. 200
Fullerton, CA 92832
Ph: (714)871-3100
Fax: (714)871-2871
E-mail: questions@fullertonchamber.com
URL: http://fullertonchamber.com
Promotes business and community development in Fullerton, CA.

14546 ■ Garden Grove Chamber of Commerce
12866 Main St., Ste. 102
Garden Grove, CA 92840-5298
Ph: (714)638-7950
Fax: (714)636-6672
Fr: 800-959-5560
E-mail: jeremy@gardengrovechamber.org
URL: http://gardengrovechamber.org
Promotes business and community development in Garden Grove, CA.

14547 ■ Garland Chamber of Commerce
520 N. Glenbrook Dr.
Garland, TX 75040
Ph: (972)272-7551
Fax: (972)276-9261
E-mail: information@garlandchamber.com
URL: http://www.garlandchamber.com
Promotes business and community development in Garland, TX.

14548 ■ Gary Chamber of Commerce
9 Broadway, Ste. S103
Gary, IN 46402
Ph: (219)885-7407
Fax: (219)885-7408
E-mail: info@garychamber.com
URL: http://www.garychamber.com
Promotes business and community development in the Gary, IN area.

14549 ■ Genesee Regional Chamber of Commerce
519 S Saginaw St., Ste. 200
Flint, MI 48502-1802

Ph: (810)600-1404
Fax: (810)600-1461
E-mail: info@thegrcc.org
URL: http://www.thegrcc.org
Business and professional organizations that promote business and community development in the Flint, MI area.

14550 ■ Georgia Chamber of Commerce
233 Peachtree St. NE, Ste. 2000
Atlanta, GA 30303-1564
Ph: (404)233-2264
Fax: (404)223-2290
Fr: 800-241-2286
URL: http://www.gachamber.com
Promotes business and community development in the state of Georgia.

14551 ■ Gilbert Chamber of Commerce
119 N Gilbert Rd., Ste. 101
PO Box 527
Gilbert, AZ 85299-0527
Ph: (480)892-0056
Fax: (480)892-1980
E-mail: info@gilbertchamber.com
URL: http://www.gilbertaz.com
Promotes business and community development in Gilbert, AZ.

14552 ■ Glendale (AZ) Chamber of Commerce
7105 N 59th Ave.
PO Box 249
Glendale, AZ 85311
Ph: (623)937-4754
Fax: (623)937-3333
Fr: 800-437-8669
E-mail: info@glendaleazchamber.org
URL: http://www.glendaleazchamber.org
Promotes business and community development in Glendale, AZ.

14553 ■ Glendale (CA) Chamber of Commerce
701 N Brand Blvd., Ste. 120
Glendale, CA 91203
Ph: (818)240-7870
Fax: (818)240-2872
E-mail: info@glendalechamber.com
URL: http://www.glendalechamber.com
Promotes business and community development in Glendale, CA.

14554 ■ Grand Prairie Chamber of Commerce
900 Conover Dr.
Grand Prairie, TX 75051
Ph: (972)264-1558
E-mail: info@grandprairiechamber.org
URL: http://www.grandprairiechamber.org
Promotes business and community development in Grand Prairie, TX.

14555 ■ Greater Aiken Chamber of Commerce
121 Richland Ave. E
PO Box 892
Aiken, SC 29801
Ph: (803)641-1111
E-mail: chamber@aikenchamber.net
URL: http://www.aikenchamber.net
Promotes business and community development in Aiken, SC.

14556 ■ Greater Bethesda-Chevy Chase Chamber of Commerce
7910 Woodmont Ave., Ste. 1204
Bethesda, MD 20814
Ph: (301)652-4900
Fax: (301)657-1973
E-mail: staff@bccchamber.org
URL: http://www.bccchamber.org

Promotes business and community development in the Bethesda and Chevy Chase communities within Maryland.

14557 ■ Greater Bloomington Chamber of Commerce
400 W 7th St., Ste. 102
PO Box 1302
Bloomington, IN 47404
Ph: (812)336-6381
Fax: (812)336-0651
E-mail: info@chamberbloomington.org
URL: http://www.chamberbloomington.org
Promotes business and community development in the Bloomington, IN area.

14558 ■ Greater Columbus Chamber of Commerce
1200 6th Ave.
Columbus, GA 31902
Ph: (706)327-1566
Fax: (706)327-7512
Fr: 800-360-8552
E-mail: mgaymon@columbusgachamber.com
URL: http://www.columbusgachamber.com
Promotes business and community development in Columbus, GA.

14559 ■ Greater Concord Chamber of Commerce
2280 Diamond Blvd., Ste. 200
Concord, CA 94520-5750
Ph: (925)685-1181
Fax: (925)685-5623
E-mail: mfowler@concordchamber.com
URL: http://www.concordchamber.com
Promotes business and community development in Concord, CA.

14560 ■ Greater Conejo Valley Chamber of Commerce
600 Hampshire Rd., Ste. 200
Westlake Village, CA 91361
Ph: (805)370-0035
Fax: (805)370-1083
URL: http://www.conejochamber.org
Promotes business and community development in Thousand Oaks and Westlake Village, CA. Offers networking opportunities.

14561 ■ Greater Corona Valley Chamber of Commerce
904 E 6th St.
Corona, CA 92879
Ph: (951)737-3350
Fax: (951)737-3531
E-mail: info@mychamber.org
URL: http://www.mychamber.org
Promotes business and community development in Corona, CA.

14562 ■ Greater Des Moines Partnership
700 Locust St., Ste. 100
Des Moines, IA 50309
Ph: (515)286-4950
URL: http://www.desmoinesmetro.com
Promotes business and community development in the greater Des Moines, IA area.

14563 ■ Greater Elizabeth Chamber of Commerce
456 N Broad St.
Elizabeth, NJ 07208
Ph: (908)355-7600
Fax: (908)436-2054
E-mail: gecc@juno.com
URL: http://www.elizabethchamber.com
Promotes business and community development in Elizabeth, NJ.

14564 ■ Greater Fairbanks Chamber of Commerce
100 Cushman St., Ste. 102
Fairbanks, AK 99701
Ph: (907)452-1105
Fax: (907)456-6968
E-mail: info@fairbankschamber.org
URL: http://www.fairbankschamber.org

Promotes business and community development in the Greater Fairbanks, AK area.

14565 ■ Greater Fort Lauderdale Chamber of Commerce
512 NE 3rd Ave.
Fort Lauderdale, FL 33301
Ph: (954)462-6000
E-mail: dan@ftlchamber.com
URL: http://www.ftlchamber.com

Promotes business, tourism, and community development in the Greater Ft. Lauderdale, FL area.

14566 ■ Greater Hollywood Chamber of Commerce
330 N Federal Hwy.
Hollywood, FL 33020
Ph: (954)923-4000
Fax: (954)923-8737
Fr: 800-231-5562
E-mail: information@hollywoodchamber.org
URL: http://www.hollywoodchamber.org

Promotes business and community development in the Hollywood, FL area.

14567 ■ Greater Hot Springs Chamber of Commerce
659 Ouachita Ave.
PO Box 6090
Hot Springs, AR 71901
Ph: (501)321-1700
Fax: (501)321-3551
Fr: 800-467-INFO
E-mail: info@hotspringschamber.com
URL: http://www.hotspringschamber.com

Promotes business and community development in the Hot Springs, AR area.

14568 ■ Greater Irving - Las Colinas Chamber of Commerce
5201 N O'Connor Blvd., Ste. 100
Irving, TX 75039
Ph: (214)217-8484
Fax: (214)384-2513
E-mail: chamber@irvingchamber.com
URL: http://www.irvingchamber.com

Promotes business and community development in Irving, TX.

14569 ■ Greater Lafayette Commerce
337 Columbia St.
PO Box 348
Lafayette, IN 47901
Ph: (765)742-4044
Fax: (765)742-6276
E-mail: information@greaterlafayettecommerce.com
URL: http://www.lafayettechamber.com

Promotes business and community development in the Lafayette, IN area.

14570 ■ Greater Lafayette (LA) Chamber of Commerce
804 E St. Mary Blvd.
PO Box 51307
Lafayette, LA 70503
Ph: (337)233-2705
Fax: (337)234-8671
E-mail: carley@lafchamber.org
URL: http://www.lafchamber.org

Promotes business and community development in the Lafayette, LA area.

14571 ■ Greater Las Cruces Chamber of Commerce
760 W Picacho Ave.
Las Cruces, NM 88005
Ph: (575)524-1968
Fax: (575)527-5546
URL: http://www.lascruces.org

Promotes business and community development in Las Cruces, NM.

14572 ■ Greater Lowell Chamber of Commerce
131 Merrimack St.
Lowell, MA 01852
Ph: (978)459-8154
Fax: (978)452-4145
E-mail: info@greaterlowellchamber.org
URL: http://www.greaterlowellchamber.org

Promotes business and community development in the Lowell, MA area.

14573 ■ Greater Manchester Chamber of Commerce
54 Hanover St.
Manchester, NH 03101
Ph: (603)666-6600
Fax: (603)626-0910
E-mail: membership@manchester-chamber.org
URL: http://www.manchester-chamber.org

Promotes business and community development in Manchester and northern Hillsborough County, NH.

14574 ■ Greater North Dakota Chamber of Commerce
2000 Schafer St.
PO Box 2639
Bismarck, ND 58501
Ph: (701)222-0929
Fax: (701)222-1611
Fr: 800-382-1405
URL: http://www.ndchamber.com

Promotes business and community development in the state of North Dakota.

14575 ■ Greater Paterson Chamber of Commerce
100 Hamilton Plaza, Ste. 1201
Paterson, NJ 07505
Ph: (973)881-7300
Fax: (973)881-8233
E-mail: gpcc@greaterpatersoncc.org
URL: http://www.greaterpatersoncc.org

Promotes business and community development in the Paterson, NJ area.

14576 ■ Greater Portsmouth Chamber of Commerce
500 Market St.
Portsmouth, NH 03802
Ph: (603)610-5510
Fax: (603)436-5118
E-mail: info@portsmouthchamber.org
URL: http://www.portsmouthchamber.org

Promotes business and community development in the Portsmouth, New Hampshire area and southwestern Maine.

14577 ■ Greater Pueblo Chamber of Commerce
302 N Santa Fe Ave.
Pueblo, CO 81003
Ph: (719)542-1704
Fr: 800-233-3446
E-mail: info@pueblochamber.org
URL: http://www.pueblochamber.org

Promotes business and community development in Pueblo County, CO.

14578 ■ Greater Sarasota Chamber of Commerce
1945 Fruitville Rd.
Sarasota, FL 34236

Ph: (941)955-8187
Fax: (941)366-5621
URL: http://www.sarasotachamber.org

Promotes business and community development in Sarasota County, FL.

14579 ■ Greater Scranton Chamber of Commerce
222 Mulberry St.
PO Box 431
Scranton, PA 18501-0431
Ph: (570)342-7711
E-mail: jstetz@scrantonchamber.com
URL: http://www.scrantonchamber.com

Promotes business and community development in the greater Scranton, PA area.

14580 ■ Greater Springfield Chamber of Commerce
1011 S 2nd St.
Springfield, IL 62704-3004
Ph: (217)525-1173
Fax: (217)525-8768
E-mail: hfowler@gscc.org
URL: http://www.gscc.org

Promotes business and community development in the Springfield, IL area.

14581 ■ Greater Stockton Chamber of Commerce
445 W Weber Ave., No. 220
Stockton, CA 95203
Ph: (209)547-2770
Fax: (209)466-5271
E-mail: schamber@stocktonchamber.org
URL: http://www.stocktonchamber.org

Promotes business and community development in the Stockton, CA area.

14582 ■ Greater Vancouver Chamber of Commerce
1101 Broadway, Ste. 100
Vancouver, WA 98660
Ph: (360)694-2588
Fax: (360)693-8279
E-mail: yourchamber@vancouverusa.com
URL: http://www.vancouverusa.com/

Promotes business and community development in the Vancouver and Clark County, WA areas.

14583 ■ Greater Waco Chamber of Commerce
101 S 3rd St.
PO Box 1220
Waco, TX 76701
Ph: (254)757-5600
E-mail: info@wacochamber.com
URL: http://www.waco-chamber.com

Promotes business and community development in the Waco, TX area.

14584 ■ Hawaii Island Chamber of Commerce
117 Keawe St., Ste. 205
Hilo, HI 96720
Ph: (808)935-7178
Fax: (808)961-4435
E-mail: admin@hicc.biz
URL: http://hicc.biz

Promotes business and community development in the Hawaiian Islands.

14585 ■ Hayward Chamber of Commerce
22561 Main St.
Hayward, CA 94541
Ph: (510)537-2424
Fax: (510)537-2730
E-mail: info@hayward.org
URL: http://www.hayward.org

Promotes business and community development in Hayward, CA.

14586 ■ Henderson Chamber of Commerce
590 S Boulder Hwy.
Henderson, NV 89015
Ph: (702)565-8951
Fax: (702)565-3115
E-mail: info@hendersonchamber.com
URL: http://www.hendersonchamber.com

Promotes business and community development in Henderson, NV.

14587 ■ Houston Metropolitan Chamber of Commerce
12 Greenway Plz., Ste. 1100
Houston, TX 77046
Ph: (713)666-1521
Fax: (713)666-1523
E-mail: info@gswhcc.org
URL: http://www.gswhcc.org

Promotes business and community development in Bellaire and Greater Southwest Houston, TX.

14588 ■ Huntington Beach Chamber of Commerce
2134 Main St., Ste. 100
Huntington Beach, CA 92648
Ph: (714)536-8888
Fax: (714)960-7654
E-mail: hbchamber@hbcoc.com
URL: http://hbchamber.com

Strives to promote a favorable business climate to support and develop the city.

14589 ■ Idaho Association of Commerce and Industry
PO Box 389
816 W Bannock St., Ste. 5B
Boise, ID 83701-0389
Ph: (208)343-1849
Fax: (208)338-5623
E-mail: iaci@iaci.org
URL: http://www.iaci.org

Promotes business and community development in the state of Idaho.

14590 ■ Illinois State Chamber of Commerce
300 S Wacker Dr., Ste. 1600
Chicago, IL 60606
Ph: (312)983-7100
Fax: (312)983-7101
URL: http://ilchamber.org

Promotes business and community development in Illinois.

14591 ■ Independence Chamber of Commerce
210 W Truman Rd.
PO Box 1077
Independence, MO 64051
Ph: (816)252-4745
Fax: (816)252-4917
E-mail: info@independencechamber.org
URL: http://www.independencechamber.org

Promotes business and community development in Independence, MO.

14592 ■ Indiana Chamber of Commerce
115 W Washington St., Ste. 850S
Indianapolis, IN 46204
Ph: (317)264-3110
Fax: (317)264-6855
E-mail: kbrinegar@indianachamber.com
URL: http://www.indianachamber.com

Businesses and other organizations. Promotes free enterprise and the preservation and advancement of the business climate. Monitors legislative activity. Holds seminars and workshops.

14593 ■ Inglewood - Airport Area Chamber of Commerce
330 E Queen St.
Inglewood, CA 90301
Ph: (310)677-1121

Fax: (310)677-1001
E-mail: inglewoodchamber@sbcglobal.net
URL: http://www.inglewoodchamber.com

Promotes business and community development in Inglewood, CA.

14594 ■ Irvine Chamber of Commerce
2485 McCabe Way, Ste. 150
Irvine, CA 92614
Ph: (949)660-9112
Fax: (949)660-0829
E-mail: icc@irvinechamber.com
URL: http://www.irvinechamber.com

Promotes business and community development in Irvine, CA.

14595 ■ Joliet Region Chamber of Commerce and Industry
63 N Chicago St.
PO Box 752
Joliet, IL 60434-0752
Ph: (815)727-5371
Fax: (815)727-5374
E-mail: info@jolietchamber.com
URL: http://www.jolietchamber.com

Promotes business and community development in the Joliet, IL area.

14596 ■ Kansas Chamber of Commerce and Industry
835 SW Topeka Blvd.
Topeka, KS 66612-1671
Ph: (785)357-6321
Fax: (785)357-4732
E-mail: president@kansaschamber.org
URL: http://www.kansaschamber.org

Promotes business and community development in Kansas.

14597 ■ Kentucky Chamber of Commerce
464 Chenault Rd.
Frankfort, KY 40601
Ph: (502)695-4700
Fax: (502)695-5051
E-mail: info@kychamber.com
URL: http://www.kychamber.com

Promotes business and community development in Kentucky.

14598 ■ Lancaster Chamber of Commerce and Industry
100 S Queen St.
PO Box 1558
Lancaster, PA 17603
Ph: (717)397-3531
Fax: (717)293-3159
URL: http://www.lancasterchamber.com

Promotes business and community development in Lancaster, PA.

14599 ■ Lansing Regional Chamber of Commerce
500 E Michigan, Ste. 200
PO Box 14030
Lansing, MI 48901
Ph: (517)487-6340
Fax: (517)484-6910
E-mail: tdaman@lansingchamber.org
URL: http://www.lansingchamber.org

Promotes business and community development in the Lansing, MI area.

14600 ■ The Laredo Chamber of Commerce
2310 San Bernardo Ave.
Laredo, TX 78040
Ph: (956)722-9895
Fax: (956)791-4503
Fr: 800-292-2122
E-mail: chamber@laredochamber.com
URL: http://laredochamber.com/home/

Promotes business and community development in Laredo, TX.

14601 ■ Livonia Chamber of Commerce
33233 Five Mile Rd.
Livonia, MI 48154
Ph: (734)427-2122
Fax: (734)427-6055
URL: http://www.livonia.org

Business association that promotes economic and community development in the city of Livonia, MI.

14602 ■ Louisiana Association of Business and Industry
3113 Valley Creek Dr.
PO Box 80258
Baton Rouge, LA 70898-0258
Ph: (225)928-5388
Fax: (225)929-6054
Fr: 888-816-5224
E-mail: labi@labi.org
URL: http://www.labi.org

Promotes business and community development in the state of Louisiana.

14603 ■ Macomb County Chamber of Commerce
28 First St., Ste. B
Mount Clemens, MI 48043
Ph: (586)493-7600
Fax: (586)493-7602
E-mail: nicole@macombcountychamber.com
URL: http://www.macombcountychamber.com

Promotes business and community development in Macomb County, MI.

14604 ■ Maine State Chamber of Commerce
125 Community Dr., Ste. 101
Augusta, ME 04330
Ph: (207)623-4568
Fax: (207)622-7723
E-mail: rstoddard@mainechamber.org
URL: http://www.mainechamber.org

Promotes business and community development in Maine.

14605 ■ Maryland Chamber of Commerce
60 West St., Ste. 100
Annapolis, MD 21401
Ph: (410)269-0642
Fax: (410)269-5247
E-mail: mcc@mdchamber.org
URL: http://www.mdchamber.org

Promotes business and community development in the state of Maryland.

14606 ■ McAllen Chamber of Commerce
1200 Ash Ave.
PO Box 790
McAllen, TX 78501
Ph: (956)682-2871
Fax: (956)687-2917
E-mail: steve@mcallenchamber.com
URL: http://www.mcallenchamber.com

Promotes business and community development in McAllen, TX.

14607 ■ Mesquite Chamber of Commerce and CVB
617 N Ebrite St.
Mesquite, TX 75149
Ph: (972)285-0211
Fax: (972)285-3535
E-mail: info@mesquitechamber.com
URL: http://www.mesquitechamber.com

Promotes business and community development in the Mesquite, TX area.

14608 ■ Metrocrest Chamber of Commerce
5100 Belt Line Rd., Ste. 430
Addison, TX 75254
Ph: (469)587-0420
Fax: (469)587-0428
E-mail: info@metrocrestchamber.com
URL: http://metrocrestchamber.com

Promotes business and community development in Carrollton, TX.

14609 ■ Michigan Chamber of Commerce
600 S Walnut St.
Lansing, MI 48933
Ph: (517)371-2100
Fax: (517)371-7228
Fr: 800-748-0266
URL: http://www.michamber.com

Promotes business and community development in the state of Michigan.

14610 ■ Miramar-Pembroke Pines Regional Chamber of Commerce
10100 Pines Blvd., 4th Fl.
Pembroke Pines, FL 33026-3900
Ph: (954)432-9808
Fax: (954)432-9193
E-mail: membership@miramarpembrokepines.org
URL: http://www.miramarpembrokepines.org/

Promotes business and community development in Miramar and Pembroke Pines, FL.

14611 ■ Mississippi Economic Council
PO Box 23276
248 E Capitol St., Ste. 940
Jackson, MS 39225-3276
Ph: (601)969-0022
Fax: (601)353-0247
Fr: 800-748-7626
E-mail: bwilson@mec.ms
URL: http://www.msmec.com

Promotes business and community development in the state of Mississippi.

14612 ■ Missoula Area Chamber of Commerce and Convention and Visitors' Bureau
825 E Front St.
PO Box 7577
Missoula, MT 59802-7577
Ph: (406)543-6623
Fax: (406)543-6625
E-mail: info@missoulachamber.com
URL: http://www.missoulachamber.com

Promotes business and community development in the Missoula, MT area.

14613 ■ Missouri Chamber of Commerce
428 E Capitol Ave.
PO Box 149
Jefferson City, MO 65102
Ph: (573)634-3511
Fax: (573)634-8855
E-mail: kbuschmann@mochamber.com
URL: http://www.mochamber.com/mx/
  hm.asp?id=home

Promotes business and community development in the state of Missouri.

14614 ■ Montana Chamber of Commerce
PO Box 1730
Helena, MT 59624-1730
Ph: (406)442-2405
Fax: (406)442-2409
Fr: 800-847-4868
E-mail: dee@montanachamber.com
URL: http://www.montanachamber.com

Promotes business and community development in the state of Montana.

14615 ■ Morgantown Area Chamber of Commerce
1029 University Ave., Ste. 101
Morgantown, WV 26505-5586
Ph: (304)292-3311
Fax: (304)296-6619
E-mail: info@morgantownchamber.org
URL: http://www.mgnchamber.org

Promotes business and community development in the Morgantown, WV area.

14616 ■ Naperville Area Chamber of Commerce
55 S Main St., Ste. 351
Naperville, IL 60540
Ph: (630)355-4141
Fax: (630)355-8335
E-mail: chamber@naperville.net
URL: http://www.naperville.net

Promotes business and community development in the Naperville, IL area.

14617 ■ Nebraska Chamber of Commerce and Industry
PO Box 95128
1320 Lincoln Mall
Lincoln, NE 68509-5128
Ph: (402)474-4422
Fax: (402)474-5681
URL: http://www.nechamber.net/dnn

Promotes business and community development in Nebraska.

14618 ■ New Hampshire's Statewide Chamber of Commerce
122 N Main St.
Concord, NH 03301
Ph: (603)224-5388
Fax: (603)224-2872
E-mail: mail@nhbia.org
URL: http://www.nhbia.org

Promotes business and community development in the state of New Hampshire.

14619 ■ New Jersey Chamber of Commerce
216 W State St.
Trenton, NJ 08608
Ph: (609)989-7888
Fax: (609)989-9696
Fr: 800-561-4602
URL: http://www.njchamber.com

Promotes business and community development in the state of New Jersey.

14620 ■ North Carolina Chamber
701 Corporate Center Dr., Ste. 400
PO Box 2508
Raleigh, NC 27607
Ph: (919)836-1400
Fax: (919)836-1425
E-mail: lebert@ncchamber.net
URL: http://www.ncchamber.net

Promotes business and community development in the state of North Carolina.

14621 ■ North Las Vegas Chamber of Commerce
3365 W Craig Rd., Ste. 25
North Las Vegas, NV 89032
Ph: (702)642-9595
Fax: (702)642-0439
URL: http://www.northlasvegaschamber.com

Promotes business and community development in North Las Vegas, NV and neighboring communities.

14622 ■ Norwalk Chamber of Commerce
12040 Foster Rd.
Norwalk, CA 90650
Ph: (562)864-7785
Fax: (562)864-8539
E-mail: info@norwalkchamber.com
URL: http://www.norwalkchamber.com

Promotes business and community development in Norwalk, CA.

14623 ■ Oceanside Chamber of Commerce
928 N Coast Hwy.
Oceanside, CA 92054
Ph: (760)722-1534
Fax: (760)722-8336
E-mail: info@oceansidechamber.com
URL: http://www.oceansidechamber.com

Promotes business and community development in Oceanside, CA.

14624 ■ Ohio Chamber of Commerce
230 E Town St.
PO Box 15159
Columbus, OH 43215-0159
Ph: (614)228-4201
Fax: (614)228-6403
Fr: 800-622-1893
E-mail: occ@ohiochamber.com
URL: http://www.ohiochamber.com

Businesses organized to foster economic and industrial growth in Ohio. Serves as liaison between government and business. Keeps members informed of employment conditions, economic developments, and pertinent regulations. Conducts lobbying activities.

14625 ■ Overland Park Chamber of Commerce
9001 W 110th St., Ste. 150
Overland Park, KS 66210
Ph: (913)491-3600
Fax: (913)491-0393
E-mail: opcc@opchamber.org
URL: http://www.opks.org

Promotes business and community development in Overland Park and Johnson County, KS.

14626 ■ Oxnard Chamber of Commerce
400 E Esplanade Dr., Ste. 302
Oxnard, CA 93036
Ph: (805)983-6118
Fax: (805)604-7331
E-mail: info@oxnardchamber.org
URL: http://www.oxnardchamber.org

Promotes business and community development in Oxnard, CA area.

14627 ■ Palmdale Chamber of Commerce
817 E Ave. Q9
Palmdale, CA 93550
Ph: (661)273-3232
Fax: (661)273-8508
URL: http://www.palmdalechamber.org

Promotes business and community development in Palmdale, CA.

14628 ■ Pasadena Chamber of Commerce
4334 Fairmont Pkwy.
Pasadena, TX 77504-3306
Ph: (281)487-7871
Fax: (281)487-5530
E-mail: info@pasadenachamber.org
URL: http://www.pasadenachamber.org

Promotes business and community development in Pasadena, TX.

14629 ■ Pasadena Chamber of Commerce and Civic Association
844 E Green St., Ste. 208
Pasadena, CA 91101
Ph: (626)795-3355
Fax: (626)795-5603
E-mail: linda@pasadena-chamber.org
URL: http://www.pasadena-chamber.org

Promotes business and community development in Pasadena, CA.

14630 ■ Pennsylvania Chamber of Business and Industry
417 Walnut St.
Harrisburg, PA 17101
Ph: (717)255-3252
Fax: (717)255-3298
Fr: 800-225-7224
E-mail: info@pachamber.org
URL: http://www.pachamber.org

Promotes business and community development in Pennsylvania.

14631 ■ Peoria Area Chamber of Commerce
100 SW Water St.
Peoria, IL 61602
Ph: (309)676-0755
Fax: (309)676-7534
URL: http://www.peoriachamber.org
Promotes business and community development in
the Peoria, IL area.

14632 ■ Peoria Chamber of Commerce
8631 W Union Hills Dr., Ste. 203
Peoria, AZ 85382
Ph: (623)979-3601
Fax: (623)979-7175
URL: http://www.peoriachamber.com
Promotes business and community development in
the Peoria, AZ area.

14633 ■ Plano Chamber of Commerce
1200 E 15th St.
Plano, TX 75074
Ph: (972)424-7547
Fax: (972)422-5182
E-mail: info@planochamber.org
URL: http://www.planochamber.org
Promotes business and community development in
Plano, TX.

**14634 ■ Rancho Cucamonga Chamber of
Commerce**
9047 Arrow Rte., Ste. 180
Rancho Cucamonga, CA 91730-4434
Ph: (909)987-1012
Fax: (909)987-5917
E-mail: info@ranchochamber.org
URL: http://www.ranchochamber.org
Promotes business and community development in
Rancho Cucamonga, CA.

14635 ■ Ricklin-Echikson Associates Inc.
374 Millburn Ave.
Millburn, NJ 07041
Ph: (973)376-2020
Fax: (973)376-2072
Fr: 800-544-2317
E-mail: jcowan@reacareers.com
URL: http://www.r-e-a.com
Assists spouses of relocating or newly recruited
employees nationwide in the transfer or establishment of a new career, as well as entry into the
employment market. Each spouse relocation career
assistance program is customized with continuous,
on-going counseling until the spouse is properly
situated. Individual and group programs available as
well as outplacement services to clients worldwide.

**14636 ■ Rockford Area Chamber of
Commerce**
308 W State St., Ste. 190
Rockford, IL 61101
Ph: (815)987-8100
Fax: (815)987-8122
E-mail: info@rockfordchamber.com
URL: http://www.rockfordchamber.com
Promotes business and community development in
the Rockford, IL area.

**14637 ■ Salinas Valley Chamber of
Commerce**
119 E Alisal St.
Salinas, CA 93902
Ph: (831)751-7725
Fax: (831)424-8639
E-mail: info@salinaschamber.com
URL: http://www.salinaschamber.com
Promotes business and community development in
the Salinas, CA area.

14638 ■ Santa Ana Chamber of Commerce
2020 N Broadway, No. 200
Santa Ana, CA 92706
Ph: (714)541-5353

Fax: (714)541-2238
E-mail: info@santaanachamber.com
URL: http://www.santaanachamber.com
Promotes business and community development in
the Santa Ana, CA area.

**14639 ■ Santa Clara Chamber of Commerce
and Convention and Visitors Bureau**
1850 Warburton Ave., Ste. 101
Santa Clara, CA 95050
Ph: (408)244-9660
Fax: (408)244-9202
Fr: 800-272-6822
E-mail: steve.vandorn@santaclara.org
URL: http://www.santaclara.org
Promotes business, community development, tour-
ism and the convention trade in Santa Clara, CA.

**14640 ■ Santa Clarita Valley Chamber of
Commerce**
27451 Tourney Rd., Ste. 160
Santa Clarita, CA 91355
Ph: (661)702-6977
Fax: (661)702-6980
E-mail: info@scvchamber.com
URL: http://www.scvchamber.com
Promotes business and community development in
the Santa Clarita Valley, CA area. Sponsors business
expo.

14641 ■ Santa Rosa Chamber of Commerce
637 1st St.
Santa Rosa, CA 95404
Ph: (707)545-1414
Fax: (707)545-6914
E-mail: chamber@santarosachamber.com
URL: http://www.santarosachamber.com
Promotes business and community development in
Santa Rosa, CA.

**14642 ■ Scottsdale Area Chamber of
Commerce**
4725 N Scottsdale Rd., No. 210
Scottsdale, AZ 85251-4498
Ph: (480)355-2700
Fax: (480)355-2710
E-mail: info@scottsdalechamber.com
URL: http://www.scottsdalechamber.com
Promotes business and community development in
the Scottsdale, AZ area.

14643 ■ Simi Valley Chamber of Commerce
40 W Cochran St., No. 100
Simi Valley, CA 93065
Ph: (805)526-3900
Fax: (805)526-6234
E-mail: info@simichamber.org
URL: http://www.simivalleychamber.org
Promotes business and community development in
Simi Valley, CA.

**14644 ■ South Carolina Chamber of
Commerce**
1301 Gervais St., Ste. 1100
Columbia, SC 29201
Ph: (803)799-4601
Fax: (803)779-6043
Fr: 800-799-4601
E-mail: chamber@scchamber.net
URL: http://www.scchamber.net
Promotes business and community development in
South Carolina.

**14645 ■ South Dakota Chamber of
Commerce and Industry**
180 N Euclid Ave.
PO Box 190
Pierre, SD 57501
Ph: (605)224-6161
Fax: (605)224-7198
Fr: 800-742-8112
E-mail: contactus@sdchamber.biz
URL: http://www.sdchamber.biz

Promotes business and community development in
the state of South Dakota.

**14646 ■ Springfield Area Chamber of
Commerce**
202 S John Q. Hammons Pkwy.
PO Box 1687
Springfield, MO 65806
Ph: (417)862-5567
URL: http://www.springfieldchamber.com
Promotes business and community development in
the Springfield, MO area.

**14647 ■ State Chamber - Oklahoma's
Association of Business and Industry**
330 NE 10th St.
Oklahoma City, OK 73104-3220
Ph: (405)235-3669
Fax: (405)235-3670
E-mail: info@okstatechamber.com
URL: http://www.okstatechamber.com
Promotes business and community development in
Oklahoma.

**14648 ■ Sterling Heights Regional Chamber
of Commerce & Industry**
12900 Hall Rd., Ste. 100
Sterling Heights, MI 48313
Ph: (586)731-5400
Fax: (586)731-3521
E-mail: lcolton@shrcci.com
URL: http://www.shrcci.com
Promotes business and community development in
the Sterling Heights, Utica, Shelby Township, MI area.

14649 ■ Sunnyvale Chamber of Commerce
260 S Sunnyvale Ave., Ste. 4
Sunnyvale, CA 94086
Ph: (408)736-4971
Fax: (408)736-1919
E-mail: communications@svcoc.org
URL: http://www.svcoc.org
Promotes business and community development in
Sunnyvale, CA.

14650 ■ Tempe Chamber of Commerce
909 E Apache Blvd.
PO Box 28500
Tempe, AZ 85281
Ph: (480)967-7891
Fax: (480)966-5365
E-mail: info@tempechamber.org
URL: http://www.tempechamber.org
Promotes business and community development in
Tempe, AZ.

**14651 ■ Tennessee Chamber of Commerce
and Industry**
611 Commerce St., Ste. 3030
Nashville, TN 37203-3742
Ph: (615)256-5141
Fax: (615)256-6726
E-mail: info@tnchamber.org
URL: http://www.tnchamber.org
Promotes business and community development in
the state of Tennessee.

**14652 ■ Texas Association of Business and
Chamber of Commerce**
1209 Nueces St.
Austin, TX 78701-1209
Ph: (512)477-6721
Fax: (512)477-0836
E-mail: info@txbiz.org
URL: http://www.txbiz.org
Promotes business and community development in
the state of Texas.

**14653 ■ Torrance Area Chamber of
Commerce**
3400 Torrance Blvd., Ste. 100
Torrance, CA 90503

Ph: (310)540-5858
Fax: (310)540-7662
E-mail: info@torrancechamber.com
URL: http://www.torrancechamber.com

Promotes business and community development in the Torrance, CA area.

14654 ■ Utah Department of Commerce
Heber M. Wells Bldg.
160 E 300 S
Salt Lake City, UT 84111
Ph: (801)530-6674
Fax: (801)530-7655
E-mail: mbeck@utah.gov
URL: http://www.commerce.state.ut.us

Promotes business and community development in the state of Utah.

14655 ■ Vallejo Chamber of Commerce
427 York St.
Vallejo, CA 94590
Ph: (707)644-5551
Fax: (707)644-5590
E-mail: info@vallejochamber.com
URL: http://www.vallejochamber.com

Promotes business and community development in Vallejo, CA.

14656 ■ Ventura Chamber of Commerce
505 Poli St., 2nd Fl.
Ventura, CA 93003
Ph: (805)643-7222
URL: http://www.venturachamber.com

Promotes business and community development in the Ventura, CA area.

14657 ■ Vermont Chamber of Commerce
PO Box 37
Montpelier, VT 05601
Ph: (802)223-3443
Fax: (802)223-4257
E-mail: info@vtchamber.com
URL: http://www.vtchamber.com

Promotes business and community development in the state of Vermont. Conducts educational programs. Lobbies state government.

14658 ■ Virginia Chamber of Commerce
9 S 5th St.
Richmond, VA 23219
Ph: (804)644-1607
Fax: (804)783-6112
E-mail: d.flannery@vachamber.com
URL: http://www.vachamber.com

Promotes business and community development in Virginia.

14659 ■ Virginia Peninsula Chamber of Commerce
21 Enterprise Pkwy., Ste. 100
Hampton, VA 23666
Ph: (757)262-2000
Fax: (757)262-2009
E-mail: info@vpcc.org
URL: http://www.virginiapeninsulachamber.com

Promotes the economic and business interests of the Virginia Peninsula.

14660 ■ West Chamber of Commerce Serving Jefferson County
1667 Cole Blvd., Bldg. 19, Ste. 400
Lakewood, CO 80401
Ph: (303)233-5555
Fax: (303)237-7633
E-mail: info@westchamber.org
URL: http://www.westchamber.org

Promotes business and community development in Lakewood and Jefferson County, CO.

14661 ■ West Covina Chamber of Commerce
811 S Sunset Ave.
West Covina, CA 91790-3599
Ph: (626)338-8496
Fax: (626)960-0511
URL: http://www.westcovinachamber.com

Promotes business and community development in West Covina, CA.

14662 ■ West Virginia Chamber of Commerce
1624 Kanawha Blvd., E
Charleston, WV 25311
Ph: (304)342-1115
Fax: (304)342-1130
E-mail: forjobs@wvchamber.com
URL: http://www.wvchamber.com

Promotes business and community development in West Virginia. Sponsors seminars.

14663 ■ Wichita Falls Chamber of Commerce and Industry
900 8th St., Ste. 218
PO Box 1860
Wichita Falls, TX 76307
Ph: (940)723-2741
Fax: (940)723-8773
E-mail: chamber@wf.net
URL: http://www.wichitafallscommerce.com

Promotes business and community development in Wichita Falls, TX.

14664 ■ Wisconsin Manufacturers and Commerce
501 E Washington Ave.
PO Box 352
Madison, WI 53703-2944
Ph: (608)258-3400
Fax: (608)258-3413
URL: http://www.wmc.org

Promotes business and community development in the state of Wisconsin.

14665 ■ Yonkers Chamber of Commerce
55 Main St., 2nd Fl.
Yonkers, NY 10701
Ph: (914)963-0332
Fax: (914)963-0455
E-mail: info@yonkerschamber.com
URL: http://www.yonkerschamber.com

Promotes business and community development in Yonkers, NY.

REFERENCE WORKS

14666 ■ Give Me More Money: Smart Salary Negotiation Tips for Getting Paid What You're Really Worth
Impact Publications
9104 Manassas Dr., Ste. N
Manassas Park, VA 20111
Ph: (703)361-7300
Fax: (703)335-9486
URL: http://www.impactpublications.com

Ron and Caryl Krannich, 2008. $17.95 (paper). 208 pages. Supplies sample negotiating scripts and tips for raising salaries. Includes salary calculators, checklists, key websites, salary ranges and stock options.

14667 ■ Knock 'Em Dead: The Ultimate Job Seeker's Handbook
Adams Media Corp.
4700 E Galbraith Rd.
Cincinnati, OH 45236
Ph: (513)531-2690
Fax: (513)531-4082
Fr: 800-289-0963
URL: http://www.adamsmediastore.com/product/1359/careers

Martin Yate. 2010. $15.95 (paper). 384 pages. Prepares the job seeker for the interview with advice on dress, manner, how to answer the toughest questions, and how to spot illegal questions. Discusses how to respond to questions of salary to maximize income. Features sections on executive search firms and drug testing.

14668 ■ Negotiating Your Salary: How to Make $1,000 a Minute
Ten Speed Press
PO Box 7123
Berkeley, CA 94707
Ph: (510)559-1600
Fax: (510)559-1629
Fr: 800-841-2665
URL: http://www.randomhouse.com/crown/tenspeed/

Jack Chapman, 2008. $15.95 (paper). 220 pages. Describes what to say and do in order to obtain the best possible compensation. Provides step-by-step instructions for negotiation.

14669 ■ Negotiation Fieldbook
McGraw-Hill Professional
Two Penn Plaza
23rd Fl.
New York, NY 10121
URL: http://www.mhprofessional.com/product.php?isbn=0071454748

Grande Lum, 2004. $14.95 (paper). 204 pages. Includes information on structuring negotiations, and gives tips on how to begin a negotiation.

14670 ■ Next-Day Salary Negotiation
Jist Publishing
875 Montreal Way
St. Paul, MN 55102
Fr: 800-648-5478
URL: http://www.jist.com

Maryanne L. Wegerbauer, 2008. $8.95 (paper). 224 pages. Covers extensive government data for salary averages. Provides worksheets for evaluations and quick tips for salary negotiation.

14671 ■ Perfect Phrases for Negotiating Salary and Job Offers
McGraw-Hill Professional
PO Box 182604
Columbus, OH 43272
Ph: 877-833-5524
Fax: (614)759-3749
E-mail: pbg.ecommerce_custserv@mcgraw-hill.com
URL: http://www.mhprofessional.com/product.php?isbn=0071475516

Matthew J. DeLuca, Nanette F. DeLuca. 2006. $9.95 (paperback). 160 pages. Provides quick, easy steps that prepare readers for salary negotiations, job interviews, or performance reviews, giving them the competitive edge.

14672 ■ Salary Facts Handbook
JIST Publishing
875 Montreal Way
St. Paul, MN 55102
Fr: 800-648-5478
E-mail: info@jist.com
URL: http://www.jist.com

Editors at JIST. 2008. $49.95 (hardcover). $39.95 (softcover). 912 pages. Gives pay information on 800 jobs at 11 levels of education and training. Includes details on salary ranges by training, educational attainments, and by locations. Contains advice on salary negotiation, factors affecting earnings, and lists of federal jobs, industries, states, and metro areas ranked by pay.

14673 ■ Salary Negotiation Tips for Professionals
Impact Publications
9104 Manassas Dr.
Manassas Park, VA 20111
Ph: (703)361-7300
Fax: (703)335-9486
URL: http://www.impactpublications.com

Ron and Caryl Krannich, 2005. $16.95 (paper). 144 pages. Designed for individuals making $50,000+ per year. Provides tips and strategies for effectively negotiating a compensation package.

14674 ■ Secrets of Power Negotiating
Career Press
220 West Pkwy., Unit 12
Pompton Plains, NJ 07444
Ph: (201)848-0310
Fax: (201)848-1727
Fr: 800-CAREER-1
URL: http://www.careerpress.com

Roger Dawson, 2006. $16.99 (hardcover). 320 pages. Covers every aspect of the negotiating process. Includes analyses of different negotiating styles.

14675 ■ Six Figure Salary Negotiation
Adams Media, F+W Publications Inc.
4700 E Galbraith Rd.
Cincinnati, OH 45236
URL: http://www.adamsmedia.com

Michael Zwell, 2008. $14.95 (paper). 272 pages. Gives tips for negotiating a satisfying job offer or raise. Supplies questions and suggestions for closing the offer at the right moment for the best salary and benefits.

AUDIO/VISUAL RESOURCES

14676 ■ Quick Interview and Salary Negotiation Video (DVD)
JIST Publishing
875 Montreal Way
St. Paul, MN 55102
Fr: 800-648-5478
E-mail: info@jist.com
URL: http://www.jist.com

2007. $149. 30 minutes. Covers strategies for landing interviews fast, being effective during the interview, and negotiating the salary.

ONLINE AND DATABASE SERVICES

14677 ■ JobStar Central
E-mail: electrajobstar@earthlink.net
URL: http://www.jobstar.org

Description: Offers salary negotiation strategies and links to other resources.

14678 ■ PayScale, Inc.
E-mail: service@payscale.com
URL: http://www.payscale.com

Online resource provides detailed information concerning salary, vacation time, bonuses and commute time. Also gives tips for salary negotiation and career planning.

14679 ■ Salary.com
URL: http://www.salary.com

Description: Offers salary reports based upon occupation. Also provides self-tests, learning and career links.

14680 ■ SalaryExpert.com
E-mail: techsupport@salaryexpert.com
URL: http://www.salaryexpert.com

Description: Salary reports.

14681 ■ SalaryNegotiations.com
URL: http://www.salarynegotiations.com

Description: Includes advice for maximizing salary. Provides video, FAQs and links to career advice.

SOFTWARE

14682 ■ ERI's Salary Assessor & Survey
ERI Economic Research Institute
8575 164th Ave. NE, Ste. 100
Redmond, WA 98052

Ph: (425)556-0205
Fax: (425)885-5091
Fr: 800-627-3697
E-mail: info.eri@erieri.com
URL: http://www.erieri.com
CD-ROM. $889 for professional; $2,389 for consultant. Program that reports competitive wage, salary, and incentive survey data.

REFERENCE WORKS

14683 ■ *33 Million People in the Room: How to Create, Influence and Run a Successful Business with Social Networking*
FT Press
1 Lake St.
Upper Saddle River, NJ 07458
URL: http://www.ftpress.com

Juliette Powell, 2009. $17.59 (hardcover). 200 pages. Discusses the power of social networking on the business world. Describes getting started and making social networks work for the user.

14684 ■ *101 Successful Networking Strategies*
Course Technology PTR
20 Channel Center St.
Boston, MA 02210
Ph: (617)289-7700
Fax: (617)289-7844
Fr: 800-354-9706
URL: http://www.courseptr.com

Eric P. Kramer. 2011. $12.99 (paper). 160 pages. Aims to equip business professionals and job seekers with strategies to maximize networking opportunities. Provides expert advice on how to improve networking skills.

14685 ■ *Business Networking and Sex: Not What You Think*
Entrepreneur Press/McGraw-Hill
2445 McCabe Way, Ste. 400
Irvine, CA 92614
Ph: (949)261-2325
Fax: (949)261-7729
Fr: 800-864-6864
URL: http://www.mhprofessional.com

Ivan Misner, Hazel Walker and Frank De Raffelle. 2011. $21.95. 256 pages. Serves as guide for professionals in successfully talking business and networking with the opposite sex.

14686 ■ *Guerilla Networking: A Proven Battle Plan to Attract the Very People You Want to Meet*
Morgan James Publishing
1225 Franklin Ave.
Ste. 325
Garden City, NY 11530
Ph: (516)620-2528
Fax: (516)908-4496
Fr: 800-485-4943
URL: http://publishing.morgan-james.com

Jay Conrad Levinson and Monroe Mann, 2007. $19.95 (paper). 305 pages. Teaches networking by focusing on how to get peers interested in meeting and working with the reader.

14687 ■ *Highly Effective Networking: Meet the Right People and Get a Great Job*
Career Press
220 West Pkwy., Unit 12
Pompton Plains, NJ 07444
Ph: (201)848-0310
Fax: (201)848-1727
Fr: 800-227-3371
E-mail: sales@careerpress.com
URL: http://www.careerpress.com

Orville Pierson. 2009. $15.99 (paper). 224 pages. Teaches individuals to use a small network to reach dozens of insiders and decision makers, get the message, create a project plan to organize networking efforts, speak effectively and comfortably with networking contacts, and talk to decision makers before the job opening is announced.

14688 ■ *I'm on LinkedIn, Now What??? A Guide to Getting the Most Out of LinkedIn*
Happy About
20660 Stevens Creek Blvd., Ste. 210
Cupertino, CA 95014
Ph: (408)257-3000
E-mail: questions@happyabout.info
URL: http://www.happyabout.com

Jason Alba. 2008. $16.96 (paper). 148 pages. Offers a perspective on networking that's of interest to a job seeker, entrepreneur, or networking enthusiast. Helps readers understand and develop an online social networking strategy with LinkedIn.

14689 ■ *Make Your Contacts Count*
American Management Association
1601 Broadway
New York, NY 10019
Ph: (212)586-8100
Fax: (212)903-8353
URL: http://www.amacombooks.org/
     book.cfm?isbn=9780814474020

Anne Baber, Lynne Waymon, 2007. $14.95 (paper). 272 pages. Helps the reader create a fully developed network. A step-by-step guide for capitalizing on networking relationships and opportunities.

14690 ■ *Networking Like a Pro: Turning Contacts into Connections*
Entrepreneur Press
2445 McCabe Way, Ste. 400
Irvine, CA 92614
Ph: (949)261-2325
Fax: (949)261-7729
Fr: 800-864-6864
E-mail: press@entrepreneur.com
URL: http://www.entrepreneurpress.com

Ivan Misner, David Alexander and Brian Hilliard. 2010. $21.95 (paper). 252 pages. Contains information on key networking concepts and strategies. Aims to teach readers how to reach quality prospects, leverage contacts, motivate ongoing referrals and get results.

14691 ■ *Networking for People Who Hate Networking: A Field Guide for Introverts, the Overwhelmed, and the Underconnected*
Berrett-Koehler Publishers
235 Montgomery St., Ste. 650
San Francisco, CA 94104
Ph: (415)288-0260
Fax: (415)362-2512
E-mail: bkpub@bkpub.com
URL: http://www.bkconnection.com

Devora Zack. 2010. $16.95 (paper). Features guidelines designed to help people who are not too keen on doing networking. Includes field-tested tips and techniques.

14692 ■ *The Networking Survival Guide: Get the Success You Want by Tapping into People You Know*
McGraw-Hill Trade
PO Box 182604
Columbus, OH 43272
Ph: 877-833-5524
Fax: (614)759-3749
E-mail: customer.service@mcgraw-hill.com
URL: http://www.mhprofessional.com/
     product.php?isbn=0071717587

Diane Darling. 2010. $16.95. Walks readers through the process of networking, including setting goals, identifying and developing potential contacts, and following up on leads and turning them into opportunities.

14693 ■ *Networking Works!: The WetFeet Insider Guide to Networking*
WetFeet, Inc.
1518 Walnut St., Ste. 1800
Philadelphia, PA 19102
URL: http://www.wetfeet.com

2008. $19.95. 88 pages. Shows how to network effectively by tapping into an existing network, reading about alternative means of networking, and using alternative means of networking.

14694 ■ *Never Eat Alone*
Random House, Inc.
1745 Broadway
New York, NY 10019
Ph: (212)782-9000
URL: http://www.randomhouse.com

Keith Ferrazzi and Tahl Raz, 2005. $26.00 (hardcover). 320 pages. A different networking technique is described in each chapter. Focuses on establishing a strong network of relationships.

14695 ■ *Resumes, Cover Letters, Networking and Interviewing*
Cengage Learning
PO Box 6904
Florence, KY 41022-6904
Fax: 800-487-8488
Fr: 800-354-9706
URL: http://www.cengage.com

Clifford W. Eischen and Lynn A. Eischen. 2012. $57.95 (paper). 128 pages. Takes job seekers through a step-by-step process of polishing a resume and developing strong interview techniques. Includes topics on using online resources in job hunting, employment databases, cover letters, networking, and job applications.

14696 ■ *Seven Days to Online Networking*
JIST Publishing
875 Montreal Way
St. Paul, MN 55102
Fr: 800-648-5478
E-mail: info@jist.com
URL: http://www.jist.com

Ellen Sautter and Diane Crompton. 2008. $9.95 (softcover). 192 pages. Helps individuals maximize online networking for job search and career success by showing them where, how, and why they can benefit from making professional connections online.

14697 ■ *The Skinny on Networking*
Rand Media Co.
265 Post Rd., W
Westport, CT 06880
Ph: (203)226-8727
E-mail: info@randmediaco.com
URL: http://www.randmediaco.com

Jim Randel. 2010. $14.95 (paper). 188 pages. Covers essential information about networking concepts.

AUDIO/VISUAL RESOURCES

14698 ■ *Job Search Strategies*
The Learning Seed
641 W Lake St., Ste. 301
Chicago, IL 60661

Fax: 800-998-0854
Fr: 800-634-4941
E-mail: info@learningseed.com
URL: http://www.learningseed.com

Video. $99.00. 23 minutes. Learn how to network with companies without going through the personnel department.

ONLINE AND DATABASE SERVICES

14699 ■ Linkedin.com
URL: http://www.linkedin.com

Description: Networking Web site for professionals. Represents 170 industries and 200 countries.

14700 ■ MeetTheBoss.com
URL: http://www.meettheboss.tv

Description: A business networking tool that combines video calling, instant messaging and email between members.

14701 ■ Monster Networking
URL: http://login.monster.com

An online community of professionals that provide jobseekers with the opportunity to learn about various companies, industries, and fields through personal contact.

14702 ■ Networking For Professionals
URL: http://www.networkingforprofessionals.com

Description: Seeks to provide a better alternative to building business contacts quickly and efficiently. Facilitates business networking among professionals across all fields.

14703 ■ Talkbiznow.com
URL: http://talkbiznow.com

Description: A free business networking Web site. Users may search for like-minded busines professionals.

14704 ■ The Virtual Handshake
URL: http://www.thevirtualhandshake.com

Description: Online resource guide for networking. Provides a weblog and online discussion groups.

OTHER SOURCES

14705 ■ Business Network International
9903 Santa Monica Blvd., Ste. 812
Beverly Hills, CA 90212
Ph: (818)667-8967
Fax: (323)395-0987
Fr: (866)889-3466
URL: http://www.bni.la

Description: Offers a structured system of giving and receiving business by providing an environment in which individuals can develop personal relationships with other business professionals.

14706 ■ Expo Experts, LLC
7770 Cooper Rd., Ste. 3, 1st Fl.
Cincinnati, OH 45242
Ph: (513)561-5422
Fax: (513)561-5402
Fr: 877-842-3976
E-mail: admin@expoexpertsllc.com
URL: http://www.expoexpertsllc.com

Description: Job fair provider in North America. Brings a combined experience in the U.S. and Canadian job fair industry. Offers advertising exposure to exhibitors.

REFERENCE WORKS

14707 ■ *Alternatives to the Peace Corps*
Food First Books
398 60th St.
Oakland, CA 94618
Ph: (510)654-4400
Fax: (510)654-4551
URL: http://www.foodfirst.org/en/store/book/
  Alternatives_to_the_P

Annual, latest edition 12th edition. $11.95 for individuals. Covers: More than 100 foreign service organizations (excluding the Peace Corps) that offer long- or short-term volunteer service or travel opportunities in developing countries and U.S.-based volunteer opportunities. Entries include: Program name, address, phone, e-mail, website, description of program, including geographical areas served and admission requirements. Arrangement: Classified by type of program. Indexes: Organization.

14708 ■ *Career Opportunities in the Nonprofit Sector*
Facts On File Inc.
132 W 31st St., 17th Fl.
New York, NY 10001
Fr: 800-322-8755
E-mail: custserv@factsonfile.com
URL: http://factsonfile.infobasepublishing.com

2006. $49.50. 352 pages. Features job and career descriptions in the nonprofit sector, followed by the descriptions of certification, education, special skills and training required.

14709 ■ *Careers in Focus: Nonprofit Organizations*
Ferguson Publishing
132 W 31st St., 17th Fl.
New York, NY 10001
Fr: 800-322-8755
E-mail: custserv@factsonfile.com
URL: http://factsonfile.infobasepublishing.com

2008. $32.95. 192 pages. Cover an overview of nonprofit organizations, followed by a selection of jobs profiled in detail, including the nature of the job, earnings, prospects for employment, what kind of training and skills it requires and sources for further information.

14710 ■ *Careers for Good Samaritans and Other Humanitarian Types*
The McGraw-Hill Companies
PO Box 182604
Columbus, OH 43272
Fax: (614)759-3749
Fr: 877-883-5524
E-mail: customer.service@mcgraw-hill.com
URL: http://www.mhprofessional.com

Marjorie Eberts and Margaret Gisler. Third edition, 2006. $16.95 (paper). 160 pages. Contains hundreds of ideas for turning good work into paid work.

Inventories opportunities in service organizations like the Red Cross, Goodwill, and the Salvation Army; religious groups, VISTA, the Peace Corps, and UNICEF; and agencies at all levels of the government. Part of Careers for You series.

14711 ■ *Directory of Catholic Charities USA Directories*
Catholic Charities USA
66 Canal Center Pl., Ste. 600
Alexandria, VA 22314-1583
Ph: (703)549-1390
Fax: (703)549-1656
URL: http://www.catholiccharitiesusa.org

Annual. $25.00 for individuals. Covers: Nearly 1,200 Catholic community and social service agencies. Listings include diocesan agencies, state Catholic conferences. Entries include: Organization name, address, name and title of director, phone, fax. Arrangement: Geographical by state, then classified by diocese.

14712 ■ *Great Jobs for Business Majors*
The McGraw-Hill Companies
PO Box 182604
Columbus, OH 43272
Fax: (614)759-3749
Fr: 877-883-5524
E-mail: customer.service@mcgraw-hill.com
URL: http://www.mhprofessional.com/
  product.php?isbn=0071544836

Stephen Lambert. Third edition, 2008. $16.95 (paper). 240 pages.

14713 ■ *National Directory of Nonprofit Organizations*
Taft Group
27500 Drake Rd.
Farmington Hills, MI 48331-3535
Ph: (248)699-4253
Fax: (248)699-8061
Fr: 800-877-4253
URL: http://www.gale.cengage.com

Annual, latest edition 27th; February 2012. $718.00 for individuals; $484.00 for individuals. Covers: Over 265,000 nonprofit organizations; volume 1 covers organizations with annual incomes of over $100,000; volume 2 covers organizations with incomes between $25,000 and $99,999. Entries include: Organization name, address, phone, annual income, IRS filing status, employer identification number, tax deductible status, activity description. Arrangement: Alphabetical. Indexes: Area of activity, geographical.

14714 ■ *The Nonprofit Career Guide: How to Land a Job That Makes a Difference*
Fieldstone Alliance
60 Plato Blvd. E, Ste. 150
St. Paul, MN 55107
Ph: (651)556-4500

Fax: (651)556-4517
E-mail: info@fieldstonealliance.org
URL: http://www.fieldstonealliance.org/
  productdetails.cfm?PC=78

Shelly Cryer. 2008. $18.95 (paper). 300 pages. Provides advice from people working at all levels of diverse non-profits. Provides information on how to prepare for a nonprofit career, conduct targeted job searches and network, handle interviews, write cover letters and resumes, and negotiate a compensation package.

14715 ■ *Nonprofit Management Resources Directory*
National Council for International Visitors
1420 K St. NW, Ste. 800
Washington, DC 20005
Ph: (202)842-1414
Fax: (202)289-4625
Fr: 800-523-8101
E-mail: info@nciv.org
URL: http://www.nciv.org/pr_publications.asp

Covers: Nonprofit organizations. Entries include: Name, address, phone, fax, email, and website address.

14716 ■ *Nonprofits and Government: Field Guides to Finding a New Career*
Facts On File
132 W 31st St., 17th Fl.
New York, NY 10001
Fax: 800-678-3633
Fr: 800-322-8755
E-mail: custserv@factsonfile.com
URL: http://factsonfile.infobasepublishing.com

Amanda Kirk. 2009. $39.95 (hardcover). 176 pages. Guides career changers in exploring career possibilities in the nonprofits and government fields. Contains tips and advice from professionals. Provides readers with an overview of nonprofits and government, ways to map out career goals for the future, and self-assessment questions.

14717 ■ *Public Human Services Directory*
American Public Human Services Association
1133 19th St., NW, Ste. 400
Washington, DC 20036-3631
Ph: (202)682-0100
Fax: (202)289-6555
URL: http://www.aphsa.org

Annual, Latest edition 2009. $225.00 for individuals; $200.00 for members; $350.00 for institutions. Covers: Federal, state, territorial, county, and major municipal public human service agencies. Entries include: Agency name, address, phone, fax, e-mail address, web site address, names of key personnel, program area. Arrangement: Geographical.

14718 ■ *Real Resumes for Jobs in Non-Profit Organizations*
PREP Publishing
1110 1/2 Hay St., Ste. C
Fayetteville, NC 28305

Ph: (910)483-6611
Fax: (910)483-2439
E-mail: preppub@aol.com
URL: http://www.prep-pub.com/Bookstore/non-
  profit.htm

Anne McKinney (Editor). April 2004. $16.95 (paper).
Illustrated. 192 pages. Real-Resumes Series.

**14719 ■ Start and Grow an Effective
  Non-Profit Organization**
Cengage Learning
PO Box 6904
Florence, KY 41022
Fax: 800-487-8488
Fr: 800-354-9706
URL: http://www.cengage.com

Lyn Scott. 2012. $29.99 (paperback). 320 pages.
Provides specific steps and action plan to establishing a non-profit organization. Includes guide on as-
sembling the right business team, crafting a strategic
plan and seeking supporters.

**14720 ■ Starting and Managing a Nonprofit
  Organization: A Legal Guide**
John Wiley and Sons, Inc.
1 Wiley Dr.
Somerset, NJ 08875-1272
Fax: (732)302-2300
Fr: 800-225-5945
E-mail: custserv@wiley.com
URL: http://as.wiley.com/WileyCDA/WileyTitle/
  productCd-0470397934.html

Bruce R. Hopkins. Fifth edition, 2009. $45.00 (paper).
364 pages.

**14721 ■ Vault Guide to the Top Government
  & Nonprofit Employers**
Vault.com Inc.
150 W 22nd St., 5th Fl.
New York, NY 10011
Ph: (212)366-4212
Fax: (212)366-6117
Fr: 888-562-8285
URL: http://www.vault.com/wps/portal/usa/search/
  guide

Latest edition 2008. $19.95 for individuals; $19.95 for
members. Covers: Government and nonprofit
agencies. Entries include: Name, address, phone,
fax, website, and branch office location. Also include
company overviews, recent company news, information on the hiring process, key competitors, and
employment contact. Arrangement: Alphabetical by
company name.

NEWSPAPERS, MAGAZINES, AND
JOURNALS

14722 ■ The Chronicle of Philanthropy
The Chronicle of Philanthropy
1255 23rd St. NW, Ste. 700
Washington, DC 20037
Ph: (202)466-1200
E-mail: editor@philanthropy.com
URL: http://philanthropy.com

$72.00/year for individuals; $125.00/year for two
years; $72.00/year for individuals, online access only;
$99.75/year for Canada; $72.00/year for Canada, online access only; $135.00/year for other countries;
$72.00/year for other countries, online access only.
Magazine covering fundraising, philanthropy, and
non-profit organizations. Includes information on tax
rulings, new grants, and statistics, reports on grant
makers, and profiles of foundations.

14723 ■ The NonProfit Times
NPT Publishing Group Inc.
201 Littleton Rd., 2nd Fl.
Morris Plains, NJ 07950
Ph: (973)401-0202

Fax: (973)401-0404
E-mail: ednchief@nptimes.com
URL: http://www.nptimes.com/

$49.95/year for individuals, print; $19.95/year for
individuals, digital only; $59.95/year for individuals,
digital & print. Trade journal serving nonprofit
organizations.

AUDIO/VISUAL RESOURCES

14724 ■ Careers in the Non-Profit Sector
JIST Publishing
875 Montreal Way
St. Paul, MN 55102
Fr: 800-648-5478
URL: http://www.jist.com

2010. $129.95. 17 minutes. Explores various job
types in the nonprofit sector.

ONLINE AND DATABASE SERVICES

14725 ■ Bridgestar
E-mail: bridgestar@bridgespan.org
URL: http://www.bridgestar.org

Description: Serves as a job board dedicated to
senior leadership positions within nonprofit
organizations. Offers resources and tools for individuals looking for nonprofit careers.

14726 ■ ExecSearches.com
E-mail: info@execsearches.com
URL: http://www.execsearches.com

Description: Job site specializing in matching seekers with non-profit, public sector, academic and
"socially conscious" positions. Contains job board,
resume databank, e-mail alert system and reference
articles. Employers may also post jobs and check
resume references.

14727 ■ Locate Nonprofit Jobs
URL: http://www.locatenonprofitjobs.com

Description: Offers employment opportunities and
career information for the nonprofit sector.

14728 ■ New Non Profit Jobs
URL: http://www.newnonprofitjobs.com

Description: Provides an online listing of companies
with available nonprofit jobs in all specialties.

14729 ■ Nonprofit Executive Jobs
URL: http://www.nonprofitexecutivejobs.com

Description: Serves as a nonprofit executive job
board and career search resource.

14730 ■ Nonprofit Jobs Cooperative
URL: http://www.nonprofitjobscoop.org

Description: Provides a one-stop source of nonprofit
jobs all over the country. Includes geographic region,
job title, category, organization name, and salary of
the position.

14731 ■ nonProfit-jobs.org
URL: http://www.nonprofit-jobs.org

Description: Lists executive level positions for
nonprofit job seekers. Features search job functions
that sorts jobs by industry and region.

14732 ■ Nonprofit Manager Jobs
URL: http://www.nonprofitmanagerjobs.com

Description: Provides nonprofit manager employment opportunities.

14733 ■ NonprofitJobMarket.org
E-mail: admin@nonprofitjobmarket.org
URL: http://www.nonprofitjobmarket.org/search.aspx

Description: Provides job opportunities, consulting
services and volunteer opportunities for nonprofit
professionals.

14734 ■ NonProfitJobs.org
E-mail: info@nonprofitjobs.org
URL: http://www.nonprofitjobs.org

Description: Exists as an online gathering place for
not-for-profit employers and management personnel.

14735 ■ NonprofitOyster.com
URL: http://www.nonprofitoyster.com

Description: Serves as a career site for the nonprofit
sector. Offers job postings and resumes.

14736 ■ OpportunityKnocks.org
100 Peachtree St. NW, Ste. 1500
Atlanta, GA 30303
Ph: (678)916-3066
Fax: (404)521-0487
Fr: 888-OKN-OCKS
E-mail: support@opportunityknocks.org
URL: http://www.opportunityknocks.org

Description: Job board website for those interested
in careers in non-profit organizations. Visitors may
search job bank, receive listserv, and subscribe to
free updates e-newsletter. Also contains career
resources.

OTHER SOURCES

**14737 ■ Association Executive Resources
  Group**
PO Box 3880
Gaithersburg, MD 20885-3880
Ph: (301)417-7045
Fax: (301)417-7049
URL: http://www.aerg.org

Executive search firm. Concentrates on non-profits.

**14738 ■ Association for Research on
  Nonprofit Organizations and Voluntary
  Action**
550 W North St., Ste. 301
Indianapolis, IN 46202
Ph: (317)684-2120
Fax: (318)684-2128
URL: http://www.arnova.org

Description: Represents professionals engaged in
research, scholarship, and programs related to
nonprofit organizations, philanthropy, civil society,
and voluntary action. Fosters research, dissemination, and application of knowledge about voluntary
action to enhance the quality of life and the general
welfare of citizens and communities.

14739 ■ Brigham Hill Consultancy
2909 Cole Ave., Ste. 220
Dallas, TX 75204
Ph: (214)871-8700
Fax: (214)871-6004
E-mail: brigham@brighamhill.com
URL: http://www.brighamhill.com

Firm provides retained executive search and related
management consulting services to not-for-profit
organizations.

14740 ■ Campaign Service Consultants
7 Andrew Cir.
Hampstead, NH 03841-0370
Ph: (603)329-4534
Fax: (603)329-4534
E-mail: cscunningham@mediaone.net

Firm provides managerial and fund-raising counsel to
nonprofit organizations. Services include: feasibility
studies, development audits, constituency analysis,
campaign management, board and staff development, special event planning and management,
interim staffing needs, computerization guidance and
assessment, and ongoing counsel and support.

14741 ■ Capability Co.
2818 Anderson Dr.
Raleigh, NC 27608
Ph: (919)791-3700

Fax: (919)882-9401
Fr: (866)832-1136
E-mail: info@capabilitycompany.com
URL: http://www.capabilitycompany.com

Executive search for nonprofits. Company helps nonprofit organizations find the best executive directors, development officers and chief financial officers.

14742 ■ Celia D. Crossley & Associates Ltd.
3011 Bethel Rd., Ste. 201
Columbus, OH 43220
Ph: (614)538-2808
Fax: (614)442-8886
E-mail: info@crosworks.com
URL: http://www.crosworks.com

Firm specializes in career planning and development, executive and organizational career coaching, assessment, key employee selection and team integration. Also offers career transition services, including in-placement, outplacement, and career coaching. Serves government, nonprofit, health-care, higher education and service industries.

14743 ■ Institutional Advantage L.L.C.
340 Lothrop Rd.
Grosse Pointe Farms, MI 48236
Ph: (313)886-6349
Fax: (313)557-1331
E-mail: kts@ia-llc.com
URL: http://www.ia-llc.com

Retained executive search for higher education and not-for-profit clients.

14744 ■ McCormack & Farrow Co.
949 S Coast Dr., Ste. 620
Costa Mesa, CA 92626

Ph: (714)549-7222
Fax: (714)549-7227
E-mail: resumes@mfsearch.com
URL: http://www.mfsearch.com

General practice retained search in most industries. Special emphasis on high-technology, start-up and emerging companies, manufacturing, healthcare, financial services, nonprofit and privately owned businesses.

14745 ■ National Council of Nonprofits
1200 New York Ave. NW, Ste. 700
Washington, DC 20005
Ph: (202)962-0322
Fax: (202)962-0321
Fr: 800-201-0779
URL: http://www.councilofnonprofits.org

Description: Strives to advance the role and capacity of the nonprofit sector in civil society. Supports the state and regional associations of nonprofit organizations.

14746 ■ Non-Profit Personnel Network
20300 W 12 Mile Rd., Ste. 101
Southfield, MI 48076
Ph: (248)569-6776
E-mail: resumes@nppn.biz
URL: http://www.nppn.biz

Description: Executive search firm that serves the nonprofit community across the United States. Offers mid to executive positions in nonprofit organizations and institutions.

14747 ■ People and Systems
315 Madison Ave., Ste. 901
New York, NY 10017

Fax: (212)501-1612
Fr: 800-738-1004
E-mail: matt@peopleandsystems.com
URL: http://www.peopleandsystems.com

Description: Provides nonprofit staffing solutions nationwide. Provides placement from the entry to executive level in all functions including finance, administration, marketing, fundraising, programs, PR, HR, and IT.

14748 ■ Professionals for Nonprofits
515 Madison Ave., Ste. 1100
New York, NY 10022
Ph: (212)546-9091
Fax: (212)546-9094
E-mail: info@nonprofitstaffing.com
URL: http://www.pnp-inc.com

Description: Provides temporary, direct hire, and consulting staff to the nonprofit sector.

14749 ■ Synergy Search Partners Inc.
11921 Freedom Dr., Ste. 550
Reston, VA 20190
Ph: (703)481-9936
Fax: (703)481-9938
E-mail: resume@synergysearchpartners.com
URL: http://www.synergysearchpartners.com

Executive Search firm provides recruitment services to a diverse client base. Firm provides consultative advice throughout the search and recruitment process. With a global network of senior-level candidates and human capital resources, firm has the reach and expertise to assist clients in finding talent with the right skill-sets, experiences, cultural compatibility, business astuteness, and leadership savvy.

REFERENCE WORKS

14750 ■ *INSIGHT Into Diversity*
INSIGHT Into Diversity
c/o Potomac Publishing, Inc.
225 Meramec Ave., Ste. 400
St. Louis, MO 63105
Ph: (314)863-2900
Fax: (314)863-2905
Fr: 800-537-0655
URL: http://www.aarjobs.com

Monthly. $15.00 for individuals; $8.00 for individuals. Covers: In each issue, about 300 positions at a professional level (most requiring advanced study) available to women, minorities, veterans, and the handicapped; listings are advertisements placed by employers with affirmative action programs. Entries include: Company or organization name, address, contact name; description of position including title, requirements, duties, application procedure, salary, etc. Arrangement: Classified by profession.

14751 ■ *Job Search Handbook for People with Disabilities, Third Edition*
JIST Publishing
875 Montreal Way
St. Paul, MN 55102
Fax: 800-547-8329
Fr: 800-648-5478
E-mail: info@jist.com
URL: http://www.jist.com/shop/
   product.php?productid=2436&cat=3426&page=1

Daniel J. Ryan, PhD. 2011. $22.95. 274 pages. Career planning guide identifies strengths, gives job search tips, and provides options for career exploration from the perspective of people who have physical or mental disabilities.

NEWSPAPERS, MAGAZINES, AND JOURNALS

14752 ■ *ADARA Update*
ADARA
PO Box 480
Myersville, MD 21773
E-mail: adaraorg@comcast.net
URL: http://www.adara.org

Description: Quarterly. Surveys news events, resources, legislation, and developments in services related to the deaf. Recurring features include notices of employment opportunities, news of the national Association and its local chapters, information on new publications, announcements of awards granted, and a calendar of events.

14753 ■ *Careers & the Disabled*
Employment Opportunity Publications
445 Broad Hollow Rd., Ste. 425
Melville, NY 11747

Ph: (631)421-9421
Fax: (631)421-1352
E-mail: info@eop.com
URL: http://www.eop.com

$11.00/year; $20.00/2 years; $30.00/3 years. Career-guidance and recruitment magazine for people with disabilities who are at undergraduate, graduate, or professional levels.

14754 ■ *Careers & the disABLED Magazine*
Equal Opportunity Publications, Inc.
445 Broadhollow Rd., Ste. 425
Melville, NY 11747
Ph: (631)421-9421
Fax: (631)421-1352
E-mail: info@eop.com
URL: http://eop.com

Three times a year. $13/year. Serves as a career-guidance and recruitment magazine for people with disabilities who are at undergraduate, graduate, or professional levels.

14755 ■ *Opportunity*
National Industries for the Blind
1310 Braddock Pl.
Alexandria, VA 22314-1691
Ph: (703)310-0500
Fr: 800-433-2304
E-mail: communications@nib.org
URL: http://www.nib.org

Description: Quarterly. Publishes news and feature articles on agencies for individuals who are blind, and describes industries, agencies, and projects that employ blind workers. Recurring features include legislative updates, conference news, and news of programs and events of various associations employing blind individuals.

14756 ■ *Paraplegia News*
PVA Publications
2111 E Highland Ave., Ste. 180
Phoenix, AZ 85016-4702
Ph: (602)224-0500
Fax: (602)224-0507
Fr: 888-888-2201
E-mail: info@pnnews.com
URL: http://pvamag.com/pn

Description: Monthly. Presents articles and briefs on wheelchair living, education, employment, housing, transportation, travel, spinal cord injury, research, legislation, new products, and sports and recreation for the wheelchair user.

14757 ■ *Vendorscope*
Randolph-Sheppard Vendors of America
940 Parc Helene Dr.
Marrero, LA 70072-2421
Ph: (504)328-6373
Fax: (504)328-6372
Fr: 800-467-5299
E-mail: rsva@comcast.net
URL: http://www.randolph-sheppard.org

Description: Quarterly. Reports on issues pertinent to the Business Enterprise Program for Blind Vendors. Recurring features include letters to the editor, interviews, news of research, a calendar of events, reports of meetings, news of educational opportunities, job listings, book reviews, notices of publications available, news of conventions and legislative action, and a column titled Mini-Mumbles from "Mean Dean."

ONLINE AND DATABASE SERVICES

14758 ■ ABILITYJobs.com
URL: http://www.abilityjobs.com

Description: Provides employment opportunities to people with disabilities. Offers employment resources and job finding services which include resume posting and searchable job listings.

14759 ■ AccessibleEmployment.org
E-mail: service@accessibleemployment.org
URL: http://accessibleemployment.org

Description: Provides assistance to qualified people with disabilities to obtain employment.

14760 ■ DisabilityCrossing.com
URL: http://www.disabilitycrossing.com

Description: Provides employment opportunities for disabled professionals.

14761 ■ Disability.gov
URL: http://www.disability.gov

Description: Features disability-related information and resources. Seeks to connect the disability community to information and opportunities. Provides tips for disabled individuals who wish to find employment in any field.

14762 ■ disABLEDperson
E-mail: info@disabledperson.com
URL: http://www.disabledperson.com

Description: Serves as a job site for individual with disabilities. Offers resume posting and job listings posted by employers around the country.

14763 ■ DisaboomJobs.com
URL: http://www.disaboomjobs.com

Description: Provides an online resource of jobs and career opportunities for people with disabilities.

14764 ■ Gettinghired.com
URL: http://gettinghired.com

Description: Offers employment opportunities for people with disabilities. Provides services to help disabled professionals prepare for the workplace and build their careers.

OTHER SOURCES

14765 ■ Abilities!
201 I.U. Willets Rd.
Albertson, NY 11507-1599

Ph: (516)465-1400
Fax: (516)465-1591
E-mail: info@abilitiesonline.org
URL: http://www.ncds.org

Description: Serves as a center providing educational, vocational, rehabilitation, and research opportunities for persons with disabilities. Work is conducted through the following: Abilities Health and Rehabilitation Services, a New York state-licensed diagnostic and treatment center which offers comprehensive outpatient programs in physical therapy, occupational therapy, speech therapy, and psychological services; Career and Employment Institute, which evaluates, trains, and counsels more than 600 adults with disabilities each year, with the goal of productive competitive employment; Henry Viscardi School, which conducts early childhood, elementary, and secondary programs, as well as adult and continuing education programs; Research and Training Institute, which conducts research on the education, employment, and career development of persons with disabilities, and holds seminars and workshops for rehabilitation services professionals. Maintains library and speakers' bureau; compiles statistics; offers placement service; conducts research and educational programs.

14766 ■ Career Opportunities for Students with Disabilities
100 Dunford Hall
Knoxville, TN 37996-4010
Ph: (865)974-7148
Fax: (865)974-6497
E-mail: info@cosdonline.org
URL: http://www.cosdonline.org

Description: Aims to improve the employment rate of college students and recent graduates with disabilities on a national basis. Works closely with employers to identify innovative methods of recruiting and hiring college graduates with disabilities, including creation of internship opportunities or encouraging participation of employers in specialized internship and recruiting programs that focus on college students with disabilities.

14767 ■ Goodwill Industries International (GII)
15810 Indianola Dr.
Rockville, MD 20855
Ph: (301)530-6500
Fr: 800-741-0186
E-mail: contactus@goodwill.org
URL: http://www.goodwill.org

Description: Federation of Goodwill Industries organizations across North America and the world concerned primarily with providing employment, training, evaluation, counseling, placement, job training, and other vocational rehabilitation services and opportunities for individual growth for people with disabilities and other special needs. Collects donated goods and sell them in Goodwill retail stores as a means of providing employment and generating income. Conducts seminars and training programs; compiles statistics.

14768 ■ Helen Keller National Center for Deaf-Blind Youths and Adults (HKNC)
141 Middle Neck Rd.
Sands Point, NY 11050-1218
Ph: (516)944-8900
Fax: (516)944-7302
E-mail: hkncinfo@hknc.org
URL: http://www.hknc.org

Description: Provides diagnostic evaluations, comprehensive vocational and personal adjustment training, job preparation and placement for adults who

are deaf-blind from every state and territory. Includes field services such as: information, referral, advocacy, and technical assistance to professionals, consumers, and families. Sponsors annual National Helen Keller Deaf-Blind Awareness Week.

14769 ■ Inspiration Ministries (IM)
N2270 State Rd. 67
Walworth, WI 53184
Ph: (262)275-6131
Fax: (262)275-3355
E-mail: info@inspirationministries.org
URL: http://www.inspirationministries.org

Description: Seeks to provide fully accessible, permanent residence with attendant care in room and board facility for physically disabled adults. Conducts summer camping program for disabled persons and retreat opportunities for groups.

14770 ■ Job Accommodation Network (JAN)
PO Box 6080
Morgantown, WV 26506-6080
Ph: (304)293-7186
Fax: (304)293-5407
Fr: 800-526-7234
E-mail: jan@askjan.org
URL: http://askjan.org

Description: A service of U.S. Department of Labor's Office of Disability Employment Policy. **Purpose:** An international toll-free consulting service that provides information about job accommodation and the employability of people with disabilities. Calls are answered by consultants who understand the limitations associated with disabilities and who have instant access to the most comprehensive and up-to-date information about accommodation methods, devices, and strategies.

14771 ■ Just One Break (JOB)
570 Seventh Ave.
New York, NY 10018
Ph: (212)785-7300
Fax: (212)785-4513
URL: http://www.justonebreak.com

Description: Serves as an employment service for people with disabilities, to help them find jobs and lead to productive lives. Finds competitive employment for qualified JOB applicants. Concentrates efforts in New York, and is working to include New Jersey and Connecticut, but advises companies nationwide. Offers placement services, employment counseling, skills evaluation, college recruitment, resume writing assistance service referrals, and computer access. Provides JOB's Student Internship Program (SIP), a hands-on work experience for college students with disabilities and works in collaboration with college disability and career service offices. Provides on-site disability awareness training to support initiatives related to interviewing, hiring, and retaining employees with disabilities.

14772 ■ Lift
PO Box 4264
Warren, NJ 07059
Ph: (908)226-1193
Fax: (908)226-1480
E-mail: inquiry@lift-inc.org
URL: http://www.lift-inc.org

Description: Works as an information resource for management and computer technology professionals who have disabilities. Offers skills development programs tailored for corporate systems, documentation standards, and working environment.

14773 ■ National Association of the Deaf (NAD)
8630 Fenton St., Ste. 820
Silver Spring, MD 20910-3819
Ph: (301)587-1788
Fax: (301)587-1791
URL: http://www.nad.org

Description: Safeguards accessibility and civil rights of America's deaf population in areas of education, employment, healthcare, and telecommunications.

14774 ■ National Business and Disability Council (NBDC)
201 I.U. Willets Rd.
Albertson, NY 11507
Ph: (516)465-1516
E-mail: jtowles@abilitiesonline.org
URL: http://www.business-disability.com

Description: Acts as a resource for employers seeking to integrate people with disabilities into the workplace and companies seeking to reach them in the consumer market.

14775 ■ NTID's Center on Employment (NCE)
Rochester Institute of Technology
Lyndon Baines Johnson Bldg.
52 Lomb Memorial Dr.
Rochester, NY 14623-5604
Ph: (585)475-6219
Fax: (585)475-7570
E-mail: ntidcoe@rit.edu
URL: http://www.ntid.rit.edu/nce

Description: Operated by the National Technical Institute for the Deaf. Promotes successful employment of Rochester Institute of Technology's deaf students and graduates. Offers resources and training for employers.

14776 ■ Special Interest Group on Accessible Computing (SIGACCESS)
2 Penn Plz., Ste. 701
New York, NY 10121-0701
Ph: (212)626-0500
Fax: (212)944-1318
Fr: 800-342-6626
E-mail: chair_sigaccess@acm.org
URL: http://www.sigaccess.org

Description: Promotes the professional interests of computing personnel with physical disabilities and the application of computing and information technology in solving relevant disability problems. Works to educate the public to support careers for the disabled.

14777 ■ Working for America Institute (WAI)
AFL-CIO
815 16th St. NW
Washington, DC 20006
Ph: (202)508-3717
Fax: (202)508-3719
E-mail: info@workingforamerica.org
URL: http://www.workingforamerica.org

Description: Serves as the employment and training arm of the AFL-CIO. Works to assure full labor participation in employment and training programs funded under the Job Training Partnership Act. Assists in developing JTPA programs for dislocated and economically disadvantaged workers; provides technical services in support of labor-operated programs. Offers job search and placement services for disabled persons and early intervention and return-to-work services for recently disabled union members. Sponsors demonstration program to develop effective ways of improving workers' skills through structured workplace training; also offers workplace literacy study. Works with affected labor groups to help workers displaced by plant closings. Provides education and training to labor members of JTPA planning councils, labor leaders, and employment and training professionals.

Opportunities for Ex-Offenders

REFERENCE WORKS

14778 ■ Best Jobs for Ex-Offenders: 101 Opportunities to Jump-Start Your New Life
Impact Publications
9104 Manassas Dr., Ste. N
Manassas Park, VA 20111-5211
Ph: (703)361-7300
Fax: (703)335-9486
E-mail: query@impactpublications.com
URL: http://www.impactpublications.com

Ron Krannich. 2008. $9.95. 128 pages. Covers profiles of 101 opportunities that includes job outlook, nature of work, qualifications, earnings, and contacts that are open to ex-offenders. Emphasizes jobs in the construction trades, with nonprofit organizations, in the manufacturing transportation, and service industries.

14779 ■ I Need a Job!: The Ex-Offender's Job Search Manual
ConquestHouse, Inc.
Po Box 611
Bladensburg, MD 20710
Ph: (240)342-3293
Fax: (202)478-1739
E-mail: info@conquestpublishers.com
URL: http://www.conquestpublishers.com/job.html

Louis Jones. May 2005. $15.00. 88 pages.

14780 ■ Prisoners' Assistance Directory
National Prison Project
125 Broad St., 18th Fl.
New York, NY 10004
Ph: (212)549-2500
URL: http://www.aclu.org

Irregular, Latest edition 2008. $35.00 for individuals. Covers: Organizations in the U.S. offering assistance to prisoners and their families, including legal, ex-offender, and family support services. Entries include: Organization name, address, phone, fax, URL, name and title of contact, geographical area served, subsidiary and branch names and locations, description of services. Arrangement: Geographical by state. Indexes: Geographical.

14781 ■ Quick Job Search for Ex-Offenders
JIST Publishing
875 Montreal Way
St. Paul, MN 55102
Fr: 800-648-5478
E-mail: info@jist.com
URL: http://www.jist.com

Michael Farr and Maurice Stevens. 2008. $46.95. 80 pages. Discusses the techniques that ex-offenders can use to search for a job. Includes appendices that job seekers can use to fill out applications or create a resume. Gives ex-offenders tips on how to keep the job they get and impress their supervisor.

AUDIO/VISUAL RESOURCES

14782 ■ Ex-offender's Guide to Job Fair Success
JIST Publishing
875 Montreal Way
St. Paul, MN 55102
Fr: 800-648-5478
E-mail: educate@emcp.com
URL: http://www.jist.com

2007. $129. 23 minutes. Covers career opportunities and other options for ex-offenders. Includes topics on preparing for the job fair, presenting to the employer, questions to be answered, networking advice, and advice from employers.

14783 ■ Expert Job Search Strategies for the Ex-offender: Career Plans and Goals
JIST Publishing
875 Montreal Way
St. Paul, MN 55102
Fr: 800-648-5478
E-mail: educate@emcp.com
URL: http://www.jist.com

2007. $149.00. 15 minutes. Helps ex-offenders learn how to get the most out of their career by examining what they like to do and what matters in their life. Offers encouragement and strategies for finding a career.

14784 ■ Expert Job Search Strategies for the Ex-offender: Interview Techniques
JIST Publishing
875 Montreal Way
St. Paul, MN 55102
Fr: 800-648-5478
E-mail: educate@emcp.com
URL: http://www.jist.com

2007. $149.00. 15 minutes. Offers advice on the different techniques that ex-offenders can use during a job interview. Helps ex-offenders learn what to wear, how to prepare before the interview, and how to handle themselves during the interview.

14785 ■ Expert Job Search Strategies for the Ex-offender: Resume Realities
JIST Publishing
875 Montreal Way
St. Paul, MN 55102
Fr: 800-648-5478
E-mail: educate@emcp.com
URL: http://www.jist.com

2007. $149.00. 15 minutes. Offers tips on what to include and what not to include when creating resume.

14786 ■ Finding a Job
Cambridge Educational
PO Box 2053
Princeton, NJ 08543-2053
Ph: 800-257-5126
Fax: (609)671-0266
Fr: 800-468-4227
E-mail: custserv@films.com
URL: http://cambridge.films.com

VHS and DVD. 2008. $89.95. 13 minutes. Covers conventional and unconventional job search methods, and which are more likely to work for ex-offenders.

14787 ■ From Parole to Payroll
Cambridge Educational
PO Box 2053
Princeton, NJ 08543-2053
Ph: 800-257-5126
Fax: (609)671-0266
Fr: 800-468-4227
E-mail: custserv@films.com
URL: http://cambridge.films.com

VHS and DVD. 2008. $311.80. Contains solid, real-world content designed to help job seekers find satisfying work, and features informative interviews, helpful tips, and colorful graphics.

14788 ■ Resumes and Job Applications
Cambridge Educational
PO Box 2053
Princeton, NJ 08543-2053
Ph: 800-257-5126
Fax: (609)671-0266
Fr: 800-468-4227
E-mail: custserv@films.com
URL: http://cambridge.films.com

$99.95. 2008. 20 minutes. Part of the "From Parole to Payroll" Series.

OTHER SOURCES

14789 ■ Court Services and Offender Supervision Agency
633 Indiana Ave., NW
Washington, DC 20004-2902
Ph: (202)220-5300
Fax: (202)220-5350
URL: http://www.csosa.gov

Description: Provides services for individuals on parole and probation.

14790 ■ Delancey Street Foundation
600 Embarcadero
San Francisco, CA 94107
Ph: (415)957-9800
Fax: (415)512-5141
URL: http://www.delanceystreetfoundation.org

Description: Provides a structured educational and living environment for ex-felons. Teaches life skills.

14791 ■ Fortune Society (FS)
29-76 Northern Blvd.
Long Island City, NY 11101
Ph: (212)691-7554

Fax: (347)510-3451
E-mail: info@fortunesociety.org
URL: http://www.fortunesociety.org

Description: Ex-offenders and others interested in penal reform. Addresses the needs of ex-offenders and high-risk youth. Promotes greater public awareness of the prison system and of the problems confronting inmates before, after, and during incarceration. Works on a personal basis with men and women recently released from prison; helps ex-offenders find jobs. Offers educational services including literacy training and G.E.D. preparation. Sends teams of ex-offenders to talk to school, church, and civic groups and on radio and television to relate first-hand experiences of prison life and to create a greater understanding of the causes of crime in the United States. Conducts Alternatives to Incarceration programs; offers AIDS and general counseling services. Acts as referral agency for half-way houses and drug and alcohol addiction programs.

14792 ■ Osborne Association
809 Westchester Ave.
Bronx, NY 10455
Ph: (718)707-2600

Fax: (718)707-3102
E-mail: info@osborneny.org
URL: http://www.osborneny.org

Description: Provides assessment, testing, career and educational counseling for ex-offenders.

14793 ■ Sentencing Project
1705 DeSales St., NW 8th Fl.
Washington, DC 20036
Ph: (202)628-0871
Fax: (202)628-1091
E-mail: staff@sentencingproject.org
URL: http://www.sentencingproject.org

Description: Provides various resources related to incarceration and the justice system.

14794 ■ Wildcat Service Corporation (WSC)
2 Washington St., 3rd Fl.
New York, NY 10004
Ph: (212)209-6000
E-mail: webresponses@wildcatnyc.org
URL: http://www.wildcatnyc.org

Description: Provides transitional employment and training for chronically unemployed persons (former

substance abusers, ex-offenders, welfare mothers, out-of-school youth, and illiterate and delinquent youth). Systematically prepares and grooms employees to accept the full responsibility of full-time work within a 12-month time period. Placement rate of terminees is about 70% in a variety of industries. Operates clerical school in basic and advanced office practices; conducts specialized "life skills" educational program. Compiles statistics; maintains placement service. Operates three high schools.

14795 ■ Women's Prison Association (WPA)
110 2nd Ave.
New York, NY 10003
Ph: (646)336-6100
Fax: (646)292-7763
E-mail: glerner@wpaonline.org
URL: http://www.wpaonline.org

Description: Purpose: Service agency that aids women involved in the criminal justice system and their families. Promotes alternatives to incarceration; sponsors transitional programs for women being released from prison; assists homeless ex-offenders seeking to reunite with their children who are in kinship or foster-care.

Opportunities for Gay and Lesbian Workers

NEWSPAPERS, MAGAZINES, AND JOURNALS

14796 ■ *The Advocate*
Here Media, Inc.
10990 Wilshire Blvd.
Penthouse
Los Angeles, CA 90024
Ph: (310)806-4288
Fax: (310)806-4268
E-mail: newsroom@advocate.com
URL: http://www.advocate.com

Biweekly. $19.95/year for individuals; $35.00/year for two years. National gay and lesbian news and lifestyle magazine.

14797 ■ *Echelon Magazine*
Echelon Business Media Inc.
6404 Wilshire Blvd., Ste. 1829
Los Angeles, CA 90048
Ph: (323)230-5548
E-mail: info@echelonmagazine.com
URL: http://www.echelonmagazine.com

Bimonthly. Publishes articles on GLBT finance, economic development, workplace advocacy, corporate diversity, education and employment.

ONLINE AND DATABASE SERVICES

14798 ■ Chicago Area Gay and Lesbian Chamber of Commerce
3179 N Clark St.
Chicago, IL 60657
Ph: (773)303-0167
E-mail: info@glchamber.org
URL: http://www.glchamber.org

Description: Site offering business, consumer and travel information to gays and lesbians in the Chicago area. Also includes classified ads for jobhunting members.

14799 ■ ProGayJobs.com
URL: http://www.progayjobs.com

Description: Serves as an online source for finding employment with companies that embrace diversity inclusive of the gay and lesbian community. Includes sections for job seekers, employers, consulting, and a directory for consumers.

14800 ■ Queer Net Online Policy Group
E-mail: info@queernet.org
URL: http://www.queernet.org

General e-mail news and discussion list dealing with gay, lesbian, bisexual, and transgender issues within the workplace.

OTHER SOURCES

14801 ■ Association for Lesbian, Gay, Bisexual and Transgender Issues in Counseling (ALGBTIC)
Oakland University
440B Pawley Hall
Rochester, MI 48309
Ph: (508)531-2721
E-mail: chaney@oakland.edu
URL: http://www.algbtic.org

Description: Counselors, personnel and guidance workers concerned with lesbian and gay issues. Seeks to eliminate discrimination against and stereotyping of gay and lesbian individuals, particularly gay counselors. Works to educate heterosexual counselors on how to overcome homophobia and to best help homosexual clients. Provides a referral network and support for gay counselors and administrators; encourages objective research on gay issues. Organizational affiliate of the American Counseling Association.

14802 ■ Gay and Lesbian Medical Association (GLMA)
1326 18th St. NW, Ste. 22
Washington, DC 20036
Ph: (202)600-8037
Fax: (202)478-1500
E-mail: info@glma.org
URL: http://www.glma.org

Description: Healthcare professionals. Seeks elimination of discrimination on the basis of gender identity and sexual orientation in the health profession; promotes unprejudiced medical care for LGBT patients through advocacy and education. Maintains a referral and support program for HIV infected health care workers. Sponsors annual continuing medical education (CME, CEU) symposium on LGBT issues. Offers support to lesbian, gay, bisexual, and transgendered health care workers; encourages research into the health needs of gays and lesbians. Maintains liaison with medical schools and other organizations concerning needs of gay patients and professionals; fosters communication and cooperation among members and other groups and individuals supportive of gay and lesbian physicians. Sponsors Lesbian Health Fund for researching lesbian health needs.

14803 ■ Gay Recruiter Network
2295N San Antonio Rd.
Palm Springs, CA 92262
Ph: (760)778-8323
Fax: (760)323-2912
E-mail: careers@gayrecruiternetwork.com
URL: http://www.gayrecruiternetwork.com

Description: Offers career management and networking opportunities. Focuses on assisting GLBT senior executives and mid-level professionals in the private and military sectors to achieve their career goals.

14804 ■ LEAGUE
208 S Akard, Ste. 810.08
Dallas, TX 75202
E-mail: league@att.com
URL: http://www.league-att.org

Description: Provides supportive environment for lesbian, gay, bisexual and transgendered employees and allies to network with one another. Promotes accepting, diverse and respectful work environment. Strengthens AT&T's presence in the lesbian, gay, bisexual and transgendered community as well as in the global community.

14805 ■ Lesbian Resource Center (LRC)
2214 S Jackson St.
Seattle, WA 98144
Ph: (206)322-3953
Fax: (206)322-0586
E-mail: lrc@lrc.net
URL: http://www.lrc.net

Description: Provides classes, groups, workshops, and information on housing, employment, and lesbian community groups and events. Represents the lesbian community in areas of political and social concern.

14806 ■ National Association of Social Workers National Committee on Lesbian, Gay and Bisexual Issues
750 First St. NE, Ste. 700
Washington, DC 20002-4241
Ph: (202)408-8600
Fr: 800-742-4089
E-mail: membership@naswdc.org
URL: http://www.socialworkers.org/governance/cmtes/nclgbi.asp

Description: A committee of the National Association of Social Workers. Seeks to ensure equal employment opportunities for lesbian, gay and bisexual individuals. Informs the NASW about: domestic, racial, and antigay violence; civil rights; family and primary associations. Encourages the NASW to support legislation, regulations, policies, judicial review, political action, and other activities that seek to establish and protect equal rights for all persons without regard to affectional and/or sexual orientation. Advises government bodies and political candidates regarding the needs and concerns of social workers and lesbian and gay people; reviews proposed legislation.

14807 ■ National Center for Lesbian Rights (NCLR)
870 Market St., Ste. 370
San Francisco, CA 94102
Ph: (415)392-6257
Fax: (415)392-8442
E-mail: info@nclrights.org
URL: http://www.nclrights.org

Description: A legal resource center specializing in sexual orientation discrimination cases, particularly those involving lesbians. Activities include: legal counseling and representation, community education, and technical assistance. Provides legal services to lesbian, gay and transgender youths, adults and elders on issues of custody and foster parenting, visitation rights second parent adoption.

14808 ■ National Gay and Lesbian Task Force (NGLTF)
1325 Massachusetts Ave. NW, Ste. 600
Washington, DC 20005
Ph: (202)393-5177
Fax: (202)393-2241
E-mail: info@thetaskforce.org
URL: http://thetaskforce.org

Description: Works to end violence and discrimination against gay, lesbian, bisexual, and transgendered people at the state, local, and federal level. Does grassroots organizing, training, and legislative advocacy. Monitors and tracks legislation in 50 states. Houses GLBT think tank producing research and analysis on GLBT issues. Maintains speakers' bureau.

14809 ■ National Organization of Gay and Lesbian Scientists and Technical Professionals (NOGLSTP)
PO Box 91803
Pasadena, CA 91109

Ph: (626)791-7689
Fax: (626)791-7689
E-mail: office@noglstp.org
URL: http://www.noglstp.org

Description: Gay and lesbian individuals employed or interested in high-technology or scientific fields; interested organizations. Works to: educate the public, especially the gay and scientific communities; improve members' employment and professional environment; provide role models through mentoring and recognition awards; interact with professional organizations; foster intercity contacts among members.

REFERENCE WORKS

14810 ■ *Photos That Sell: The Art of Successful Freelance Photography*
Watson-Guptill Publications
1745 Broadway
New York, NY 10019
Ph: (212)782-9000
Fax: (212)940-7868
Fr: 800-733-3000
E-mail: info@watsonguptill.com
URL: http://www.randomhouse.com/crown/watsonguptill
Lee Frost. 2004. $27.95 (paper). 192 pages.

14811 ■ *Self-Publishing Manual*
Para Publishing
530 Ellwood Ridge Rd.
Santa Barbara, CA 93117-1047
Ph: (805)968-7277
Fax: (805)968-1379
Fr: 800-727-2782
URL: http://www.parapublishing.com

Biennial, odd years. $19.95 for individuals. Publication includes: Lists of wholesalers, reviewers, exporters, suppliers, direct mailing list sources, publishing organizations, and others of assistance in publishing. Entries include: Organization or company name, address, email addresses and web address. Arrangement: Classified by ZIP code. Indexes: General subject.

ONLINE AND DATABASE SERVICES

14812 ■ FreelanceJobs.org
URL: http://www.freelancejobs.org

Description: Serves as an online marketplace for freelance professionals and employers.

14813 ■ Guru.com
5001 Baum Blvd., Ste. 760
Pittsburgh, PA 15213
Fax: (412)687-4466
Fr: 888-687-1316
URL: http://www.guru.com

Description: Job board specializing in contract jobs for creative and information technology professionals. Also provides online incorporation and educational opportunities for independent contractors along with articles and advice.

14814 ■ Work from Home
URL: http://www.jobs-telecommuting.com

Description: Contains a listing of over 700 companies currently looking for telecommuters. Employers may add or remove job listings. Also information on starting a home business available.

OTHER SOURCES

14815 ■ American Society of Journalists and Authors (ASJA)
1501 Broadway, Ste. 302
New York, NY 10036
Ph: (212)997-0947
Fax: (212)937-2315
E-mail: director@asja.org
URL: http://www.asja.org

Description: Represents freelance writers of nonfiction magazine articles and books. Seeks to elevate the professional and economic position of nonfiction writers, provide a forum for discussion of common problems among writers and editors, and promote a code of ethics for writers and editors. Operates writer referral service for individuals, institutions, or companies seeking writers for special projects; sponsors Llewellyn Miller Fund to aid professional writers who no longer able to work due to age, disability, or extraordinary professional crisis.

14816 ■ Association of Food Journalists (AFJ)
7 Avenida Vista Grande, Ste. B7, No. 467
Santa Fe, NM 87508-9199
Ph: (505)466-4742
E-mail: caroldemasters@yahoo.com
URL: http://www.afjonline.com

Description: Represents individuals employed as food journalists by newspapers, magazines, internet services, and broadcasters; freelance food journalists. Aims to encourage communication and professional development among food journalists and to increase members' knowledge of food and food-related issues. Promotes professional ethical standards.

14817 ■ Dance Critics Association (DCA)
PO Box 1882
Old Chelsea Sta.
New York, NY 10011
E-mail: dancecritics@hotmail.com
URL: http://www.dancecritics.org

Description: Critics who review dance as a major professional responsibility either on a regular basis or as a freelance reviewer, in print and/or broadcast media; teachers, historians, publicists, and other individuals interested in dance writing. Encourages excellence in dance criticism through education, research, and the exchange of ideas. Conducts clinics on practical topics of interest to critics.

14818 ■ National Court Reporters Association (NCRA)
8224 Old Courthouse Rd.
Vienna, VA 22182-3808
Ph: (703)556-6272
Fax: (703)556-6291
Fr: 800-272-6272
E-mail: melanie@sonntagreporting.com
URL: http://www.ncraonline.com

Description: Represents Independent state, regional, and local associations. Verbatim court reporters who work as official reporters for courts and government agencies, as freelance reporters for independent contractors, and as captioners for television programming; retired reporters, teachers of court reporting, and school officials; student court reporters. Conducts research; compiles statistics; offers several certification programs; and publishes journal.

14819 ■ National Writers Union (NWU)
256 W 38th St., Ste. 703
New York, NY 10018
Ph: (212)254-0279
Fax: (212)254-0673
E-mail: nwu@nwu.org
URL: http://www.nwu.org

Description: Freelance writers; journalists, authors, poets, and technical and public relations writers who are not represented by any existing union. Engages in collective bargaining and provides other services for members such as grievance handling and health insurance. Works to raise rates and improve treatment of freelance writers by magazine and book publishers. Holds conferences on legal, economic, trade, and craft issues affecting writers.

REFERENCE WORKS

14820 ■ *The Career Guide—Dun's Employment Opportunities Directory*
Dun & Bradstreet Corp.
103 JFK Pky.
Short Hills, NJ 07078
Ph: (973)921-5500
Fr: 800-234-3867
URL: http://dnb.com/us

Annual. Covers: More than 10,000 companies on leading employers throughout the U.S. that provide career opportunities in sales, marketing, management, engineering, life and physical sciences, computer science, mathematics, statistics planning, accounting and finance, liberal arts fields, and other technical and professional areas; based on data supplied on questionnaires and through personal interviews. Also covers personnel consultants; includes some public sector employers (governments, schools, etc.) usually not found in similar lists. Entries include: Company name, location of headquarters and other offices or plants; entries may also include name, title, address, and phone of employment contact; disciplines or occupational groups hired; brief overview of company, discussion of types of positions that may be available, training and career development programs, benefits offered, internship and work-study programs. Arrangement: Employers are alphabetical; geographically by industry, employer branch offices geographically, disciplines hired geographically, employees offering work-study or internship programs and personnel consultants. Indexes: Geographical, SIC code.

14821 ■ *College Grad Job Hunter: Insider Techniques and Tactics for Finding a Top-Paying Entry Level Job*
Adams Media Corp.
57 Littlefield St.
Avon, MA 02322
Ph: (508)427-7100
Fax: (508)427-6790
Fr: 800-872-5627
URL: http://www.adamsmediastore.com/product/the-college-grad-job-hunter-6th-edition

Brian D. Krueger. Sixth edition. $11.96 (paper). 352 pages.

14822 ■ *Great Jobs for English Majors*
The McGraw-Hill Companies
PO Box 182604
Columbus, OH 43272
Fax: (614)759-3749
Fr: 877-883-5524
E-mail: customer.service@mcgraw-hill.com
URL: http://www.mhprofessional.com

Julie DeGalan and Stephen Lambert. Third edition, 2006. $15.95 (paper). 192 pages.

14823 ■ *Great Jobs for Foreign Language Majors*
The McGraw-Hill Companies
PO Box 182604
Columbus, OH 43272
Fax: (614)759-3749
Fr: 877-883-5524
E-mail: customer.service@mcgraw-hill.com
URL: http://www.mhprofessional.com/product.php?isbn=0071476148

Julie DeGalan and Stephen Lambert. Third edition, 2007. $15.95 (paper). 192 pages. Part of "Great Jobs for...Majors" series.

14824 ■ *Great Jobs for History Majors*
The McGraw-Hill Companies
PO Box 182604
Columbus, OH 43272
Fax: (614)759-3749
Fr: 877-883-5524
E-mail: customer.service@mcgraw-hill.com
URL: http://www.mhprofessional.com

Julie DeGalan and Stephen Lambert. 2007. $16.95 (paper). 192 pages.

14825 ■ *Great Jobs for Liberal Arts Majors*
The McGraw-Hill Companies
PO Box 182604
Columbus, OH 43272
Fax: (614)759-3749
Fr: 877-883-5524
E-mail: customer.service@mcgraw-hill.com
URL: http://www.mhprofessional.com/product.php?isbn=0071482148

Blythe Camenson. Second edition, 2007. $16.95 (paper). 192 pages.

NEWSPAPERS, MAGAZINES, AND JOURNALS

14826 ■ *Current Jobs in Liberal Arts*
Foster Opportunities, Inc.
1834 Olmstead Dr.
Falls Church, VA 22043
Ph: (703)506-4400
Fr: 888-870-3069
E-mail: admin@graduatejobs.com
URL: http://www.graduatejobs.com/libarts.htm

Bimonthly. $84/year. Lists entry-level or early career job vacancies in a broad range of liberal arts fields.

14827 ■ *Liberal Arts Career News*
Foster Opportunities, Inc.
1834 Olmstead Dr.
Falls Church, VA 22043-1001
Ph: (703)506-4400
Fax: 888-870-3069
E-mail: admin@graduatejobs.com
URL: http://www.graduatejobs.com/lacn.htm

Bimonthly. $39.50/year. Provides tips and practical career information for people in all liberal arts disciplines.

ONLINE AND DATABASE SERVICES

14828 ■ *Arts & Humanities Jobs*
URL: http://artsandhumanitiesjobs.com

Description: Serves as an online source of liberal arts jobs, including hard-to-find entry-level and early-career-level employment.

14829 ■ *Current Jobs for Graduates*
E-mail: admin@graduatejobs.com
URL: http://www.graduatejobs.com

Description: Provides job vacancy bulletin for liberal arts graduates.

14830 ■ *True Careers: Campus*
URL: http://www.truecareerscampus.com

Description: Recent college graduates can post their resume and search for jobs. Also contains interviewing tips and career resources, and career expert advice posting.

Opportunities for Military Personnel and Veterans

REFERENCE WORKS

14831 ■ *150 Best Jobs Through Military Training*
JIST Publishing
875 Montreal Way
St. Paul, MN 55102
Fr: 800-648-5478
E-mail: educate@emcp.com
URL: http://www.jist.com

Laurence Shatkin. 2008. $19.95 (softcover). 432 pages. Focuses on the military jobs bridging to civilian careers. Covers military occupations and its civilian counterparts with detailed job descriptions. Contains lists that are organized by pay, growth, openings, part-time work, self-employment, gender, interest, and personality type. Includes lists of occupations held by veterans and the fields in which veterans work.

14832 ■ *Best Career For Veterans*
LearningExpress, LLC
2 Rector St., 26th Fl.
New York, NY 10006
Fr: 800-295-9556
E-mail: customerservice@learningexpressllc.com
URL: http://www.learningexpressllc.com

LearningExpress Editors. 2009. $14.95 (paper). 210 pages. Offers a career guide for military personnel who want to leverage their experience and skills into a rewarding, high-paying civilian job post-service.

14833 ■ *Career Opportunities in the Armed Forces*
Facts On File Inc.
132 W 31st St., 17th Fl.
New York, NY 10001
Ph: (212)967-8800
Fax: 800-678-3633
Fr: 800-322-8755
URL: http://factsonfile.infobasepublishing.com

Latest edition 2nd, 2007. $49.50 for individuals. Covers: 70 jobs from all branches of the service with emphasis not only on the career opportunities available in the military, but how military experience can be applied to a career in the civilian world; among the jobs profiled are communications manager, special operations officer, aerospace engineer, physicist, physician/surgeon, social worker, firefighter, and air traffic controller.

14834 ■ *Career Progression Guide for Soldiers*
Stackpole Books
5067 Ritter Rd.
Mechanicsburg, PA 17055
Ph: (717)796-0411
Fax: (717)796-0412
Fr: 800-732-3669
URL: http://www.stackpolebooks.com

Audie G. Lewis. Third edition. $14.95 (paper). 160 pages.

14835 ■ *Careers after the Armed Forces: How to Decide on the Right Career and Make a Successful Transition*
Kogan Page Publishers
1518 Walnut St., Ste. 1100
Philadelphia, PA 19102
Ph: (215)928-9112
Fax: (215)928-9113
E-mail: info@koganpage.com
URL: http://www.koganpageusa.com

Jon Mitchell. 2009. $17.95 (paper). 160 pages. Offers career options for men and women who leave the U.S. military for other work. Features exercises, tools, case studies, and tips designed to ease the transition from active duty to the civilian workforce. Includes advice on resume preparation, interview techniques, working with job recruiters, and evaluating job offers.

14836 ■ *Careers in Focus: Armed Forces*
Ferguson Publishing
132 W 31st St., 17th Fl.
New York, NY 10001
Fax: 800-678-3633
Fr: 800-322-8755
E-mail: custserv@factsonfile.com
URL: http://ferguson.infobasepublishing.com

2008. $32.95 (hardcover). 208 pages. Features career paths for students interested in joining the military.

14837 ■ *Combat Leader to Corporate Leader*
ABC-CLIO
130 Cremona Dr.
Santa Barbara, CA 93117
Fax: (866)270-3856
Fr: 800-368-6868
URL: http://www.abc-clio.com

Chad Storlie. 2010. $34.95. 184 pages (hardcover). Features military-to-civilian career transition, and how to use their military experiences and training to succeed in civilian careers.

14838 ■ *Financial Aid for Veterans, Military Personnel, and Their Dependents*
Reference Service Press
5000 Windplay Dr., Ste. 4
El Dorado Hills, CA 95762-9600
Ph: (916)939-9620
Fax: (916)939-9626
URL: http://www.rspfunding.com

Biennial, Latest edition 2010-2012. $40.00 for individuals. Covers: Organizations that offer approximately 1,100 scholarships, fellowships, loans, grants, awards, and internships to veterans, military personnel, and their families. Entries include: Organization name, address, phone, financial data, requirements for eligibility, duration, special features and limitations, deadline, number of awards. Arrange-

ment: Classified by type of program and target audience. Indexes: Organization name, program, residency, tenability, subject, and deadline date.

14839 ■ *INSIGHT Into Diversity*
INSIGHT Into Diversity
c/o Potomac Publishing, Inc.
225 Meramec Ave., Ste. 400
St. Louis, MO 63105
Ph: (314)863-2900
Fax: (314)863-2905
Fr: 800-537-0655
URL: http://www.aarjobs.com

Monthly. $15.00 for individuals; $8.00 for individuals. Covers: In each issue, about 300 positions at a professional level (most requiring advanced study) available to women, minorities, veterans, and the handicapped; listings are advertisements placed by employers with affirmative action programs. Entries include: Company or organization name, address, contact name; description of position including title, requirements, duties, application procedure, salary, etc. Arrangement: Classified by profession.

14840 ■ *Job Search: Marketing Your Military Experience*
Stackpole Books
5067 Ritter Rd.
Mechanicsburg, PA 17055
Ph: (717)796-0411
Fax: (717)796-0412
Fr: 800-732-3669
URL: http://www.stackpolebooks.com

David G. Henderson. Fifth edition. $19.95 (paper). 272 pages.

14841 ■ *Jobseeker's Guide*
The Resume Place, Inc.
89 Mellor Ave.
Baltimore, MD 21228
Ph: (410)744-4324
Fax: (410)744-0112
Fr: 888-480-8265
E-mail: resume@resume-place.com
URL: http://www.resume-place.com

Kathryn Troutman. 2010. $14.95 (paper). 150 pages. Contains essential information for military and family members who are seeking federal employment. Includes resume and cover letter samples.

14842 ■ *Life After the Military: A Handbook for Transitioning Veterans*
Government Institutes
4501 Forbes Blvd., Ste. 200
Lanham, MD 20706
Ph: (301)459-3366
Fax: (301)429-5748
URL: http://rowman.com

Janelle Hill, Cheryl Lawhorne, Don Philpott. 2011. $34.95 (hardback). 324 pages. Discusses many issues that transitioning veterans are faced with such as finding employment, going back to school, managing finances, special benefits available to veterans and a host of other issues the transitioning veteran is likely to face when making the move to civilian life.

14843 ■ Military to Federal Career Guide
The Resume Place, Inc.
89 Mellor Ave.
Baltimore, MD 21228
Ph: (410)744-4324
Fax: (410)744-0112
Fr: 888-480-8265
E-mail: resume@resume-place.com
URL: http://www.resume-place.com

Kathryn Troutman, Paulina Chen and Brian Moore. 2010. $14.95 (paper, CD-ROM included). 130 pages. Serves as a guide for military veterans who want to start a career in the federal government. Provides tips on how to design a federal resume that will translate a veteran's military skills and competencies into the federal skills, keywords and qualifications.

14844 ■ Military-to-Civilian Career Transition Guide: The Essential Job Search Handbook for Service Members
JIST Publishing
875 Montreal Way
St. Paul, MN 55102
Fax: 800-547-8329
Fr: 800-648-5478
E-mail: info@jist.com
URL: http://www.jist.com/shop/
  product.php?productid=16608&cat=0&page=1

Janet I. Farley. 2010. $14.95. 208 pages. Provides a framework for career transition for service members leaving any branch of the military; includes step-by-step directions, checklists, worksheets, and sample resumes.

14845 ■ Opportunities in Military Careers
The McGraw-Hill Companies
PO Box 182604
Columbus, OH 43272
Fax: (614)759-3749
Fr: 877-883-5524
E-mail: customer.service@mcgraw-hill.com
URL: http://www.mhprofessional.com/
  product.php?isbn=0071448527

Adrian A. Paradis. 2005. $14.95; $13.95 (paper). 159 pages. Illustrates what it's like to work in a variety of job situations unique to the armed forces. Opportunities for civilian employment are also included. Illustrated.

14846 ■ Writing your NSPS Self-Assessment, Second Edition
The Resume Place, Inc.
89 Mellor Ave.
Baltimore, MD 21228
Ph: (410)744-4324
Fax: (410)744-0112
Fr: 888-480-8265
E-mail: resume@resume-place.com
URL: http://www.resume-place.com

Kathryn K. Troutman and Nancy H. Segal. 2009. $28.95 (softcover). 186 pages. Serves as a guide to writing accomplishments for the Department of Defense employees and supervisors. Includes an appendix that details four complete NSPS self-assessment samples.

Newspapers, Magazines, and Journals

14847 ■ Air Force Times
Gannett Government Media Corporation
6883 Commercial Dr.
Springfield, VA 22159-0500
Ph: (703)750-7400
Fr: 800-368-5718
URL: http://www.airforcetimes.com

Weekly (Mon.). $55.00/year for individuals, print only;

$29.95/year for individuals, online only. Independent newspaper serving Air Force personnel worldwide.

14848 ■ Armed Forces Journal International
Defense News Media Group
6883 Commercial Dr.
Springfield, VA 22159
Ph: (703)642-7330
Fax: (703)642-7386
Fr: 800-252-5825
URL: http://www.armedforcesjournal.com/

Periodic. Free, qualified individuals. Magazine concerning the armed services, national security, and defense.

14849 ■ Army Aviation Magazine
Army Aviation Publications Inc.
755 Main St., Ste. 4D
Monroe, CT 06468-2830
Ph: (203)268-2450
Fax: (203)268-5870
URL: http://www.quad-a.org/index.php?option=com_
  content&view=arti

Monthly. $30.00/year for individuals; $3.00/year for single issue. Army aviation magazine.

14850 ■ Checkpoint
Veterans of Foreign Wars of the United States
VFW National Headquarters
406 W 34th St.
Kansas City, MO 64111
Ph: (816)756-3390
Fax: (816)968-1177
E-mail: tdyhouse@vfw.org
URL: http://www.vfw.org

Description: Six issues/year. Concerned with the organization's work of promoting patriotism. Covers national news of the VFW's community service activities, holiday observances, patriotic promotion campaigns, youth activities, safety, etc. Recurring features include editorials, legislation updates, veterans services, employment opportunities, and national security/foreign affairs.

14851 ■ Civilian Jobs News
Civilian Jobs, LLC.
1825 Barrett Lakes Blvd., Ste. 300
Kennesaw, GA 30144
Ph: (678)819-4198
Fax: (678)819-5162
Fr: (866)801-4418
E-mail: info@civilianjobs.com
URL: http://www.civilianjobnews.com

Bimonthly. $12/year. Features practical information for the military person transitioning from the military and seeking a civilian job.

14852 ■ G.I. Jobs
Victory Media Inc.
429 Mills St.
Coraopolis, PA 15108
Ph: (412)269-1663
E-mail: advertise@gijobs.com
URL: http://www.gijobs.net/

Monthly. $19.95/year for individuals. Magazine for military personnel transitioning to civilian employment or seeking civilian education.

14853 ■ Military Medicine
AMSUS - The Society of the Federal Health Agencies
9320 Old Georgetown Rd.
Bethesda, MD 20814
Ph: (301)897-8800
Fax: (301)503-5446
Fr: 800-761-9320
URL: http://www.amsus.org/index.php/journal

Monthly. $170.00/year for individuals, print and online; $225.00/year for other countries. Journal for professional personnel affiliated with the Federal medical services.

14854 ■ Navy Times
Gannett Government Media Corporation
6883 Commercial Dr.
Springfield, VA 22159-0500
Ph: (703)750-7400
Fr: 800-368-5718
URL: http://www.navytimes.com/

Weekly (Mon.). $55.00/year for individuals, print only; $29.95/year for individuals, online only. Independent newspaper serving Navy, Marine, and Coast Guard personnel.

14855 ■ The Officer
The Reserve Officers Association
1 Constitution Ave. NE
Washington, DC 20002
Ph: (202)479-2200
Fax: (202)547-1641
Fr: 800-809-9448
URL: http://www.roa.org/site/
  PageServer?pagename=publications

$12.00/year for individuals; $1.15/year for single issue. Magazine for active and reserve officers of all uniformed services.

Online and Database Services

14856 ■ CivilianJobs.com
E-mail: info@civilianjobs.com
URL: http://civilianjobs.com

Description: Offers an online recruiting solution for candidates that are currently transitioning out of the military as well as military veterans with varying amounts of business experience.

14857 ■ Government and Military Jobs
URL: http://www.governmentandmilitaryjobs.com

Description: Provides information on available government and military jobs in all specialties.

14858 ■ HirePatriots.com
URL: http://hirepatriots.com

Description: Provides a job board for troops, military spouses and veterans. Features other career resources such as education and training, business opportunities and more.

14859 ■ Military Exits
E-mail: jobs@militaryexits.com
URL: http://www.militaryexits.com

Description: Provides career and job listings for veterans and discharged military personnel returning to civilian employment.

14860 ■ Military Job Zone
URL: http://www.militaryoracle.com/95/military-job-zone.php

Description: Provides military recruiting, military placement, veteran job placement, and transition services. Assists transitioning military and veterans in finding civilian jobs.

14861 ■ Military.com
URL: http://www.military.com

Description: Works to accelerate military growth and change the playing field for career and educational opportunities for service members, veterans and military spouses. Provides a job board and other career resources such as resume posting, networking with veterans and career fairs where job seekers can meet employers looking for military experience.

14862 ■ MilitaryHire.com
URL: http://www.militaryhire.com

Description: Serves as a career network where former military personnel can seek careers and utilize their professional skills. Connects veterans of America's armed forces with employers. Helps those who are transitioning from military service to civilian life or searching for a second job.

14863 ■ Today's Military
URL: http://www.todaysmilitary.com/military-careers
Description: Site provides details on many enlisted and officer occupations and describes training, advancement, and educational services within each of the major services. Includes browsing capabilities to match positions with interests.

14864 ■ veteranjobs.us
URL: http://www.veteranjobs.us
Description: Helps job seekers find the best veteran career opportunities with the best companies. Assists employers and recruiters to further their recruiting goals by matching qualified candidates with available positions.

14865 ■ VetJobs.com
URL: http://www.vetjobs.com
Description: Serves as internet niche job board for the military market. Provides tools necessary to make job searching for veterans and translates the military experience to civilian equivalents for employers.

OTHER SOURCES

14866 ■ Air Force Association (AFA)
1501 Lee Hwy.
Arlington, VA 22209-1198
Ph: (703)247-5800
Fax: (703)247-5853
Fr: 800-727-3337
E-mail: membership@afa.org
URL: http://www.afa.org
Description: Promotes public understanding of aerospace power and the pivotal role it plays in the security of the nation.

14867 ■ American Military Retirees Association (AMRA)
5436 Peru St., Ste. 1
Plattsburgh, NY 12901
Ph: (518)563-9479
Fax: (518)324-5204
Fr: 800-424-2969
E-mail: info@amra1973.org
URL: http://amra1973.org
Description: Persons honorably retired for length of service or disability from all branches, all ranks of the United States Armed Forces and their widows or widowers. Aims to: Maintain "COLA" Program; authorization for all military retirees regardless of age; maintain adequate care at military/VA medical facilities. Works to support or oppose Legislation in the best interests of members and to protect the earned privileges and benefits of military retirees. Sponsors Letter-writing campaigns. Offers supplemental health insurance for TRICARE and CHAMPVA beneficiaries. Member of National Military and Veterans Alliance.

14868 ■ Army Aviation Association of America (AAAA)
755 Main St., Ste. 4D
Monroe, CT 06468-2830
Ph: (203)268-2450
Fax: (203)268-5870
E-mail: aaaa@quad-a.org
URL: http://www.quad-a.org
Description: Commissioned officers, warrant officers, and enlisted personnel serving in U.S. Army aviation assignments in the active U.S. Army, Army National Guard, and Army Reserve; Department of Army civilian personnel and industry representatives affiliated with army aviation. Fosters fellowship among military and civilian persons connected with army aviation, past or present; seeks to advance status, overall esprit, and general knowledge of professionals engaged in army aviation. Activities include locator and placement services, technical assistance, and biographical archives. Sponsors speakers' bureau; maintains hall of fame.

14869 ■ Army and Navy Union U.S.A. (ANU)
528 A Canton Rd.
Akron, OH 44312
Ph: (330)798-0880
Fax: (330)798-0890
URL: http://armynavyunion.com
Description: Servicemen and veterans of the armed forces during peace or war. Participates in veterans service work of all types. Provides children's services. Maintains nine county councils and 11 departments.

14870 ■ Association of Graduates of the United States Air Force Academy (AOG)
3116 Academy Dr.
USAF Academy, CO 80840-4475
Ph: (719)472-0300
Fax: (719)333-4194
E-mail: aog@aogusafa.org
URL: http://www.usafa.org
Description: Graduates and friends of the U.S. Air Force Academy. Promotes interest in and dedication to the mission, ideals, objectives, activities, and history of the Academy; encourages young people to attend the Academy; encourages and supports fundraising for the Academy; fosters camaraderie among Academy graduates and U.S. armed forces officer corps; professional development of the armed forces officer corps. Sponsors annual class reunions/homecomings. Offers scholarships to graduates of the academy and their dependents; provides placement service. Operates charitable program, including humanitarian support for next-of-kin of academy graduates. Compiles statistics.

14871 ■ Association of the United States Army (AUSA)
2425 Wilson Blvd.
Arlington, VA 22201
Ph: (703)841-4300
Fax: (703)525-9039
Fr: 800-336-4570
E-mail: gsullivan@ausa.org
URL: http://www.ausa.org
Description: Professional society of: active, retired, and reserve military personnel; West Point and Army ROTC cadets; civilians interested in national defense. Seeks to advance the security of the United States and consolidate the efforts of all who support the United States Army as an indispensable instrument of national security. Conducts industrial symposia for manufacturers of Army weapons and equipment, and those in the Department of the Army who plan, develop, test, and use weapons and equipment. Symposia subjects have included guided missiles, army aviation, electronics and communication, telemedicine, vehicles, and armor. Sponsors monthly PBS TV series, America's Army.

14872 ■ Blinded Veterans Association (BVA)
477 H St. NW
Washington, DC 20001-2617
Ph: (202)371-8880
Fax: (202)371-8258
Fr: 800-669-7079
E-mail: snelson@bva.org
URL: http://www.bva.org
Description: Veterans who lost their sight as a result of military service in the armed forces of the U.S.; associate members are veterans whose loss of sight was not connected with military service. Assists blinded veterans in attaining benefits and employment and in reestablishing themselves as adjusted, active, and productive citizens in their communities. Offers placement service; supports research programs; compiles statistics. Constructs legislative initiatives designed to improve blind rehabilitation programs for veterans.

14873 ■ Bradley-Morris
1825 Barrett Lakes Blvd., Ste. 300
Kennesaw, GA 30144
Fr: 800-330-4950
URL: http://bradley-morris.com
Description: Offers job placement services to military

job seekers who are undergoing military separation, and job seekers with military experience who have worked in the civilian sector.

14874 ■ Marine Corps Association (MCA)
715 Broadway St.
Quantico, VA 22134
Ph: (703)640-6161
Fax: (703)640-0823
Fr: 800-336-0291
E-mail: mcaf@mca-marines.org
URL: http://www.mca-marines.org
Description: Represents active duty, reserve, retired, Fleet Reserve, honorably discharged Marines, and members of other services who have served with Marine Corps units. Disseminates information about the military arts and sciences to members; assists members' professional advancement; fosters the spirit and works to preserve the traditions of the United States Marine Corps. Maintains discount book service and group insurance plan for members. Association founded by members of the Second Provisional Marine Brigade at Guantanamo Bay, Cuba.

14875 ■ Marine Corps Reserve Association (MCRA)
8626 Lee Hwy.
Fairfax, VA 22031-2135
Ph: (703)289-1204
Fax: (703)289-1206
Fr: 877-287-8780
E-mail: hqs@usmcra.org
URL: http://www.usmcra.org
Description: Marines who have served on active duty in peace or war. Seeks to: advance the professional skills of marines; represent and assist individual members; promote the interests of the U.S. Marine Corps in order to advance the welfare and preserve the security of the United States. Maintains speakers' bureau and placement service.

14876 ■ Military Officers Association of America (MOAA)
201 N Washington St.
Alexandria, VA 22314-2537
Ph: (703)549-2311
Fr: 800-234-6622
E-mail: msc@moaa.org
URL: http://www.moaa.org
Description: Active duty, retired, National Guard, Reserve, former commissioned officers, warrant officers of the following uniformed services and their surviving spouse: Army, Marine Corps, Navy, Air Force, Coast Guard, Public Health Service, NOAA. Supports strong national defense and represents and assists members, their dependents and survivors with active duty and retirement issues and benefits. Sponsors educational assistance program, survivor assistance, and travel, insurance, and career transition services.

14877 ■ MilitaryStars
PO BOX 276
Tallevast, FL 34270
Ph: (941)684-0133
Fr: 800-775-1415
E-mail: info@militarystars.com
URL: http://www.militarystars.com
Description: Provides military veteran employment through military job fair and career expos, and military hiring events. Assists transitioning military and veterans in finding civilian jobs via regional career expos throughout the United States.

14878 ■ National Association for Uniformed Services (NAUS)
5535 Hempstead Way
Springfield, VA 22151-4094
Ph: (703)750-1342
Fax: (703)354-4380
Fr: 800-842-3451
E-mail: naus@naus.org
URL: http://www.naus.org
Description: Members of the uniformed military

services, active, retired or reserve, veteran, enlisted and officers, and their spouses or widows. Develops and supports legislation that upholds the security of the U.S., sustains the morale of the uniformed services, and provides fair and equitable consideration for all service people. Protects and improves compensation, entitlements, and benefits. Provides discount rates on travel, insurance, auto rentals, charge cards, prescription medicine, and legal services.

14879 ■ National Naval Officers Association (NNOA)
PO Box 10871
Alexandria, VA 22310-0871
Ph: (703)231-8554
E-mail: ea@nnoa.org
URL: http://www.nnoa.org
Description: Active, reserve, and retired Navy, Marine, and Coast Guard officers and students in college and military sea service programs. Promotes and assists recruitment, retention, and career development of minority officers in the naval service. Conducts specialized education; maintains counseling, referral, and mentorship. Makes available non-ROTC grants-in-aid. Sponsors competitions; operates charitable program.

14880 ■ Non Commissioned Officers Association of the United States of America (NCOA)
9330 Corporate Dr., Ste. 701
Selma, TX 78154

Fr: 800-662-2620
E-mail: natdir@ncoausa.org
URL: http://www.ncoausa.org
Description: Noncommissioned and petty officers of the United States military serving in grades E1 through E9 from all five branches of the U.S. Armed Forces; includes active duty and retired personnel, members of the Reserve and National Guard components, and personnel who held the rank of NCO/PO at the time of separation from active duty under honorable conditions. Formed for patriotic, fraternal, social, and benevolent purposes. Offers veterans job assistance, legislative representation, and grants. Conducts charitable programs.

14881 ■ RecruitMilitary.com
422 W Loveland Ave.
Loveland, OH 45140
Ph: (513)683-5020
Fax: (513)683-5021
E-mail: support@recruitmilitary.com
URL: http://www.recruitmilitary.com
Description: Serves as a recruiting firm focusing on matching up military veterans and their spouses with employers across the world. Assists candidates with information about resumes, networking, and interviewing tips in the career center and also provides veteran job fairs throughout the country.

14882 ■ Vietnam Veterans Against the War (VVAW)
PO Box 2065
Station A
Chicago, IL 60690-2065

Ph: (773)276-4189
E-mail: vvaw@vvaw.org
URL: http://www.vvaw.org
Description: Works for: improvement of VA conditions and job opportunities; elimination of the possibility of future military conflicts such as Vietnam; no draft or registration; testing and treatment of Agent Orange poisoning. Offers traumatic stress disorder counseling and discharge upgrading; provides Agent Orange self-help information.

14883 ■ Vietnam Veterans of America (VVA)
8719 Colesville Rd., Ste. 100
Silver Spring, MD 20910
Ph: (301)585-4000
Fax: (301)585-0519
Fr: 800-882-1316
E-mail: communications@vva.org
URL: http://www.vva.org
Description: Acts as congressionally chartered, nationwide veterans service organization formed specifically for Vietnam veterans. Aims to work for the employment, education benefits, improved psychological assistance, and health care of Vietnam veterans. Provides referral services and research and public information programs to help veterans in developing a positive identification with their Vietnam service and with fellow veterans. Offers annual training for veterans' service representatives.

Opportunities for Minorities

REFERENCE WORKS

14884 ■ Advice from the Top: What Minority Women Say about Their Career Success
ABC-CLIO
130 Cremona Dr.
Santa Barbara, CA 93117
Fax: (866)270-3856
Fr: 800-368-6868
E-mail: customerservice@abc-clio.com
URL: http://www.abc-clio.com

Valencia Campbell. 2009. $39.95 (hardcover). 174 pages. Contains tips and advice from minority women who succeeded in their respective careers. Seeks to inspire women who want to advance their careers. Includes profiles of successful minority women.

14885 ■ American Indian National Business Directory
National Center for American Indian Enterprise Development
953 E Juanita Ave.
Mesa, AZ 85204
Ph: (480)545-1298
Fax: (480)545-4208
Fr: 800-462-2433
URL: http://www.ncaied.org

Annual, May. Covers: Firms offering professional, commercial, and industrial products and services. Entries include: Firm name, address, phone, name and title of owner or chief executive, product or service, year established, work locations, license type/specialty, bonding capacity/sales. Arrangement: Classified by line of business.

14886 ■ Black Enterprise—Top Black Businesses Issue
Earl Graves Publishing Co.
130 5th Ave., 10th Fl.
New York, NY 10011-4399
Ph: (212)242-8000
E-mail: customerservice@blackenterprise.com
URL: http://www.blackenterprise.com

Annual, June; Latest edition 2008. $3.95; $5.00. Publication includes: Lists of 100 Black-owned industrial/service companies with sales of $18 million or above; 25 banks with total assets of $3.6 billion or more; 10 insurance companies with total assets of about $689 million or more; and 100 auto dealers with sales of $17 million or above; 20 advertising agencies with total billings of $795 million or more; 15 investment banks with issues totalling $123 billion.

14887 ■ Ferguson Career Resource Guide for Women and Minorities
Impact Publications
9104 Manassas Dr., Ste. N
Manassas Park, VA 20111-5211
Ph: (703)361-7300
Fax: (703)335-9486

Fr: 800-361-1055
URL: http://www.impactpublications.com

Latest edition September, 2006. $150.00 for individuals. Covers: information on hundreds of organizations, colleges, foundations, and publications devoted to the careers and educational advancement of women minorities.

14888 ■ INSIGHT Into Diversity
INSIGHT Into Diversity
c/o Potomac Publishing, Inc.
225 Meramec Ave., Ste. 400
St. Louis, MO 63105
Ph: (314)863-2900
Fax: (314)863-2905
Fr: 800-537-0655
URL: http://www.aarjobs.com

Monthly. $15.00 for individuals; $8.00 for individuals. Covers: In each issue, about 300 positions at a professional level (most requiring advanced study) available to women, minorities, veterans, and the handicapped; listings are advertisements placed by employers with affirmative action programs. Entries include: Company or organization name, address, contact name; description of position including title, requirements, duties, application procedure, salary, etc. Arrangement: Classified by profession.

14889 ■ Latinnovating: Green American Jobs and the Latinos Creating Them
Gracefully Global, LLC
22568 Mission Blvd., No. 427
Hayward, CA 94541
Ph: (510)542-9449
URL: http://www.gracefullyglobal.com

Graciela Tiscareno-Sato. 2011. $25.00 (paper). 212 pages. Profiles ten different career paths for Latinos interested in environmental business. Shows the culturally-rooted environmental entrepreneurship in the Latino community.

14890 ■ Migrant Education
ABC-CLIO
PO Box 1911
Santa Barbara, CA 93102-1911
Ph: (805)968-1911
Fax: (866)270-3856
Fr: 800-368-6868
URL: http://www.abc-clio.com

Publication includes: List of additional resources for further information about migrant education. Principal content of publication is discussion of issues facing educators who work with migrant families. Indexes: Alphabetical.

14891 ■ Minority Business Information Center
National Minority Supplier Development Council Inc.
1359 Broadway, 10th Fl.
New York, NY 10018
Ph: (212)944-2430

Fax: (212)719-9611
URL: http://www.nmsdc.org/nmsdc

Current. Updated as needed. Database covers: Approximately 3,500 companies that are certified by the NMSDC as minority owned. Database includes: Company name, address, phone, parent company name, Standard Industrial Classification (SIC) code/North American Industry Classification System (NAICS), description of products and services, year founded, ownership structure, number of employees; name, title, ethnicity, and sex of owners; major customers, annual sales, geographical area served, most recent certification date and accrediting council.

14892 ■ National Directory of Minority-Owned Business Firms
Business Research Services Inc.
7720 Wisconsin Ave., Ste. 213
Bethesda, MD 20814
Ph: (301)229-5561
Fax: (301)229-6133
Fr: 800-845-8420
URL: http://www.sba8a.com

Annual, latest edition 15th; June 2010. $295.00 for individuals. Covers: Over 30,000 minority-owned businesses. Entries include: Company name, address, phone, name and title of contact, minority group, certification status, date founded, number of employees, description of products or services, sales volume, government contracting experience, references. Arrangement: Standard Industrial Classification (SIC) code, geographical. Indexes: Alphabetical by company name, SIC by name.

14893 ■ National Minority and Women-Owned Business Directory
Diversity Information Resources Inc.
2105 Central Ave. NE
Minneapolis, MN 55418
Ph: (612)781-6819
Fax: (612)781-0109
URL: http://www.diversityinforesources.com

Annual, Latest edition 2010. $145.00 for individuals. Covers: Over 9,000 minority-owned companies capable of supplying their goods and services on national or regional levels. Entries include: Company name, address, phone, fax, e-mail, Web site, number of employees, year established, products or services, certification status, minority identification, annual sales, NAICS code. Arrangement: Classified by product or service, then geographical and alphabetical. Indexes: Alphabetical, commodity, keyword.

14894 ■ SER Network Directory
SER-Jobs for Progress National Inc.
100 E Royal Ln., Ste. 130
Irving, TX 75039
Ph: (469)549-3600
Fax: (469)549-3687
URL: http://www.ser-national.org

Annual, Latest edition 2009. Covers: Approximately

130 affiliated agencies in 90 U.S. cities of SER ("Service, Employment, Redevelopment")-Jobs for Progress National, Inc., an organization of Hispanics that provides employment and training, services to disadvantaged youth and adults, especially Hispanics. Entries include: Organization name, address, phone, name of president, services provided, satellite offices, if any. Arrangement: Geographical.

NEWSPAPERS, MAGAZINES, AND JOURNALS

14895 ■ African-American Career World
Equal Opportunity Publications Inc.
445 Broad Hollow Rd., Ste. 425
Melville, NY 11747
Ph: (631)421-9421
Fax: (631)421-1352
URL: http://www.eop.com/advertise-AACW.php

Semiannual. $18.00/year for individuals; $34.00/year for two years; $49.00/year for individuals, three years; free to qualified subscribers. Magazine that aims to be a recruitment link between students and professionals who are African American and the major corporations that seek to hire them.

14896 ■ CAA Voice
Chinese for Affirmative Action
17 Walter U. Lum Pl.
San Francisco, CA 94108
Ph: (415)274-6750
Fax: (415)397-8770
E-mail: info@caasf.org
URL: http://www.caasf.org

Description: Biannual. Reports on legislation and court rulings which affect the civil rights of Chinese Americans. Publicizes recent acts of discrimination against Chinese Americans and examines media stereotypes of Asians. Supports affirmative action programs and informs readers of career counseling services, and employment and apprenticeship opportunities. Promotes bilingual education and services; announces events of the organization.

14897 ■ Chinese American Medical Society Newsletter
Chinese American Medical Society
41 Elizabeth St., Ste. 403
New York, NY 10013
Ph: (212)334-4760
Fax: (212)965-1876
E-mail: jseto@camsociety.org
URL: http://www.camsociety.org

Description: Two issues/year. Publishes Society news. Recurring features include recent activities of the Society, upcoming scientific meetings, excerpts of presentations at the scientific meeting, new members, job listings and a calendar of events.

14898 ■ Equal Opportunity Magazine
Equal Opportunity Publications, Inc.
445 Broadhollow Rd., Ste. 425
Melville, NY 11747
Ph: (631)421-9421
Fax: (631)421-1352
E-mail: info@eop.com
URL: http://eop.com

Three times a year. $14/year for individuals who are not minority students or professionals. Career-guidance and recruitment magazine that is distributed free of charge to African American, Hispanic, Native-American, and Asian-American college students and professionals in all fields including engineering, computer science, technology, finance, business, healthcare, liberal arts, and education.

14899 ■ Hispanic Career World
Equal Opportunity Publications Inc.
445 Broad Hollow Rd., Ste. 425
Melville, NY 11747
Ph: (631)421-9421

Fax: (631)421-1352
URL: http://www.eop.com/mags-HCW.php

Semiannual. $18.00/year for individuals; $34.00/year for two years; $49.00/year for individuals, 3 years; free to qualified subscribers. Magazine that aims to be a recruitment link between students and professionals who are Hispanic and the major corporations that seek to hire them.

14900 ■ Hispanic Link Weekly Report
Hispanic Link News Service
1420 N St. NW
Washington, DC 20005
Ph: (202)234-0280
Fax: (202)234-4090
URL: http://www.hispaniclink.org/subscribe.htm

Description: Weekly. $118.00/year for individuals; $25.00/year for students; $140.00/year for institutions. Covers Hispanic issues nationwide, including politics, employment, education, arts and entertainment, and relevant events. Recurring features include interviews, news of research, a calendar of events, reports of meetings, news of educational opportunities, and job listings.

14901 ■ Hispanic Times Magazine
Hispanic Times Magazine
PO Box 579
Winchester, CA 92596
Ph: (909)926-2119

Quarterly. $30.00/year for individuals; $3.50/year for single issue. Magazine focusing on business and careers (English and Spanish).

14902 ■ Item-Interference Technology Engineers Master
Robar Industries Inc.
3 Union Hill Rd.
West Conshohocken, PA 19428-2788
Fax: (610)834-7337
E-mail: item@rbitem.com
URL: http://www.interferencetechnology.com/
rebrand_redirect.asp

Design magazine about measurement and control of electromagnetic interference.

14903 ■ Minority Engineer Magazine
Employment Opportunity Publications
445 Broad Hollow Rd., Ste. 425
Melville, NY 11747
Ph: (631)421-9421
Fax: (631)421-1352
E-mail: info@eop.com
URL: http://www.eop.com/mags-ME.php

$18.00/year for non-minority engineering student or professional; $34.00/2 years for non-minority engineering student or professional; $49.00/3 years for non-minority engineering student or professional. Provides job listings, company profiles, and articles geared toward the engineering student and professional.

14904 ■ National Association of Black Accountants-News Plus
National Association of Black Accountants Inc.
7474 Greenway Center Dr., Ste. 1120
Greenbelt, MD 20770
Ph: (301)474-6222
Fax: (301)474-3114
Fr: 888-571-2939
E-mail: customerservice@nabainc.org
URL: http://www.nabainc.org/

Description: Quarterly. Addresses concerns of black business professionals, especially in the accounting profession. Reports on accounting education issues, developments affecting the profession, and the Association's activities on the behalf of minorities in the accounting profession. Recurring features include member profiles, job listings, reports of meetings, news of research, and a calendar of events.

14905 ■ Saludos Hispanos
Saludos Hispanos
73-121 Fred Waring Dr., Ste. 100
Palm Desert, CA 92260
Ph: (760)776-1206
Fax: (760)776-1214
Fr: 800-371-4456
URL: http://www.saludos.com/

Bimonthly. Magazine showcasing successful Hispanic Americans and promoting higher education (English and Spanish).

ONLINE AND DATABASE SERVICES

14906 ■ Academic Diversity Search
URL: http://www.academicdiversitysearch.com

Description: Specializes in placing women and minorities on university faculty and administrative, executive, scientific, or technical staff.

14907 ■ Black Collegian Online
URL: http://www.blackcollegian.com

Description: Career site for students of color. Features information on career development, self-development, job opportunities, study abroad programs, health and fitness, graduate/professional schools, internships/co-ops, and other information designed to ensure transition from college to a successful career. Targeted specifically to African-American students and other students of color.

14908 ■ DiversityCareerHub.com
URL: http://www.diversitycareerhub.com

Description: Provides jobs for underrepresented minorities and women, as well as other minority job seekers looking for employment.

14909 ■ DiversityJobs.org
URL: http://diversityjobs.org

Description: Serves as job board that connects diversity candidates with employers.

14910 ■ DiversitySearch.com
URL: http://www.diversitysearch.com

Description: Serves as a career portal for all diversity and minority job candidates.

14911 ■ EmployDIVERSITY
URL: http://www.employdiversity.com

Description: Provides multicultural professionals with employment opportunities and career development information. Offers free job search services to job seekers.

14912 ■ HireDiversity.com
E-mail: hd@hirediversity.com
URL: http://www.hirediversity.com

Description: Exists as an online service for diversity recruitment and career development. Provides services and networking opportunities while linking under-represented candidates with Fortune 1000 corporations, government agencies, and non-profit/educational institutions.

14913 ■ iHispano.com
URL: http://www.ihispano.com

Description: Serves as a professional networking site and job board for Latinos in the United States. Features a job search engine, personalized job agents, a tool for the creation of multiple resumes and cover letters, career resources and tool kits, on-line branding, professional networking, blogs, and forums.

14914 ■ IMDiversity.com
URL: http://www.imdiversity.com

Description: Provides jobs for underrepresented minorities and other diverse job seekers. Offers a job bank that lists diversity sensitive employers. Includes other job search features such as customized resume and career management tools.

14915 ■ LatinosForHire.com
URL: http://www.latinosforhire.com

Description: Identifies and lists organizations that are currently hiring and have a commitment to diversity and to the Latino and Hispanic community.

14916 ■ Latpro
E-mail: support@latpro.com
URL: http://www.latpro.com

Description: Job site dedicated to finding jobs for Spanish, Portuguese and bilingual workers. Seekers may post resumes, search the job databank and receive job alerts via e-mail. Contains e-mail newsletters, recruiter lists, relocation tools and salary calculators and ESL education opportunities, among other resources. Also available in Spanish and Portuguese.

14917 ■ MBA Careers
3934 SW Corbett Ave.
Portland, OR 97239
Ph: (503)221-7779
Fax: (503)221-7780
E-mail: eric@careerexposure.com
URL: http://mbacareers.com

Description: Job site that provides resume posting, databank search and e-mail alert services to MBA and other advanced graduate degree holders.

14918 ■ Minority Affairs
URL: http://www.minorityaffairs.com

Description: Offers career, employment, and educational resources to empower minority job seekers and preserve workplace diversity.

14919 ■ Minority Jobs
URL: http://www.minorityemployment.org

Description: Features a searchable database of employment opportunities for minorities.

14920 ■ Minority Part Time Jobs
URL: http://www.minorityparttimejobs.com

Description: Features part time job search listings for minorities.

14921 ■ MinorityJobs.net
E-mail: info@minorityresources.us
URL: http://www.minorityjobs.net

Description: Provides employment opportunities to individuals from all communities and ethnic backgrounds.

14922 ■ MinorityNurse.com
URL: http://www.minoritynurse.com

Description: Provides career and education resources for minority nursing professionals, students, and faculty.

14923 ■ NativeAmericanJobs.com
E-mail: jc@nativeamericanjobs.com
URL: http://www.nativeamericanjobs.com

Description: Provide job and career opportunities for Native Americans and others.

14924 ■ NSBE Online
URL: http://www.nsbe.org

Description: A section of the website of the National Society of Black Engineers. Main files include: Job Search (includes full-time, co-ops, internships, and student jobs), Post a Job, Post a Resume. Fee: $250 to post a job for 60 days.

14925 ■ PSI Diversity Job Fair
URL: http://www.psijobfair.com

Description: Specializes in the area of diversity and technical job fairs.

14926 ■ SpanishJobs.com
URL: http://spanishjobs.jobamatic.com/a/jbb/find-jobs

Description: Provides job opportunities for bilingual/ Spanish professionals specializing in the fields of administration, customer service, finance, human resources, management, marketing, sales, and translation. Hires for full-time, part-time, contract, seasonal, permanent, temporary, internship, and volunteer opportunities.

14927 ■ WomenAndMinorities.com
E-mail: info@womenandminorities.com
URL: http://womenandminorities.com

Description: Serves as a minority website where job ads and resumes can be easily accessed. Provides a search engine that matches qualified diverse applicants to job openings and automatically notifies employers of matching resumes and job seekers of matching job listings.

OTHER SOURCES

14928 ■ American Indian Science and Engineering Society (AISES)
PO Box 9828
Albuquerque, NM 87119-9828
Ph: (505)765-1052
Fax: (505)765-5608
E-mail: info@aises.org
URL: http://www.aises.org

Description: Represents American Indian and non-Indian students and professionals in science, technology, and engineering fields; corporations representing energy, mining, aerospace, electronic, and computer fields. Seeks to motivate and encourage students to pursue undergraduate and graduate studies in science, engineering, and technology. Sponsors science fairs in grade schools, teacher training workshops, summer math/science sessions for 8th-12th graders, professional chapters, and student chapters in colleges. Offers scholarships. Adult members serve as role models, advisers, and mentors for students. Operates placement service.

14929 ■ Asian American Architects and Engineers (AAAE)
1167 Mission St., 4th Fl.
San Francisco, CA 94103
Ph: (415)552-1118
E-mail: info@aaaenc.org
URL: http://www.aaaenc.org

Description: Minorities. Provides contracts and job opportunities for minorities in the architectural and engineering fields. Serves as a network for the promotion in professional fields.

14930 ■ Chinese for Affirmative Action (CAA)
17 Walter U. Lum Pl.
San Francisco, CA 94108
Ph: (415)274-6750
Fax: (415)397-8770
E-mail: info@caasf.org
URL: http://www.caasf.org

Description: Works towards equal rights and justice for Asian Americans, women and other people of color. Conducts policy advocacy in the areas of education, employment, hate crimes and affirmative action. Provides direct services for people interested in non-traditional blue collar work where women and people of color have been historically underrepresented.

14931 ■ Corporate Diversity Search
PO Box 1086
Webster, NY 14580
Ph: (585)787-0537
Fax: (585)787-1321
E-mail: oates@corpdiversitysearch.com
URL: http://www.corpdiversitysearch.com

Description: Serves as an executive search firm specializing in the placement of women and minorities. Provides organizations with professionals who possess the technical expertise, education, and commitment in the following areas: engineering (chemical, electrical, mechanical), optics, sciences, accounting and finance, manufacturing, and human resources.

14932 ■ Hispanic Alliance for Career Enhancement
100 S Wacker Dr., Ste. 700
Chicago, IL 60606
Ph: (312)435-0498
Fax: (312)454-7448
E-mail: info@haceonline.org
URL: http://www.haceonline.org

Description: Strives to make a positive impact on the American workplace by cultivating the pipeline of Latino talent. Fosters the career advancement of Latino professionals.

14933 ■ NAACP
4805 Mt. Hope Dr.
Baltimore, MD 21215
Ph: (410)580-5777
Fr: 877-NAACP-98
URL: http://www.naacp.org

Description: Persons "of all races and religions" who believe in the objectives and methods of the NAACP. Works to achieve equal rights through the democratic process and eliminate racial prejudice by removing racial discrimination in housing, employment, voting, schools, the courts, transportation, recreation, prisons, and business enterprises. Offers referral services, tutorials, job referrals, and day care. Sponsors seminars; maintains law library. Sponsors the NAACP National Housing Corporation to assist in the development of low and moderate income housing for families. Compiles statistics.

14934 ■ National Association of Hispanic Journalists (NAHJ)
1050 Connecticut Ave. NW, 10th Fl.
Washington, DC 20036-5334
Ph: (202)662-7145
Fax: (202)662-7144
E-mail: nahj@nahj.org
URL: http://www.nahj.org

Description: Aims to organize and support Hispanics involved in news gathering and dissemination. Encourages journalism and communications study and practice by Hispanics. Seeks recognition for Hispanic members of the profession regarding their skills and achievements. Promotes fair and accurate media treatment of Hispanics; opposes job discrimination and demeaning stereotypes. Works to increase educational and career opportunities and development for Hispanics in the field. Seeks to foster greater awareness of members' cultural identity, interests, and concerns. Provides a united voice for Hispanic journalists with the aim of achieving national visibility. Offers placement services to Hispanic students. Activities include: a census of Hispanic media professionals nationwide; writing contest for Hispanic students. Offers scholarships, seminars, and training workshops.

14935 ■ National Black MBA Association (NBMBAA)
180 N Michigan Ave., Ste. 1400
Chicago, IL 60601
Ph: (312)236-2622
Fax: (312)236-0390
E-mail: mail@nbmbaa.org
URL: http://www.nbmbaa.org

Description: Business professionals, lawyers, accountants, and engineers concerned with the role of blacks who hold advanced management degrees. Works to create economic and intellectual wealth for the black community. Encourages blacks to pursue continuing business education; assists students preparing to enter the business world. Provides programs for minority youths, students, and professionals, and entrepreneurs including workshops, panel discussions, and Destination MBA seminar.

Sponsors job fairs. Works with graduate schools. Operates job placement service.

14936 ■ National Coalition of 100 Black Women (NCBW)
1925 Adam C. Powell Jr. Blvd., Ste. 1L
New York, NY 10026
Ph: (212)222-5660
Fax: (212)222-5675
E-mail: executivedirector@nc100bw.org
URL: http://www.ncbw.org

Description: Represents African-American women actively involved with issues such as economic development, health, employment, education, voting, housing, criminal justice, the status of black families, and the arts. Seeks to provide networking and career opportunities for African-American women in the process of establishing links between the organization and the corporate and political arenas. Encourages leadership development; sponsors role-model and mentor programs to provide guidance to teenage mothers and young women in high school or who have graduated from college and are striving for career advancement.

14937 ■ National Puerto Rican Forum (NPRF)
1776 Clay Ave.
Bronx, NY 10457
Ph: (718)299-1100
Fax: (718)294-6237
Fr: 888-513-7464
E-mail: info@promesa.org
URL: http://www.promesa.org/docs/NPRF.html

Description: Concerned with the overall improvement of Puerto Rican and Hispanic communities throughout the U.S. Seeks to identify the obstacles preventing the advancement of the Puerto Rican and Hispanic communities and to develop strategies to remove them. Designs and implements programs in

areas of job counseling, training and placement, and English language skills, to deal effectively with the problems of Puerto Ricans and other Hispanics. Sponsors Career Services and Job Placement Program at the national level. Also provides specialized programs in New York, such as: Employment Placement Initiative, Access and Family Services in the schools, and job counseling.

14938 ■ National Society of Hispanic MBAs (NSHMBA)
1303 Walnut Hill Ln., Ste. 100
Irving, TX 75038
Ph: (214)596-9338
Fax: (214)596-9325
Fr: 877-467-4622
E-mail: saramos@nshmba.org
URL: http://www.nshmba.org

Description: Hispanic MBA professional business network dedicated to economic and philanthropic advancement.

14939 ■ Organization of Chinese American Women (OCAW)
4641 Montgomery Ave., Ste. 208
Bethesda, MD 20814
Ph: (301)907-3898
Fax: (301)907-3899
E-mail: info@ocawwomen.org
URL: http://www.ocawwomen.org

Description: Advances the cause of Chinese American women in the U.S. and fosters public awareness of their special needs and concerns. Seeks to integrate Chinese American women into the mainstream of women's activities and programs. Addresses issues such as equal employment opportunities at both the professional and nonprofessional levels; overcoming stereotypes; racial and sexual discrimination and restrictive traditional beliefs; assistance to poverty-stricken recent immigrants; ac-

cess to leadership and policymaking positions. Serves as networking for Chinese American women. Sponsors annual opera and Mother's Day and Award Banquet. Establishes scholarships for middle school girls in rural China.

14940 ■ SER - Jobs for Progress National
100 E Royal Ln., Ste. 130
Irving, TX 75039
Ph: (469)549-3600
Fax: (469)549-3687
E-mail: info@ser-national.org
URL: http://www.ser-national.org

Description: Aims to provide employment training and opportunities for Spanish-speaking and disadvantaged Americans. Seeks to increase business and economic opportunities for minority communities and ensure optimum participation by the Hispanic community in public policy forums. Gives funds to SER performance contracts that are funded by the federal government. (The acronym SER stands for service, employment, and redevelopment.) Organizes its own training and management program and is responsible for recruitment and selection of job trainees, counseling, pre-job orientation and vocational preparation, basic education, employer relations, and follow-up services to trainees after training and job placement.

14941 ■ Wealth in Diversity Consulting Group Inc.
544 Black Mountain
Cambridge, VT 05444
Ph: (802)644-5140
Fax: (802)644-2140
E-mail: info@wealthindiversity.com
URL: http://www.wealthindiversity.com

Group specializes in diversity initiatives, leadership and management development, organizational culture, team building, coaching, assessments, recruitment, conflict resolution, career development and health care educational development.

REFERENCE WORKS

14942 ■ *Career of Gold: Defeat Age Bias by Re-Careering for the Second Half of Your Life*
Today's Books
c/o History Publishing Company, LLC
PO Box 700
Palisades, NY 10964
Ph: (845)398-8161
URL: http://www.historypublishingco.com/authors/bracken/careerofgold.php

Don Bracken. 2006. $ 15.95 (paper). 232 pages. Deals with age bias confronting the post-fifty generation and the means of dealing with it. Encourages and guides older individuals wishing to start a new career.

14943 ■ *Finding a Job After 50*
Career Press
220 West Pkwy., Unit 12
Pompton Plains, NJ 07444
Ph: (201)848-0310
Fax: (201)848-1727
Fr: 800-227-3371
URL: http://www.careerpress.com

Jeannette Woodward. 2007. $14.99 (paper). 224 pages. Provides guides and tools for older workers who are looking for a job.

14944 ■ *INSIGHT Into Diversity*
INSIGHT Into Diversity
c/o Potomac Publishing, Inc.
225 Meramec Ave., Ste. 400
St. Louis, MO 63105
Ph: (314)863-2900
Fax: (314)863-2905
Fr: 800-537-0655
URL: http://www.aarjobs.com

Monthly. $15.00 for individuals; $8.00 for individuals. Covers: In each issue, about 300 positions at a professional level (most requiring advanced study) available to women, minorities, veterans, and the handicapped; listings are advertisements placed by employers with affirmative action programs. Entries include: Company or organization name, address, contact name; description of position including title, requirements, duties, application procedure, salary, etc. Arrangement: Classified by profession.

14945 ■ *Over 40 and You're Hired!*
Penguin Group (USA)
375 Hudson St.
New York, NY 10014-3657
Ph: (212)366-2000
Fax: (212)366-2933
E-mail: ecommerce@us.penguingroup.com
URL: http://us.penguingroup.com

Robin Ryan. 2009. $15.00 (paper). 256 pages. Inspires people, aged forty and above, to jump-start their careers and secure new, better-paying jobs. Offers advice and detailed explanations that people over forty will find indispensable as they look for work.

14946 ■ *Resumes for Re-Entering the Job Market*
The McGraw-Hill Companies
PO Box 182604
Columbus, OH 43272
Fax: (614)759-3749
Fr: 877-883-5524
E-mail: customer.service@mcgraw-hill.com
URL: http://www.mhprofessional.com/product.php?isbn=007164203X

Second edition, 2008. $12.95 (paper). 144 pages. Part of VGM Professional Resumes series.

ONLINE AND DATABASE SERVICES

14947 ■ RetiredBrains.com
URL: http://www.retiredbrains.com

Description: Serves older boomers, seniors, retirees and those about to retire who are looking to find jobs, volunteer opportunities, educational resources and retirement information. Offers nationwide job listings searchable by industry or state. Includes important senior-focused material including information on health concerns, insurance products, cruises and vacations, financial planning, retirement living and more.

14948 ■ RetiredStars.com
URL: http://www.retiredstars.com

Description: Features job listings for retirees who want to work again. Includes useful resources pertaining to job search and career options.

14949 ■ RetireeWorkforce.com
URL: http://www.retireeworkforce.com

Description: Provides employment opportunities for experienced and motivated retirees. Offers part-time, flexible, seasonal and full-time positions.

14950 ■ RetirementCrossing
URL: http://www.retirementcrossing.com

Description: Provides lists of all available retirement job openings across employer career webpages, job boards, organizations' websites, newspaper classifieds, and recruiter sites.

14951 ■ Senior Job Bank
URL: http://www.seniorjobbank.com

Description: Job postings for seniors.

14952 ■ SeniorJobBank
URL: http://www.seniorjobbank.org

Description: Serves as job site for people who are over 50 years of age. Offers job postings, job search, resume, and job alert registration for job seekers as well as career and education information.

14953 ■ Seniors 4 Hire
E-mail: info@seniors4hire.org
URL: http://www.seniors4hire.org

Description: Online career center for people 50 and over.

14954 ■ Workforce50.com
URL: http://www.workforce50.com

Description: Serves older workers with a full service job board and career site. Provides employment and education resources that cater to mature workers searching for employment, in transition or approaching retirement.

OTHER SOURCES

14955 ■ Experience Works
4401 Wilson Blvd., Ste. 1100
Arlington, VA 22203
Ph: (703)522-7272
Fax: (703)522-0141
Fr: (866)EXP-WRKS
E-mail: info@experienceworks.org
URL: http://www.experienceworks.org

Description: Provides training and employment services for mature workers. Reaches more than 125,000 mature individuals.

14956 ■ Gray is Green: The National Senior Conservation Corps
26 Broadway
North Haven, CT 06473
Fr: 800-684-5889
E-mail: rosikerr@grayisgreen.org
URL: http://www.grayisgreen.org

Description: Enables people over 65 to actively participate in creating a positive environmental change. Provides resources to seniors in three distinct areas: greening, advocacy and learning and teaching. Serves as a clearinghouse for senior citizens interested in greening their lives, learning about sustainability, developing second careers in conservation, advocating for sound climate change policy and in serving as resources for younger people involved in sustainability.

14957 ■ National Indian Council on Aging, Inc.
10501 Montgomery Blvd. NE, Ste. 210
Albuquerque, NM 87111
Ph: (505)292-2001
Fax: (505)292-1922
E-mail: info@nicoa.org
URL: http://www.nicoa.org

Description: Offers MaturityWorks-a partnership that places mature workers with jobs.

14958 ■ Senior Employment Resources
4201 John Marr Dr., Ste. 236
Annandale, VA 22003-3204

Ph: (703)750-1936
Fax: (703)750-0269

E-mail: office@seniorjobs.org
URL: http://www.seniorjobs.org
Description: Job placement service that matches

companies and job seekers age 50 and above.

Opportunities for Teenagers

REFERENCE WORKS

14959 ■ *Peterson's Summer Opportunities for Kids and Teenagers*
Peterson's Guides
2000 Lenox Dr.
Box 67005
Lawrenceville, NJ 08648
Ph: (609)896-1800
Fax: (609)896-4531
Fr: 800-338-3282
E-mail: custsvc@petersons.com
URL: http://www.petersons.com/books/internships.asp
Peterson's. Twenty-fifth edition, 2005. $26.95 (paper). 768 pages. In addition to information about 1,400 summer activities and programs, covers job opportunities for high school and college students. Part of Summer Opportunities for Kids and Teenagers series.

14960 ■ *Resumes for High School Graduates*
The McGraw-Hill Companies
PO Box 182604
Columbus, OH 43272
Fax: (614)759-3749
Fr: 877-883-5524
E-mail: customer.service@mcgraw-hill.com
URL: http://www.mhprofessional.com/product.php?isbn=0071448918
Third edition, 2005. $11.95. 144 pages. Designed for the person with little or no full-time work experience. Shows how to emphasize part-work experience and highlight educational, extra-curricular and volunteer experience. Provides sample resumes and cover letters.

14961 ■ *Teens and the Job Game*
iUniverse Inc.
1663 Liberty Dr.
Bloomington, IN 47403
Fax: (812)355-4085
Fr: 800-288-4677
URL: http://www.iuniverse.com

Beverly Slomka. 2011. $11.95 (perfect bound softcover). 120 pages. Serves as start-up guide for young adults in the job preparation process.

ONLINE AND DATABASE SERVICES

14962 ■ Acting-for-Teens.com
URL: http://www.acting-for-teens.com
Description: Provides information on all available acting jobs for teens.

14963 ■ GrooveJob.com
URL: http://www.groovejob.com
Description: Serves as a job board that lists part-time jobs for students and teens. Includes summer and seasonal jobs.

14964 ■ MyFirstPaycheck.com
URL: http://www.myfirstpaycheck.com
Description: Exists as a job-listing site for teenagers. Offers advice and resources, including an interactive resume builder to help young people have a more successful job application process.

14965 ■ TeenagerCrossing.com
URL: http://www.teenagercrossing.com
Description: Job board that caters to the job-search needs of teen job seekers.

14966 ■ Teens4Hire.org
E-mail: info@teens4hire.org
URL: http://www.teens4hire.org
Description: Online recruitment site for teenagers. Features full and part time jobs, internships, apprenticeships, work-based learning experiences, volunteer positions, and reputable business opportunities.

OTHER SOURCES

14967 ■ National Youth Employment Coalition (NYEC)
1836 Jefferson Pl. NW
Washington, DC 20036

Ph: (202)659-1064
Fax: (202)659-0399
E-mail: nyec@nyec.org
URL: http://www.nyec.org
Description: A network of over 180 community-based organizations, research organizations, public interest groups, policy analysis organizations, and others dedicated to promoting improved policies and practices related to youth employment/development, to help youth succeed in becoming lifelong learners, productive workers and self-sufficient citizens.

14968 ■ Operation Enterprise
American Management Association
1601 Broadway
New York, NY 10019-7420
Fr: 800-634-4262
E-mail: operationenterprise@amanet.org
URL: http://www.amanet.org/advantage/Operation-Enterprise.aspx
Description: Gives high school and college students an opportunity to learn about management by working with executives and managers. Learning techniques used include small group discussions, panel forums, a business simulation, and role playing. Sponsors Career Skills program, to encourage development of job skills. Candidates are sponsored in a variety of ways by companies, civic organizations, or individuals.

14969 ■ Way to Work (WW)
52 Broadway, 6th Fl.
New York, NY 10004
Ph: (212)823-1035
E-mail: erodriguez@waytoworknyc.org
URL: http://www.waytoworknyc.org/front
Description: Serves as a free voluntary vocational training, guidance, and job placement service for economically and educationally disadvantaged young people (ages 16-21) who are referred by other accredited public and voluntary agencies in New York City. **Purpose:** Seeks to aid high school dropouts and young people with correctional and drug abuse histories. Conducts GED prop and testing.

REFERENCE WORKS

14970 ■ *Harvard Business School Guide to Careers in Management Consulting*
Harvard Business School Publishing
60 Harvard Way
Boston, MA 02163
Ph: (617)783-7400
Fax: (617)783-7489
Fr: 888-500-1016
URL: http://www.hbsp.harvard.edu

$10.83 for individuals. Publication includes: Well-known consulting firms, a mailing list of recruiting contacts, and a selective bibliography of relevant books and directories compiled by the Harvard Business School.

ONLINE AND DATABASE SERVICES

14971 ■ Adecco
URL: http://www.adecco.com/en-US/Pages/default.aspx

Description: Offers temporary staffing, permanent placement, outsourcing, outplacement, training and consulting.

14972 ■ SummerJobs.com
URL: http://www.summerjobs.com

Description: Database listing seasonal and part-time job opportunities. Job listings are organized by country, state, region, and city. Primary focus is on summer jobs for students and education professionals.

OTHER SOURCES

14973 ■ Ambassador Personnel Services Inc.
1541 Fording Island Rd., Ste. 4
Hilton Head Island, SC 29926
Ph: (843)837-9066
Fax: (843)837-6477
E-mail: bluffton@teamambassador.com
URL: http://www.teamambassador.com

Full service employment agency that includes local temporary and permanent placements, medical home health provider and regional and national hospitality placement. Industries served: locally: administrative and clerical, home health; regionally: food and beverage and hospitality.

14974 ■ Elite Staffing
1400 W Hubbard St.
Ste. 200
Chicago, IL 60642
Ph: (773)235-3000
Fax: (773)235-7443
Fr: 800-423-5595
E-mail: info@elitestaffinginc.com
URL: http://www.elitestaffinginc.com

Description: Provides contract, temporary, part-time and full-time staffing services. Provides placement in the following industries: administrative, light industrial and skilled industrial.

14975 ■ Integrity Staffing Solutions
750 Shipyard Dr.
Ste. 300
Wilmington, DE 19801
Fr: 888-458-TEMP
E-mail: info@integritystaffing.com
URL: http://www.integritystaffing.com

Description: Offers temporary and permanent staffing solutions. Services offered include office/clerical staffing, professional staffing, light industrial staffing and direct placement.

14976 ■ Kelly Services
999 W Big Beaver Rd.
Troy, MI 48084
Ph: (248)362-4444
E-mail: kfirst@kellyservices.com
URL: http://www.kellyservices.com/web/global/services/en/pages/index.html

Description: Placement service for temporary and permanent positions. Opportunities are available in several industries, including science, law, healthcare, engineering and education.

14977 ■ Labor Finders International Inc.
11426 N Jog Rd.
Palm Beach Gardens, FL 33418
Ph: (561)627-6507
Fr: 800-864-7749
URL: http://www.laborfinders.com

Description: Provides temporary staffing services for industrial, commercial and construction projects.

14978 ■ Legend Global Search, Inc.
28 W 44th St., Ste. 218
New York, NY 10036
Ph: (212)293-8920
Fax: (212)293-8925
E-mail: staffing@legendglobalsearch.com
URL: http://legalcareers.com

Description: Specializes in the placement for direct-hire, contract and temporary positions at every level of the enterprise.

14979 ■ The Linde Group, Inc.
301 Sovereign Ct.
Ballwin, MO 63021
Ph: (636)207-1118
Fax: (636)207-1371
E-mail: lincoln@thelindegroup.com
URL: http://www.thelindegroup.com

Permanent placement and temporary help service.

14980 ■ Preferred Temporaries
Sears Crescent Bldg.
Ste. 550
100 City Hall Plaza
Boston, MA 02108
Ph: (617)723-1919
Fax: (617)523-0202
E-mail: information@preferredtemps.com
URL: http://www.preferredtemps.com

Description: Provides temporary staffing solutions for companies in the Boston, MA area.

14981 ■ RO-LAN Associates Inc.
725 Sabattus St.
Lewiston, ME 04240
Ph: (207)784-1010
Fax: (207)782-3446
E-mail: rlapointe@aol.com

Professional placement specialists for permanent and temporary positions. Also offers executive search and recruiting expertise, outplacements, complete resume service, new business consulting and job and career transition coaching.

14982 ■ Spear-Izzo Associates L.L.C.
651 Holiday Dr., Ste. 300
Pittsburgh, PA 15220
Ph: (412)928-3290
Fax: (724)940-1959
E-mail: info@siasearch.com
URL: http://www.siasearch.com

An executive search management company. Provides permanent, temporary, and contract placements, for the consulting industry.

REFERENCE WORKS

14983 ■ *Advice from the Top: What Minority Women Say about Their Career Success*
ABC-CLIO
130 Cremona Dr.
Santa Barbara, CA 93117
Fax: (866)270-3856
Fr: 800-368-6868
E-mail: customerservice@abc-clio.com
URL: http://www.abc-clio.com

Valencia Campbell. 2009. $39.95 (hardcover). 174 pages. Contains tips and advice from minority women who succeeded in their respective careers. Seeks to inspire women who want to advance their careers. Includes profiles of successful minority women.

14984 ■ *Career GPS: Strategies for Women Navigating the New Corporate Landscape*
Amistad
c/o HarperCollins Publishers
10 E 53rd St.
New York, NY 10022
Ph: (212)207-7000
Fr: 800-242-7737
URL: http://www.harpercollins.com

Ella L.J. Edmondson Bell and Linda Villarosa. 2011. $14.99 (paper). 256 pages. Serves as a guide for career women looking to advance up the corporate ladder. Includes guidelines and tips for maximizing a review, and networking.

14985 ■ *Creative Girl: The Ultimate Guide for Turning Talent and Creativity into a Real Career*
Running Press
2300 Chestnut St., Ste. 200
Philadelphia, PA 19103
Ph: (215)567-5080
E-mail: perseus.promos@perseusbooks.com
URL: http://www.perseusbooksgroup.com

Katharine Sise. 2010. $16.95 (paper). Teaches women how to turn their talents and creativity into a profitable career.

14986 ■ *The Digital Mom Handbook: How to Blog, Vlog, Tweet, and Facebook Your Way to a Dream Career at Home*
HarperCollins Publishers
10 E 53rd St.
New York, NY 10022
Ph: (212)207-7000
URL: http://www.harpercollins.com

Audrey McClelland and Colleen Padilla. 2011. $10.98. 256 pages. Guides stay-at-home moms to create successful careers from home using the internet.

14987 ■ *Ferguson Career Resource Guide for Women and Minorities*
Impact Publications
9104 Manassas Dr., Ste. N
Manassas Park, VA 20111-5211
Ph: (703)361-7300
Fax: (703)335-9486
Fr: 800-361-1055
URL: http://www.impactpublications.com

Latest edition September, 2006. $150.00 for individuals. Covers: information on hundreds of organizations, colleges, foundations, and publications devoted to the careers and educational advancement of women minorities.

14988 ■ *INSIGHT Into Diversity*
INSIGHT Into Diversity
c/o Potomac Publishing, Inc.
225 Meramec Ave., Ste. 400
St. Louis, MO 63105
Ph: (314)863-2900
Fax: (314)863-2905
Fr: 800-537-0655
URL: http://www.aarjobs.com

Monthly. $15.00 for individuals; $8.00 for individuals. Covers: In each issue, about 300 positions at a professional level (most requiring advanced study) available to women, minorities, veterans, and the handicapped; listings are advertisements placed by employers with affirmative action programs. Entries include: Company or organization name, address, contact name; description of position including title, requirements, duties, application procedure, salary, etc. Arrangement: Classified by profession.

14989 ■ *National Directory of Woman-Owned Business Firms*
Business Research Services Inc.
7720 Wisconsin Ave., Ste. 213
Bethesda, MD 20814
Ph: (301)229-5561
Fax: (301)229-6133
Fr: 800-845-8420
URL: http://www.sba8a.com

Annual, latest edition 13th. $295.00 for individuals. Covers: 30,000 woman-owned businesses. Entries include: Company name, address, phone, name and title of contact, minority group, certification status, date founded, number of employees, description of products or services, sales volume, government contracting experience, references. Arrangement: Standard Industrial Classification (SIC) code, geographical. Indexes: Alphabetical by company.

14990 ■ *Wisconsin Women's Resource Directory*
Wisconsin Women's Council
101 E Wilson St., 8th Fl.
Madison, WI 53702
Ph: (608)266-2219

Fax: (608)267-0626
URL: http://womenscouncil.wi.gov/
section.asp?linkid=41&locid=2

Latest edition 2005-2006. Covers: Agencies, organizations, services, and other programs of interest to and concerned with women, including career planning, displaced homemaker services, legal aid, women's studies programs, child care services, etc. Entries include: Organization name, address, phone, e-mail, URL, purpose. Arrangement: Classified by area of concern.

14991 ■ *Women in Engineering, Science and Technology: Education and Career Challenges*
IGI Global
701 E Chocolate Ave.
Hershey, PA 17033
Ph: (717)533-8845
Fax: (717)533-8661
Fr: (866)342-6657
E-mail: cust@igi-global.com
URL: http://www.igi-global.com

Aileen Cater-Steel and Emily Cater. 2010. $180 (hardcover). 384 pages. Provides a collection of empirical studies related to the education and careers of women in Engineering.

14992 ■ *The Work-at-Home Success Bible*
Adams Media
57 Littlefield St.
Avon, MA 02322
Ph: (508)427-7100
Fax: (508)427-6790
URL: http://www.adamsmedia.com

Leslie Truex. 2009. $14.95 (paper). 336 pages. Serves as a guide for women interested in working from home. Features topics on finding the right job fit, setting up a home office, organizing and scheduling daily business tasks and avoiding home distractions.

NEWSPAPERS, MAGAZINES, AND JOURNALS

14993 ■ *American Association of Women Dentists Chronicle*
American Association of Women Dentists
216 W Jackson Blvd, Ste. 625
Chicago, IL 60606
Fax: (312)750-1203
Fr: 800-920-2293
E-mail: info@aawd.org
URL: http://www.aawd.org/

Description: Quarterly. Includes articles of interest on dentistry, nutrition, research, education, and federal services. Provides information on the association, the practice of dentistry, and women in dentistry.

14994 ■ Association for Women in Mathematics Newsletter
Association for Women in Mathematics
11240 Waples Mill Rd., Ste. 200
Fairfax, VA 22030
Ph: (703)934-0163
Fax: (703)359-7562
E-mail: awm@awm-math.org
URL: http://www.awm-math.org/newsletter.html

Description: Six issues/year. Has a circulation of 3,500. $50/year for libraries, women's studies centers, and non-mathematics departments. Concerned with the progress of women in professional fields, particularly in mathematics and related careers. Recounts facets of the history of women in mathematics, discusses issues related to education, and highlights women being honored for studies and achievements. Recurring features include letters to the editor and a section on job openings.

14995 ■ The Broadcast
EYH Network
Mills College
5000 Macarthur Blvd.
Oakland, CA 94613
Ph: (510)430-2222
Fax: (510)430-2090
E-mail: msneyh@mills.edu
URL: http://www.expandingyourhorizons.org/news/
newsletters.php

Description: Quarterly. Carries news of the Network, which is interested in promoting the continuing development in mathematics and science of all people, with special emphasis on the needs of women. Recurring features include information on career education conferences, teacher education programs which encourage girls and women to pursue scientific careers, and news of resources available.

14996 ■ Business Woman Magazine
Business and Professional Women/USA
1718 M St. NW, Ste. 148
Washington, DC 20036
Ph: (202)293-1100
Fax: (202)861-0298
Fr: 888-491-8833
E-mail: foundation@bpwfoundation.org
URL: http://www.bpwusa.org

$30.00/year for individuals; $35.00/year for two years. Magazine for working women that promotes workplace equity issues.

14997 ■ Center for Research on Women-Standpoint
Center for Research on Women
The University of Memphis
337 Clement Hall
Memphis, TN 38152-3550
Ph: (901)678-2770
Fax: (901)678-3652
E-mail: crow@memphis.edu
URL: http://www.memphis.edu/crow/

Description: 2/year. Features news on issues of concern to women, including careers, education, ethnic minority affairs, sexual harassment, violence, and economics. Includes information on Center activities and conferences, and Race, Class, and Gender Scholarship.

14998 ■ FEW's News and Views
Federally Employed Women Inc.
700 N Fairfax St., No. 510
Alexandria, VA 22314
Ph: (202)898-0994
Fax: (202)898-1535
E-mail: few@few.org
URL: http://www.few.org/publications.asp

Description: Bimonthly. Concerned with women's issues, particularly those involving women in the federal government. Reports on administration actions affecting the status of women and analyzes significant legislation. Recurring features include letters to the editor, news of members, a calendar of events, book reviews, and notices of career development and training opportunities.

14999 ■ International Women Pilots
The Ninety-Nines Inc.
4300 Amelia Earhart Rd.
Oklahoma City, OK 73159
Ph: (405)685-7969
Fax: (405)685-7985
Fr: 800-994-1929
E-mail: 99s@ninety-nines.org
URL: http://www.ninety-nines.org/index.cfm/99_
news_magazine.htm

Description: Bimonthly. $20 for non-members. Includes material of interest to the members of The Ninety-Nines, Inc., an international organization of women pilots. Recurring features include interviews, news of research, letters to the editor, news of educational opportunities, a calendar of events, and columns titled President's and Careers.

15000 ■ Making Bread
Making Bread Magazine
1528 Walnut St., Ste. 1925
Philadelphia, PA 19102
URL: http://www.makingbreadmagazine.com/
NEWHome.htm

Irregular. $20.00/year for individuals. Online magazine for professional and entrepreneurial women.

15001 ■ The NAWIC Image
National Association of Women in Construction
327 S Adams St.
Fort Worth, TX 76104
Ph: (817)877-5551
Fax: (817)877-0324
Fr: 800-552-3506
E-mail: nawic@nawic.org
URL: http://www.nawic.org

Description: Bimonthly. Fosters career advancement for women in construction. Features women business owners, training for construction trades and educational programs. Recurring features include columns titled "Issues and Trends," "Road to Success," "Chapter Highlights," "Members on the Move," and "Q&A."

15002 ■ Southern Association for Women Historians Newsletter
Southern Association for Women Historians
c/o Shannon Frystak
Dept. of History
409 Stroud Hall
East Stroudsburg University of Pennsylvania
East Stroudsburg, PA 18301-2999
E-mail: h-sawh-request@h-net.msu.edu
URL: http://www.h-net.org/~sawh

Description: Three issues/year. Informs members of the Association's activities aimed at advancing the professional development of women historians and historians of women. Carries minutes of the annual meeting, announcements of awards and prizes available for work published in a variety of areas, and calls for papers at various conferences. Recurring features include notices of publications available, job listings, and member updates.

15003 ■ WEPANEWS
Women in Engineering Programs & Advocates Network
1901 E Asbury Ave., Ste. 220
Denver, CO 80208
Ph: (303)871-4643
Fax: (303)871-4628
E-mail: dmatt@wepan.org
URL: http://www.wepan.org

Description: 2/year. Seeks to provide greater access for women to careers in engineering. Includes news of graduate, undergraduate, freshmen, pre-college, and re-entry engineering programs for women. Recurring features include job listings, faculty, grant, and conference news, international engineering program news, action group news, notices of publications available, and a column titled Kudos.

15004 ■ Woman Engineer
Equal Opportunity Publications, Inc.
445 Broadhollow Rd., Ste. 425
Melville, NY 11747
Ph: (631)421-9421
Fax: (631)421-1352
E-mail: info@eop.com
URL: http://www.eop.com

Annual. Magazine that is offered at no charge to qualified female engineering, computer-science, and information-technology students and professionals seeking to find employment and advancement in their careers.

15005 ■ Women in Business
The ABWA Company Inc.
9100 Ward Pky.
PO Box 8728
Kansas City, MO 64114-0728
Fax: (816)361-4991
Fr: 800-228-0007
E-mail: abwa@abwa.org
URL: http://www.abwa.org

Bimonthly. $32.00/year for nonmembers. Women's business magazine.

15006 ■ Women in Higher Education
Wenniger Co.
5376 Farmco Dr.
Madison, WI 53704
Ph: (608)251-3232
Fax: (608)284-0601
E-mail: career@wihe.com
URL: http://www.wihe.com/

Description: Monthly. Focuses on leadership, career strategies, gender equity, and harassment of women administrators. Recurring features include interviews, news of research, reports of meetings and presentations, news of educational opportunities, job listings, book reviews, notices of publications available, columns titled Profile, Research Briefs, Newswatch, What Should She Do?, Moveable Type, and The Last Laugh.

AUDIO/VISUAL RESOURCES

15007 ■ Work Talk: Women in Nontraditional Careers in Their Own Words
Her Own Words
PO Box 5264
Madison, WI 53705
Ph: (608)271-7083
Fax: (608)271-0209
E-mail: jocelynriley@herownwords.com
URL: http://www.herownwords.com

Video. Jocelyn Riley. $95.00. 15 minutes. Resource guide also available for $45.00.

ONLINE AND DATABASE SERVICES

15008 ■ Career-Intelligence.com
URL: http://www.career-intelligence.com

Description: Serves as an online career resource for women looking for employment. Features topics on career assessment, career management, transition, advancement, starting up a business, and other relevant issues for career enhancement.

15009 ■ CareerWomen.com
URL: http://careerwomen.com

Description: Serves as an online career center by and for women. Provides job seekers access to employers and recruiters who are actively looking for female talent, workers and professionals.

15010 ■ MBA Careers
3934 SW Corbett Ave.
Portland, OR 97239
Ph: (503)221-7779
Fax: (503)221-7780
E-mail: eric@careerexposure.com
URL: http://mbacareers.com

Description: Job site that provides resume posting, databank search and e-mail alert services to MBA and other advanced graduate degree holders.

15011 ■ MomsToWork.com
E-mail: contactus@momstowork.com
URL: http://www.momstowork.com

Description: Features job opportunities for all mothers.

15012 ■ Womans-Work.com
URL: http://www.womans-work.com

Description: Focuses on helping women find professional flexible work jobs. Offers life balance tips, wage comparisons, resume writing guidelines, and tips on interviewing.

15013 ■ Women For Hire
URL: http://womenforhire.com

Description: Provides career advancement services for professional women. Offers career-related information and an online job board to help employers connect with professional women from all fields.

15014 ■ Women in Legal Jobs
URL: http://www.legaljobsforwomen.com

Description: Serves as an online resource for women seeking legal jobs.

15015 ■ Women at Work
3871 E Colorado Blvd.
Pasadena, CA 91107
Ph: (626)796-6870
Fax: (626)793-7396
E-mail: jobs@womenatwork1.org
URL: http://womenatwork.org

Description: Site of nonprofit job and career resource center, serving the greater Los Angeles area.

15016 ■ WomenAndMinorities.com
E-mail: info@womenandminorities.com
URL: http://womenandminorities.com

Description: Serves as a minority website where job ads and resumes can be easily accessed. Provides a search engine that matches qualified diverse applicants to job openings and automatically notifies employers of matching resumes and matching job listings.

15017 ■ WomensJobList.com
URL: http://www.womensjoblist.com

Description: Serves as a job board dedicated to professional women. Provides employers with exclusive access to highly qualified candidates.

OTHER SOURCES

15018 ■ 9 to 5, National Association of Working Women
207 E Buffalo St., No. 211
Milwaukee, WI 53202
Ph: (414)274-0925
Fax: (414)272-2870
Fr: 800-522-0925
E-mail: 9to5@9to5.org
URL: http://www.9to5.org

Description: Represents women office workers. Seeks to build a national network of local office worker chapters that strives to gain better pay, proper use of office automation, opportunities for advancement, elimination of sex and race discrimination, and improved working conditions for women office workers. Works to introduce legislation or regulations

at state level to protect video display terminal operators. Produces studies and research in areas such as reproductive hazards of Video Display Terminals (VDTs), automation's effect on clerical employment, family and medical leaves, and stress. Conducts annual summer school for working women. Maintains speakers' bureau.

15019 ■ 9 to 5 Working Women Education Fund (WWEF)
207 E Buffalo St., No. 211
Milwaukee, WI 53202
Ph: (414)274-0925
Fax: (414)272-2870
Fr: 800-522-0925
E-mail: 9to5@9to5.org
URL: http://www.9to5.org

Description: Conducts research on the concerns of women workers. Includes topics such as: work/family, anti-discrimination, welfare/workfare, contingent work. Conducts public presentations and seminars upon request; provides speakers and trainers on sexual harassment. Compiles statistics of women in the workforce.

15020 ■ Association for Women Geoscientists (AWG)
12000 N Washington St., Ste. 285
Thornton, CO 80241
Ph: (303)412-6219
Fax: (303)253-9220
E-mail: office@awg.org
URL: http://www.awg.org

Description: Represents men and women geologists, geophysicists, petroleum engineers, geological engineers, hydrogeologists, paleontologists, geochemists, and other geoscientists. Aims to encourage the participation of women in the geosciences. Exchanges educational, technical, and professional information. Enhances the professional growth and advancement of women in the geosciences. Provides information through web site on opportunities and careers available to women in the geosciences. Sponsors educational booths and programs at geological society conventions. Operates charitable program. Maintains speaker's bureau, and Association for Women Geoscientists Foundation.

15021 ■ Business and Professional Women's Foundation (BPWF)
1718 M St. NW, No. 148
Washington, DC 20036
Ph: (202)293-1100
Fax: (202)861-0298
E-mail: foundation@bpwfoundation.org
URL: http://www.bpwfoundation.org

Description: Dedicated to improving the economic status of working women through their integration into all occupations. Conducts and supports research on women and work, with special emphasis on economic issues. Maintains Marguerite Rawalt Resource Center of 20,000 items on economic issues involving women and work and provides public reference and referral service.

15022 ■ Catalyst
120 Wall St., 5th Fl.
New York, NY 10005-3904
Ph: (212)514-7600
Fax: (212)514-8470
E-mail: info@catalyst.org
URL: http://www.catalystwomen.org

Description: Works to advance women in Business and the professions. Serves as a source of information on women in business for past four decades. Helps companies and women maximize their potential. Holds current statistics, print media, and research materials on issues related to women in business.

15023 ■ Center for Economic Options (CEO)
910 Quarrier St., Ste. 206
Charleston, WV 25301

Ph: (304)345-1298
Fax: (304)342-0641
E-mail: info@economicoptions.org
URL: http://www.centerforeconomicoptions.org

Description: Seeks to improve the economic position and quality of life for women, especially low-income and minority women. Works to provide access to job training and employment options to women. Supports self-employed women and small business owners by offering training and technical assistance and information. Advocates women's legal right to employment, training, education, and credit. Seeks to inform the public on economic issues related to women; while activities are conducted on local and state levels, group cooperates with national and international organizations on issues relating to employment and economic justice for women. Maintains speakers' bureau and library. Compiles statistics; conducts research.

15024 ■ Corporate Diversity Search
PO Box 1086
Webster, NY 14580
Ph: (585)787-0537
Fax: (585)787-1321
E-mail: oates@corpdiversitysearch.com
URL: http://www.corpdiversitysearch.com

Description: Serves as an executive search firm specializing in the placement of women and minorities. Provides organizations with professionals who possess the technical expertise, education, and commitment in the following areas: engineering (chemical, electrical, mechanical), optics, sciences, accounting and finance, manufacturing, and human resources.

15025 ■ Federally Employed Women (FEW)
700 N Fairfax St., No. 510
Alexandria, VA 22314
Ph: (202)898-0994
Fax: (202)898-1535
E-mail: few@few.org
URL: http://www.few.org

Description: Represents men and women employed by the federal government. Seeks to end sexual discrimination in government service; to increase job opportunities for women in government service and to further the potential of all women in the government; to improve the merit system in government employment; to assist present and potential government employees who are discriminated against because of sex; to work with other organizations and individuals concerned with equal employment opportunity in the government. Provides speakers and sponsors seminars to publicize the Federal Women's Program; furnishes members with information on pending legislation designed to end discrimination against working women; informs and provides members opportunities for training to improve their job potential; issuesfact sheets interpreting civil service rules and regulations and other legislative issues; provides annual training conference for over 3,000 women and men

15026 ■ Feminist Majority Foundation
1600 Wilson Blvd., Ste. 801
Arlington, VA 22209
Ph: (703)522-2214
Fax: (703)522-2219
URL: http://feminist.org

Description: Promotes women's equality, reproductive health and non-violence. Engages in research and public policy development, public education programs, grassroots organizing projects, leadership training and development programs. Participates and organizes forums on issues of women's equality and empowerment.

15027 ■ The International Alliance for Women (TIAW)
1760 Old Meadow Rd., Ste. 500
McLean, VA 22102

Fr: (866)533-8429
E-mail: info@tiaw.org
URL: http://www.tiaw.org

Description: Local networks comprising 50,000 professional and executive women in 12 countries; individual businesswomen without a network affiliation are alliance associates. Promotes recognition of the achievements of women in business. Encourages placement of women in senior executive positions. Maintains high standards of professional competence among members. Facilitates communication on an international scale among professional women's networks and their members. Represents members' interests before policymaking business and government. Sponsors programs that support equal opportunity and enhance members' business and professional skills. Operates appointments and directors service. Maintains speakers' bureau.

15028 ■ National Association for Female Executives
PO Box 3052
Langhorne, PA 19047
Fr: 800-927-6233
E-mail: carol.evans@workingmother.com
URL: http://www.nafe.com

Description: Represents women executives, business owners, and entrepreneurs. Provides networking opportunities for all members. Advocates for the advancement of women in the workplace.

15029 ■ National Coalition of 100 Black Women (NCBW)
1925 Adam C. Powell Jr. Blvd., Ste. 1L
New York, NY 10026
Ph: (212)222-5660
Fax: (212)222-5675
E-mail: executivedirector@nc100bw.org
URL: http://www.ncbw.org

Description: Represents African-American women actively involved with issues such as economic development, health, employment, education, voting, housing, criminal justice, the status of black families, and the arts. Seeks to provide networking and career opportunities for African-American women in the process of establishing links between the organization and the corporate and political arenas. Encourages leadership development; sponsors role-model and mentor programs to provide guidance to teenage mothers and young women in high school or who have graduated from college and are striving for career advancement.

15030 ■ Organization of Chinese American Women (OCAW)
4641 Montgomery Ave., Ste. 208
Bethesda, MD 20814
Ph: (301)907-3898
Fax: (301)907-3899
E-mail: info@ocawwomen.org
URL: http://www.ocawwomen.org

Description: Advances the cause of Chinese American women in the U.S. and fosters public awareness of their special needs and concerns. Seeks to integrate Chinese American women into the mainstream of women's activities and programs. Addresses issues such as equal employment opportunities at both the professional and nonprofessional levels; overcoming stereotypes; racial and sexual discrimination and restrictive traditional beliefs; assistance to poverty-stricken recent immigrants; access to leadership and policymaking positions. Serves as networking for Chinese American women. Sponsors annual opera and Mother's Day and Award Banquet. Establishes scholarships for middle school girls in rural China.

15031 ■ Wealth in Diversity Consulting Group Inc.
544 Black Mountain
Cambridge, VT 05444
Ph: (802)644-5140
Fax: (802)644-2140
E-mail: info@wealthindiversity.com
URL: http://www.wealthindiversity.com

Group specializes in diversity initiatives, leadership and management development, organizational culture, team building, coaching, assessments, recruitment, conflict resolution, career development and health care educational development.

15032 ■ Wider Opportunities for Women (WOW)
1001 Connecticut Ave. NW, Ste. 930
Washington, DC 20036
Ph: (202)464-1596
Fax: (202)464-1660
E-mail: vstaples@wowonline.org
URL: http://www.wowonline.org

Description: Expands employment opportunities for women through information, employment training, technical assistance, and advocacy. Works to overcome barriers to women's employment and economic equity, including occupational segregation, sex stereotyped education and training, discrimination in employment practices and wages. Sponsors Women's Work Force Network, a national network of 500 women's employment programs and advocates. Monitors current policies to increase the priority given to employment needs of women; provides information to congressional staffs to clarify the impact of various legislative proposals on women; issues public policy alerts and informational materials when relevant federal policy is being proposed or undergoing revision; conducts investigative projects to assess how legislative programs are implemented and their impact on women. Offers technical assistance to education institutions, government agencies, and private industry on programs to increase women's participation in non-traditional employment and training. Maintains National Commission on Working Women and Industry Advisory Councils.

15033 ■ Women in Management (WIM)
PO Box 1032
Dundee, IL 60118-7032
Ph: (708)386-0496
Fax: (847)683-3751
Fr: 877-946-6285
E-mail: nationalwim@wimonline.org
URL: http://www.wimonline.org

Description: Supports network of women in professional and management positions that facilitate the exchange of experience and ideas. Promotes self-growth in management; provides speakers who are successful in management; sponsors workshops and special interest groups to discuss problems and share job experiences.

Outplacement

AUDIO/VISUAL RESOURCES

15034 ■ Getting Fired, Getting Hired: Job Hunting From A to Z
Career Lab
8310 S Valley Hwy., Ste. 300
Englewood, CO 80112-5815
Ph: (303)790-0505
Fax: (303)790-0606
Fr: 800-723-9675
E-mail: wsfrank@careerlab.com
URL: http://www.careerlab.com/craig_lincoln/startup_fired_hired.htm
Six-part video series.

ONLINE AND DATABASE SERVICES

15035 ■ CareerCounselingServices.com
URL: http://www.careercounselingservices.com
Description: Provides consulting services for career transitioning.

15036 ■ CareerFYI.com
URL: http://www.careerfyi.com
Description: Provides career transition services for downsized employees.

15037 ■ Careerpro.com
E-mail: info@careerpro.com
URL: http://www.careerpro.com
Description: Provides resume and career tips for job hunters. Outplacement services are provided.

15038 ■ HR-Guide.com
URL: http://www.hr-guide.com
Description: Online guide to outplacement services.

15039 ■ Outplacing.com
E-mail: info@outplacing.com
URL: http://outplacing.com
Description: Provides online and personalized outplacement services to increase success in finding a new career.

15040 ■ Transition Solutions: Executive Center for Transition
Fr: 888-424-0003
E-mail: info@transitionsolutions.com
URL: http://www.transitionsolutions.com
Description: Provides tailored transition support for senior executives with compensation of six figures or more.

OTHER SOURCES

15041 ■ Allen and Associates
2600 Lake Lucien Dr.
Ste. 410
Maitland, FL 32751
Ph: (407)475-5500
Fr: (866)953-8800
URL: http://www.allenandassociates.com
Description: Outplacement firm offering career transition services.

15042 ■ Association of Career Firms North America (ACFI)
8509 Crown Crescent C., Ste. ACF
Charlotte, NC 28227
Ph: (704)849-2500
Fax: (704)845-2420
E-mail: bcrigger@oipartners.net
URL: http://www.acf-northamerica.com
Description: Represents firms providing displaced employees, who are sponsored by their organization, with counsel and assistance in job searching and the techniques and practices of choosing a career. Develops, improves and encourages the art and science of outplacement consulting and the professional standards of competence, objectivity, and integrity in the service of clients. Cooperates with other industrial, technical, educational, professional, and governmental bodies in areas of mutual interest and concern.

15043 ■ Career Transitions, LLC
4101 Edison Lakes Pkwy., Ste. 200
Mishawaka, IN 46545
Ph: (574)968-1860
Fax: (574)968-1871
Fr: 800-800-3617
URL: http://www.careertransitionsllc.com
Description: Provides contract staffing as well as professional search, recruiting, and outplacement services.

15044 ■ CareerSoar.com
PO Box 905
Wappingers Falls, NY 12590
Ph: (845)235-9233
E-mail: info@careersoar.com
URL: http://www.careersoar.com
Description: Provides consulting services solutions.

15045 ■ CPIworld.com
6340 Quadrangle Dr., Ste. 160
Chapel Hill, NC 27517
Ph: (919)401-4273
URL: http://www.cpiworld.com
Description: Provides outplacement services for corporations. Transitions talent to improve corporate profitability.

15046 ■ Five O'Clock Club
300 E 40th St., Ste. 6L
New York, NY 10016
Ph: (212)286-4500
Fax: (212)286-9571
Fr: 800-538-6645
URL: http://www.fiveoclockclub.com
Description: Career Counseling network.

15047 ■ The Miles/LeHane Group Inc.
205 N King St.
Leesburg, VA 20176
Ph: (703)777-3370
Fax: (703)777-4861
E-mail: feedback@mileslehane.com
URL: http://www.mileslehane.com
Description: Provides transition support consultants to facilitate transition report process.

15048 ■ National Career Development Association (NCDA)
305 N Beech Cir.
Broken Arrow, OK 74012
Ph: (918)663-7060
Fax: (918)663-7058
Fr: (866)367-6232
E-mail: dpennington@ncda.org
URL: http://associationdatabase.com/aws/NCDA/pt/sp/Home_Page
Description: Represents professionals and others interested in career development or counseling in various work environments. Supports counselors, education and training personnel, and allied professionals working in schools, colleges, business/industry, community and government agencies, and in private practice. Provides publications, support for state and local activities, human equity programs, and continuing education and training for these professionals. Provides networking opportunities for career professionals in business, education, and government.

15049 ■ Peter K. Studner Associates
Jamenair Ltd.
PO Box 241957
Los Angeles, CA 90024-9757
Ph: (310)470-6688
Fax: (310)470-8106
Fr: 800-581-5953
URL: http://www.superjobsearch.com
Description: Provides outplacement services helping individuals in career transitions through all stages of preparation to identify, attain, negotiate and achieve their next opportunity.

15050 ■ Quest Outplacement
11436 Marketplace Dr. N, Ste. 217
Champlin, MN 55316
Fax: (763)447-3379
Fr: 888-430-2637
E-mail: info@questoutplacement.com
URL: http://www.questoutplacement.com
Description: Provides transition support consultants to facilitate career transition process.

15051 ■ RiseSmart, Inc.
2055 Gateway Pl., Ste. 150
San Jose, CA 95110
Ph: (408)436-9100

Fr: 877-384-0004
E-mail: support@risesmart.com
URL: http://www.risesmart.com

Description: Helps displaced employees find new jobs. Utilizes a common technology and service

platform to provide solutions for recruitment and outplacement.

15052 ■ Sai Strategies
E-mail: info@saistrategies.com
URL: http://www.saistrategies.com

Description: Private firm offering outplacement services.

Self Employment

REFERENCE WORKS

15053 ■ *Careers in Focus—Entrepreneurs*
Facts On File Inc.
132 W 31st St., 17th Fl.
New York, NY 10001
Ph: (212)967-8800
Fax: 800-678-3633
Fr: 800-322-8755
URL: http://www.infobasepublishing.com
Latest edition 3rd; Published July, 2009. $32.95 for individuals. Covers: An overview of entrepreneurship, followed by a selection of jobs profiled in detail, including the nature of the job, earnings, prospects for employment, what kind of training and skills it requires, and sources for further information.

15054 ■ *Careers for Self-Starters and Other Entrepreneurial Types*
The McGraw-Hill Companies
PO Box 182604
Columbus, OH 43272
Fax: (614)759-3749
Fr: 877-883-5524
E-mail: customer.service@mcgraw-hill.com
URL: http://www.mhprofessional.com
Blythe Camenson. Second edition, 2004. $13.95 (paper). 129 pages.

15055 ■ *Change Your Job, Change Your Life: Careering and Re-Careering in the New Boom/Bust Economy*
Impact Publications
9104 Manassas Dr., Ste. N
Manassas Park, VA 20111-5211
Ph: (703)361-7300
Fax: (703)335-9486
Fr: 800-361-1055
E-mail: query@impactpublications.com
URL: http://www.impactpublications.com
Ronald Krannich. Ninth edition, 2004. $21.95 (paper). 367 pages. Details trends in the marketplace, how to identify opportunities, how to retrain for them, and how to land jobs. Includes a chapter on starting a business. Contains index, bibliography, and illustrations.

15056 ■ *A Consumer Guide to Buying a Franchise*
Franchise Rule Information Hotline
600 Pennsylvania Ave., NW
Washington, DC 20580
Ph: (202)326-2222
URL: http://www.ftc.gov
2005. 21 pages. Describes owning and selecting a franchise.

15057 ■ *Expert Resumes for Baby Boomers*
JIST Publishing
875 Montreal Way
St. Paul, MN 55102
Fr: 800-648-5478
E-mail: educate@emcp.com
URL: http://www.jist.com
Louise M. Kursmark and Wendy S. Enelow. 2007. $16.95 (softcover). 288 pages. Presents written sample resumes for people facing career crossroads: advancing, downsizing, retiring, returning to work after an absence, changing careers, starting their own business, and more. Includes step-by-step instructions and strategies for writing perfectly targeted and professional resumes for all situations.

15058 ■ *Making a Living Without a Job: Winning Ways for Creating Work That You Love*
Bantam Books
c/o Random House, Inc.
1745 Broadway
New York, NY 10019
Ph: (212)782-9000
URL: http://www.randomhouse.com
Barbara J. Winter. 2009. $16.00 (paperback). 288 pages. Serves as guide to self-employment. Includes topics on: finding opportunities in a tough economy; using the internet to market the business; avoiding the common pitfalls of self-employment; and developing multiple profit centers.

15059 ■ *Self-Employment: From Dream to Reality!*
Jist Publishing
875 Montreal Way
St. Paul, MN 55102
Fr: 800-648-5478
E-mail: info@jist.com
URL: http://www.jist.com/shop/
product.php?productid=16252
Linda D. Gilkeson and Theresia Paauwe. Third edition, 2008. $23.95. 176 pages. An interactive workbook for starting a small business.

15060 ■ *Small Business Sourcebook*
Gale
PO Box 6904
Florence, KY 41022-6904
Fr: 800-354-9706
URL: http://www.gale.cengage.com
Annual, Latest edition 29th; March, 2012. $681.00 for individuals. Contains profiles for 340 specific types of small business. Each profile contains sources of start-up information, associations, educational programs, reference works, sources of supplies, statistical sources, trade periodicals, videos, trade shows and conventions, consultants, franchises, databases, business systems and software, libraries, research centers, and Internet databases. Publications also lists 99 general small business topics of interest to entrepreneurs, and sources of small business information and assistance. Entries include: Organization, individual, event, or publication name, address, contact numbers; description of contents, activities, services, publications, or programs; and other details relevant to the type of source, such as show dates and location, investment preferences and limitations, etc. Arrangement: Volume 1 contains small business profiles A-Z; volume 2 contains general small business topics, state listings, federal government assistance. Indexes: Alphabetical.

15061 ■ *Small Time Operator: How to Start Your Own Small Business, Keep Your Books, Pay Your Taxes, and Stay out of Trouble!*
Bell Springs Publishing
PO Box 1240
Willits, CA 95490
Ph: (707)459-6372
Fax: (707)459-8614
Fr: 800-515-8050
E-mail: publisher@bellsprings.com
URL: http://www.bellsprings.com
Bernard Kamoroff. Eighth edition, 2004. $18.95 (paper). 208 pages.

15062 ■ *Start Your Own Business and Hire Yourself: Insider Tips for Successful Self-Employment in Any Economy*
JIST Publishing
875 Montreal way
St. Paul, MN 55102
Fr: 800-648-5478
URL: http://www.jist.com
Suzanne Caplan. 2010. $14.95 (softcover). 208 pages. Serves as guide for professionals considering self-employment. Provides strategies and advice on starting a business, writing business plans, finding clients, and managing costs and gaining profit.

15063 ■ *Supplier Diversity Information Resource Guide*
Diversity Information Resources Inc.
2105 Central Ave. NE
Minneapolis, MN 55418
Ph: (612)781-6819
Fax: (612)781-0109
URL: http://www.diversityinforesources.com
Annual, latest edition 2011. $82.00 for individuals. Covers: Business opportunity fairs, seminars, and workshops; National Supplier Development Council regional offices; Small Business Administration and Minority Business Development Administration offices; minority and women-owned business directories; and other resources for minority and women-owned businesses.

NEWSPAPERS, MAGAZINES, AND JOURNALS

15064 ■ *Entrepreneur Magazine*
Entrepreneur Media Inc.
2445 McCabe Way, Ste. 400
Irvine, CA 92614

Ph: (949)261-2325
Fr: 800-274-6229
E-mail: entmag@entrepreneur.com
URL: http://www.entrepreneur.com/magazine/
entrepreneur/index.html

Monthly. $11.97/year for individuals. Magazine covering small business management and operation.

15065 ■ Franchising World
International Franchise Association
1501 K St. NW, Ste. 350
Washington, DC 20005
Ph: (202)628-8000
Fax: (202)628-0812
Fr: 800-543-1038
URL: http://www.franchise.org/

Monthly. $50.00/year for individuals. Trade magazine covering topics of interest to franchise company executives and the business world.

15066 ■ Innkeeping
Professional Association of Innkeepers International
207 White Horse Pike
Haddon Heights, NJ 08035
Ph: (856)310-1102
Fax: (856)895-0432
Fr: 800-468-7244
E-mail: membership@paii.org
URL: http://www.innkeeping.org

Description: Monthly. Addresses topics of interest to innkeepers who own and operate bed and breakfast operations. Recurring features include letters to the editor, news of research, news of educational opportunities, and notices of publications available.

OTHER SOURCES

15067 ■ National Association for the Self-Employed (NASE)
PO Box 241
Annapolis Junction, MD 20701-0241
Fr: 800-232-6273
URL: http://www.nase.org

Description: Self-employed and small independent businesspersons. Acts as an advocate at the state and federal levels for self-employed people. Provides discounts on products and services important to self-employed and small business owners.

Using Recruiters and Employment Agencies

REFERENCE WORKS

15068 ■ Federal Resume Guidebook
JIST Publishing
875 Montreal Way
St. Paul, MN 55102
Fr: 800-648-5478
E-mail: educate@emcp.com
URL: http://www.jist.com

Kathryn Kraemer Troutman. 2011. $21.95 (softcover). 448 pages. Teaches readers how to develop resumes online and how to write KSAs, ECQs, essays, and short answers that will impress employers. Features sample resumes in actual online builder format. Contains tips for writing KSAs (knowledge, skills and abilities statements) and tips on security clearance requirements.

15069 ■ Headhunters Revealed
Hunter Arts Publishing
PO Box 66578E
Los Angeles, CA 90066
Ph: (310)842-8864
Fax: (310)842-8868
URL: http://www.headhuntersrevealed.com

Quarterly. $14.95 for individuals; $12.50 for out of country. Covers: Online career sites, career associations, and organizations.

15070 ■ Job Seeker's Guide To Working With Recruiters
Kennedy Information
1 Phoenix Mill Ln., 3rd Fl.
Peterborough, NH 03458
Ph: (603)924-1006
Fax: (603)924-4460
Fr: 800-531-0007
E-mail: support@kennedyinfo.com
URL: http://www.kennedyinfo.com

Kennedy Information. 2009. $24.95 (paper). 190 pages. Provides tips on how to successfully work with recruiters and land the next job.

15071 ■ Knock 'Em Dead: The Ultimate Job Seeker's Handbook
Adams Media Corp.
4700 E Galbraith Rd.
Cincinnati, OH 45236
Ph: (513)531-2690
Fax: (513)531-4082
Fr: 800-289-0963
URL: http://www.adamsmediastore.com/product/1359/careers

Martin Yate. 2010. $15.95 (paper). 384 pages. Prepares the job seeker for the interview with advice on dress, manner, how to answer the toughest questions, and how to spot illegal questions. Discusses how to respond to questions of salary to maximize income. Features sections on executive search firms and drug testing.

15072 ■ National Directory of Personnel Service Firms
National Association of Personnel Services
131 Prominence Ct., Ste. 130
Dawsonville, GA 30534
Ph: (706)531-0060
Fax: (866)739-4750
URL: http://www.recruitinglife.com

Annual, spring. Covers: Over 1,100 member private (for-profit) personnel service firms and temporary service firms. Entries include: Firm name, address, phone, fax, contact, area of specialization. Arrangement: Same information given geographically by employment specialty.

15073 ■ The Professional Recruiter's Handbook
Kogan Page Publishers
1518 Walnut St., Ste. 1100
Philadelphia, PA 19102
Ph: (215)928-9112
Fax: (215)928-9113
E-mail: info@koganpage.com
URL: http://www.koganpageusa.com

Ann Swain and Jane Newell Brown. 2009. $39.95 (paper). 256 pages. Serves as a guide to achieving success as a recruiting consultant. Includes practical advice on attracting the right candidates and finding and retaining new clients. Features case studies and interviews with recruitment professionals.

ONLINE AND DATABASE SERVICES

15074 ■ Association of Executive Search Consultants
E-mail: aesc@aesc.org
URL: http://www.aesc.org/eweb

Description: Partnership with BlueSteps.com allows member search consultants to add their names to a directory of firms, which may then be referred to senior executives who contact the organization to help fill executive vacancies within their own organizations.

15075 ■ Corporate Search Consultants, Inc.
PO Box 236
Oakland, FL 34760
Fax: (321)221-1732
Fr: 800-800-7231
E-mail: webmanager@corpsearch.com
URL: http://www.corpsearch.com

Description: Job search consultants. Job board and resume posting for jobs in the healthcare and medical community.

15076 ■ FutureStep.com
1900 Ave. of the Stars, Ste. 2600
Los Angeles, CA 90067

Fr: (866)RPO-GO71
E-mail: info@futurestep.com
URL: http://www.futurestep.com

Description: An executive search service for management professionals. Seekers can register for free, and search for jobs posted. Also contains assessment information, career resources, and useful links.

15077 ■ GlocapSearch.com
156 W 56th St., 4th Fl.
New York, NY 10019
Ph: (212)333-6400
URL: http://www.glocap.com

Description: Recruitment firm for the private equity, venture capital and hedge fund marketplaces. After registering with website, seekers will be notified weekly of positions available that may interest them. Through returned e-mail, the firm will forward resumes and schedule preliminary interviews with prospective employers.

15078 ■ MRINetwork.com
URL: http://www.mrinetwork.com

Description: Management-level job seekers can review job board and/or contact an executive recruiter seeking for prospective candidates. Site also contains resume building and career transitioning resources.

15079 ■ The Recruiter Directory
URL: http://therecruiterdirectory.com

Description: Features a searchable database of headhunters and recruiters across the United States.

15080 ■ SearchFirm.com
URL: http://www.searchfirm.com

Description: Serves as an online executive recruiter directory. Seeks to connect corporate recruiters with leading executive search firms.

15081 ■ Spherion
2050 Spectrum Blvd.
Fort Lauderdale, FL 33309
Ph: (954)308-7600
Fr: 800-774-3746
E-mail: help@spherion.com
URL: http://www.spherion.com

Description: Recruitment firm specializing in accounting and finance, sales and marketing, interim executives, technology, engineering, retail and human resources.

15082 ■ TheRecruiterNetwork.com
URL: http://www.therecruiternetwork.com/recruiter/index.php

Description: Maintains an active and up-to-date database of recruiters from all industries and job seeker resumes. Facilitates resume distribution to potential recruiters.

SOFTWARE

15083 ■ **Executive Search System**
Custom Databanks, Inc.
60 Sutton Pl. S, Ste. 14BN
New York, NY 10022-4168
Fr: 800-445-3557
E-mail: email@customdatabanks.com
URL: http://www.customdatabanks.com
$300.00 (latest update). Databases contain 25,700+

search firms. Can download and merge data directly into your cover letters.

OTHER SOURCES

15084 ■ **NPA, The Worldwide Recruiting Network**
1680 Viewpond Dr. SE
Grand Rapids, MI 49508

Ph: (616)455-6555
Fax: (616)455-8255
E-mail: npa@npaworldwide.com
URL: http://www.npaworldwide.com

Description: Connects premier independent recruiting firms located throughout Europe, Asia, Australia, Africa and the Americas to facilitate cooperative, split-fee placements. Works direct placement jobs where fees are always paid by the employer.

Working at Home

REFERENCE WORKS

15085 ■ The Digital Mom Handbook: How to Blog, Vlog, Tweet, and Facebook Your Way to a Dream Career at Home
HarperCollins Publishers
10 E 53rd St.
New York, NY 10022
Ph: (212)207-7000
URL: http://www.harpercollins.com
Audrey McClelland and Colleen Padilla. 2011. $10.98. 256 pages. Guides stay-at-home moms to create successful careers from home using the internet.

15086 ■ Homemade Money
M. Evans & Company Inc.
4501 Forbes Blvd., Ste. 200
Lanham, MD 20706-4346
Ph: (301)459-3366
Fax: (301)429-5743
Fr: 800-462-6420
URL: http://www.rlpgtrade.com
Published in two volumes. $24.95 for individuals. Publication includes: A special 76 page, updated "A-Z Crash Course" on business basics and a directory of 300 listings.

15087 ■ The Ultimate Job Directory
Outskirts Press, Inc.
10940 S Parker Rd., No. 515
Parker, CO 80134
Fr: 888-672-6657
URL: http://www.outskirtspress.com
SM Consulting. 2010. $29.95 (paper). 379 pages. Contains an extensive listing of 1,000 legitimate work from home companies.

15088 ■ Undress for Success: The Naked Truth about Making Money at Home
John Wiley & Sons, Inc.
111 River St.
Hoboken, NJ 07030
Ph: (201)748-6000
Fax: (201)748-6088
E-mail: info@wiley.com
URL: http://www.wiley.com
Kate Lister and Tom Harnish. 2009. $24.95 (hardcover). 288 pages. Guides professionals interested in starting a home-based job or business. Provides tips and advice on: available home-based jobs and how to land one; using the Web for opportunities without being scammed; and turning professional talents into a freelance business.

15089 ■ The Work-at-Home Success Bible
Adams Media
57 Littlefield St.
Avon, MA 02322
Ph: (508)427-7100
Fax: (508)427-6790
URL: http://www.adamsmedia.com
Leslie Truex. 2009. $14.95 (paper). 336 pages. Serves as a guide for women interested in working from home. Features topics on finding the right job fit, setting up a home office, organizing and scheduling daily business tasks and avoiding home distractions.

15090 ■ Work@home
New Hope Publishers
PO Box 12065
Birmingham, AL 35202
Ph: (205)991-8100
Fr: 800-968-7301
URL: http://www.newhopepublishers.com
Glynnis Whitwer. 2007. $15.99. 240 pages (paper). Offers practical guides in all aspects of the transition from working in a corporate workplace to working from home.

ONLINE AND DATABASE SERVICES

15091 ■ At-Homeworks.com
URL: http://www.at-homeworks.com
Description: Provides resources and ideas for working at home. Job postings are available, as well as networking opportunities.

15092 ■ HEA-Employment.com
URL: http://www.hea-employment.com
Description: Helps job seekers locate work at home employment opportunities. Aims to connect job seekers with reputable employers.

15093 ■ Home-Based Working Moms
URL: http://www.hbwm.com
Description: Users can create profiles and network with others who work at home. Provides job opportunities and a support system.

15094 ■ LegitimateOnlineJobs.com
URL: http://www.legitimateonlinejobs.com
Description: Serves as a job search engine for finding telecommuting employment opportunities.

15095 ■ ProgrammingFromHome.com
URL: http://www.programmingfromhome.com
Description: Serves as a site that helps programmers bring their programming careers back home. Provides job openings posted by employers who are looking for part-time and full-time computer programming help.

15096 ■ StayHomeJobs.com
URL: http://www.stayhomejobs.com
Description: Serves as a niche job board for job seekers who wish to work from home.

15097 ■ Telecommuting Jobs
URL: http://www.tjobs.com
Description: Job hunters may enter a resume or post a job-wanted listing. Employers may search talent available and post job availabilities. Site also includes tools to connect telecommuters with employers and job news about telecommuting.

15098 ■ Work-At-Home-Directory.com
URL: http://www.work-at-home-directory.com
Description: Exists as an online site designed and developed to help visitors find legitimate work at home income and/or an online home based business.

15099 ■ Work At Home Jobs
URL: http://www.workathomejobs.org
Description: Serves as a job aggregator for work from home opportunities. Enables users to receive job email alerts, save work at home jobs that they're interested in, post their resumes and portfolio, and network with others working from home.

15100 ■ Work from Home
URL: http://www.jobs-telecommuting.com
Description: Contains a listing of over 700 companies currently looking for telecommuters. Employers may add or remove job listings. Also information on starting a home business available.

15101 ■ WorkAtHomeCareers.com
URL: http://www.workathomecareers.com
Description: Serves as a search engine for work-at-home jobs, careers, home businesses, work from home articles and companies that hire workers.

15102 ■ WorkAtHomeCrossing.com
URL: http://www.workathomecrossing.com
Description: Provides job consolidation service in the employment industry for individuals who wish to work at home.

15103 ■ WorldwideWorkAtHome.com
URL: http://www.worldwideworkathome.com
Description: Offers information and resources relating to work at home jobs, telecommuting, freelance work, home business ideas, and more.

OTHER SOURCES

15104 ■ Home Employment Directory
National Homeworkers Association
1450 W 7th Ave.
Eugene, OR 97402
Ph: (541)485-4741
Fax: (541)683-6385
Fr: 800-356-0473
URL: http://www.national-homeworkers-association.com

Lists companies that pay weekly incomes for work performed at home.

Working Part-Time, Summer Employment, and Internships

REFERENCE WORKS

15105 ■ All Work, No Pay: Finding an Internship, Building Your Resume, Making Connections, and Gaining Job Experience
Ten Speed Press
6001 Shellmound St.
Emeryville, CA 94608
Ph: (510)285-3000
Fax: (510)285-2979
URL: http://www.randomhouse.com/crown/tenspeed
Lauren Berger. 2012. $12.99 (paper). 208 pages. Covers essential information that students and alternative career-changers need to get ahead. Contains tips on scoring the best internship, building connections and developing skills.

15106 ■ The Counseling Practicum and Internship Manual
Springer Publishing Company
11 W 42nd St., 15th Fl.
New York, NY 10036
Ph: (212)431-4370
Fax: (212)941-7842
Fr: 877-687-7476
URL: http://www.springerpub.com
Shannon Hodges. 2010. $35.00. 311 pages (softcover). Covers practicum and internships in all settings and provides detailed guidelines in selecting and applying for a job, performing responsibly on the job, and maintaining ethical standards.

15107 ■ Directory of Child Life Programs
Child Life Council Inc.
11821 Parklawn Dr., Ste. 310
Rockville, MD 20852-2539
Ph: (301)881-7090
Fax: (301)881-7092
URL: http://www.childlife.org
Biennial, latest edition 14th, 2006. Covers: Over 400 child life programs. Entries include: Facility name, address, phone, name of child life department and director, reporting structure, staff statistics, educational requirements for employment, and internship or educational opportunities. Arrangement: Geographical. Indexes: Speciality areas, internship sessions, program size, fellowships.

15108 ■ Directory of International Internships
Dean's Office of International Studies and Programs
Michigan State University
209 International Ctr.
East Lansing, MI 48824-1035
Ph: (517)355-2350
Fax: (517)353-7254
E-mail: infonew@isp.msu.edu
URL: http://www.isp.msu.edu/students/internships/intlguide
Irregular, latest edition 5th. $34.00 for individuals; $27.00 for students; $30.00 for students; $37.00 for

individuals. Covers: International internships sponsored by academic institutions, private sector, and the federal government. Entries include: Institution name, address, phone, names and titles of key personnel, subject areas in which internships are available, number available, location, duration, financial data, academic credit available, evaluation procedures, application deadline, requirements of participation. Arrangement: Classified by type of sponsor, then alphabetical. Indexes: Sponsor, subject, geographical.

15109 ■ Grants, Fellowships, and Prizes of Interest to Historians
American Historical Association
400 A St. SE
Washington, DC 20003-3889
Ph: (202)544-2422
Fax: (202)544-8307
E-mail: grantguide@theaha.org
URL: http://www.historians.org
Annual, latest edition 2006. for members. Covers: Over 450 sources of funding (scholarships, fellowships, internships, awards, and book and essay prizes) in the United States and abroad for graduate students, postdoctoral researchers, and institutions in the humanities. Entries include: Name of source, institution name or contact, address, phone, eligibility and proposal requirements, award or stipend amount, location requirements for research, application deadlines. Arrangement: Alphabetical in three categories: support for individual research and teaching; grants for groups and organizations for research and education; and book, article, essay, and manuscript prizes.

15110 ■ The Internship, Practicum and Field Placement Handbook: A Guide for the Helping Professions
Prentice Hall PTR
1 Lake St.
Upper Saddle River, NJ 07458
Ph: (201)236-7000
Fr: 800-922-0579
URL: http://www.pearsonhighered.com
Brian N. Baird. Fifth edition, 2008. $93.40. 264 pages.

15111 ■ Internships in Recreation and Leisure Services: A Practical Guide for Students
Venture Publishing, Inc.
1999 Cato Ave.
State College, PA 16801
Ph: (814)234-4561
Fax: (814)234-1651
E-mail: vpublish@venturepublish.com
URL: http://www.venturepublish.com/product.php?id=154
Edward E. Seagle, Jr., Ralph W. Smith. Fourth edition, 2008. $33.95 (paper). 204 pages.

15112 ■ Internships in Sport Management
Venture Publishing, Inc.
1999 Cato Ave.
State College, PA 16801
Ph: (814)234-4561
Fax: (814)234-1651
URL: http://www.venturepublish.com
Robin Ammon, Jr., Matthew Walker, Edward E. Seagle and Ralph W. Smith. 2010. $29.95. 170 pages. Seeks to prepare promising sport management majors for internship in sport event management, intercollegiate athletics, minor league sport, sport facility management, sport marketing, sport promotions, or other areas of the expanding sport/business and sport/entertainment industries. Contains real-life examples presented by previous sport management students.

15113 ■ National Directory of Arts Internships
National Network for Artist Placement
935 West Ave. 37
Los Angeles, CA 90065
Ph: (323)222-4035
E-mail: info@artistplacement.com
URL: http://www.artistplacement.com
Biennial, odd years; latest edition 11th. $95.00 for individuals. Covers: Over 5,000 internship opportunities in dance, music, theater, art, design, film, and video & over 1,250 host organizations Entries include: Name of sponsoring organization, address, name of contact; description of positions available, eligibility requirements, stipend or salary (if any), application procedures. Arrangement: Classified by discipline, then geographical.

15114 ■ Part Time Prospects: International Comparison of Part Time Work in Europe, North America and the Pacific Rim
Taylor & Francis
325 Chestnut St., 8th Fl.
Philadelphia, PA 19106
Ph: (215)625-8900
Fax: (215)269-0363
Fr: 800-821-8312
URL: http://www.taylorandfrancis.com
Jacqueline O'Reilly and Colette Fagan. $55.95 (paper). 304 pages. Presents for the first time a systematically comparative analysis of the common and divergent patterns in the use of part-time work in Europe, America and the Pacific Rim.

15115 ■ Peterson's Summer Opportunities for Kids and Teenagers
Peterson's Guides
2000 Lenox Dr.
Box 67005
Lawrenceville, NJ 08648
Ph: (609)896-1800
Fax: (609)896-4531

Fr: 800-338-3282
E-mail: custsvc@petersons.com
URL: http://www.petersons.com/books/
internships.asp

Peterson's. Twenty-fifth edition, 2005. $26.95 (paper). 768 pages. In addition to information about 1,400 summer activities and programs, covers job opportunities for high school and college students. Part of Summer Opportunities for Kids and Teenagers series.

15116 ■ A Practical Guide to Sport Management Internships
Carolina Academic Press
700 Kent St.
Durham, NC 27701
Ph: (919)489-7486
Fax: (919)493-5668
URL: http://www.cap-press.com

John Miller and Todd Seidler. 2010. $30.00 (paper). 246 pages. Provides an overview of the role of internships in sport management programs. Offers in-depth pedagogical and legal insights on sport management industries.

15117 ■ Summer Theater Directory
American Theatre Works Inc.
2349 West Rd.
PO Box 159
Dorset, VT 05251
Ph: (802)867-9333
Fax: (802)867-2297
URL: http://www.theatredirectories.com

Annual, Latest edition 2009. $38.50 for individuals. Covers: Summer theater companies, theme parks and cruise lines that offer employment opportunities in acting, design, production, and management; summer theater training programs. Entries include: Company name, address, phone, name and title of contact; type of company, activities and size of house; whether union affiliated, whether nonprofit or commercial; year established; hiring procedure and number of positions hired annually, season; description of stage; internships; description of company's artistic goals and audience. Arrangement: Geographical. Indexes: Company name.

15118 ■ Vault Guide to Top Internships
Vault.com Inc.
150 W 22nd St., 5th Fl.
New York, NY 10011
Ph: (212)366-4212
Fax: (212)366-6117
Fr: 888-562-8285
URL: http://www.vault.com

Latest edition 2010. $14.95 for individuals; $14.95 for members. Covers: More than 700 internships. Entries include: Information on qualification, pay, number of interns, length of internship, and contact information. Also include background information on the company or organization.

NEWSPAPERS, MAGAZINES, AND JOURNALS

15119 ■ NRPA Career Center
National Recreation and Park Association, Professional Services Div.
22377 Belmont Ridge Rd.
Ashburn, VA 20148
Ph: (703)858-0784
Fax: (703)858-0794
Fr: 800-626-6772
E-mail: customerservice@nrpa.org
URL: http://www.nrpa.org

Description: Provides listings of employment opportunities in the park, recreation, and leisure services field.

ONLINE AND DATABASE SERVICES

15120 ■ Aplus-SummerJobs.com
URL: http://www.aplus-summerjobs.com

Description: Provides summer and seasonal work opportunities for students and recent graduates.

15121 ■ Backdoorjobs.com
URL: http://www.backdoorjobs.com

Description: Provides an online listing of short-term employment opportunities for job seekers.

15122 ■ CampPage - Summer Camp Jobs
URL: http://www.summercampstaff.com

Description: Contains an online listing of summer camp jobs.

15123 ■ CoolWorks.com
URL: http://www.coolworks.com

Description: Provides seasonal job and career opportunities. Focuses on jobs in places which include national parks, resorts, ranches, camps, ski resorts, conservation corps, jobs on water, and more.

15124 ■ GrooveJob.com
URL: http://www.groovejob.com

Description: Serves as a job board that lists part-time jobs for students and teens. Includes summer and seasonal jobs.

15125 ■ InternJobs.com
URL: http://www.internjobs.com

Description: Serves as a database of internships and entry-level positions for students, recent graduates and career changers.

15126 ■ InternshipCrossing.com
URL: http://www.internshipcrossing.com

Description: Provides internship opportunities in a wide variety of fields.

15127 ■ Internships4You
URL: http://www.internships4you.com

Description: Lists internship opportunities for college students worldwide.

15128 ■ Internweb.com
URL: http://www.internweb.com

Description: Connects job seekers, specifically students, with an employer and the kind of internship that they need.

15129 ■ InternZoo.com
URL: http://www.internzoo.com

Description: Serves as an online internship database for students across the country. Offers internships, summer internships, paid internships, college internships and also provides job opportunities.

15130 ■ PartTimeCrossing
URL: http://www.parttimecrossing.com

Description: Provides lists of all available part-time jobs across employer career webpages, job boards, organizations' websites, newspaper classifieds, and recruiter sites.

15131 ■ Rising Star Internships
URL: http://www.rsinternships.com

Description: Lists internship opportunities for various fields and industries. Features other internship links, college/university lists, and a career resource center.

15132 ■ Snagajob.com
URL: http://www.snagajob.com

Description: Job site for part-time and full-time hourly jobs.

15133 ■ SummerJobs411.com
E-mail: info@summerjobs411.com
URL: http://www.summerjobs411.com

Description: Provides information, as well as job listings, for different summer jobs such as cruise ship jobs, jobs in the Alaska fishing industry, tour guiding positions, daycare and babysitting, lifeguard jobs, retail jobs, and summer internships.

15134 ■ WetFeet.com
URL: http://www.wetfeet.com

Description: Job board website with free membership for job seekers. Contains job board, resume listing, self assessment guides, company and city research, discussion forums, e-guides and online bookstore, salary calculators and listings of internship opportunities.

OTHER SOURCES

15135 ■ Association of Psychology Postdoctoral and Internship Centers (APPIC)
10 G St. NE, Ste. 440
Washington, DC 20002
Ph: (202)589-0600
Fax: (202)589-0603
E-mail: appic@aol.com
URL: http://www.appic.org

Description: Veterans administration hospitals, medical centers, state hospitals, university counseling centers, and other facilities that provide internship and postdoctoral programs in professional psychology. Promotes activities that assist in the development of professional psychology training programs. Serves as a clearinghouse to provide Ph.D. candidates with internship placement assistance at member facilities. Conducts workshops and seminars on training procedures in clinical psychology at the PhD level.

15136 ■ Experience International
PO Box 680
Everson, WA 98247
Ph: (360)966-3876
Fax: (360)966-4131
E-mail: info@expint.org
URL: http://www.expint.org

Description: Promotes international understanding and human resource development. Provides projects in international development and training in agricultural extension and education. Fosters technical and cultural exchange among members.

15137 ■ INROADS
10 S Broadway, Ste. 300
St. Louis, MO 63102
Ph: (314)241-7488
Fax: (314)241-9325
E-mail: info@inroads.org
URL: http://www.inroads.org

Description: Provides internships for ethnically diverse students which lead to full-time career opportunities for the interns. Aims to develop and place talented Black, Hispanic/Latino, and Native American Indian high school and college students in business and industry and to prepare them for corporate and community leadership. Recruits, trains, and matches over 5000 individuals with paid internships for over 500 business corporations per year. Offers professional training seminars on time management, business presentation skills, team building, and decision making. Provides personal and professional guidance to pre-college and college interns. Operates in the U.S.; Mexico City; and Toronto and Saskatchewan, Canada.

15138 ■ National Association of Part-Time and Temporary Employees (NAPTE)
5800 Barton, Ste. 201
PO Box 3805
Shawnee, KS 66203

Ph: (913)962-7740
E-mail: napte-champion@worldnet.att.net
URL: http://www.members.tripod.com/~napte

Description: Purpose: Promotes the economic and social interests of persons working on a part-time, contingent, or temporary basis through research, advocacy, and member services. Offers short-term portable health insurance.

15139 ■ New Ways to Work (NWW)
103 Morris St., Ste. A
Sebastopol, CA 95472
Ph: (707)824-4000
Fax: (707)824-4410
E-mail: newways@newwaystowork.org
URL: http://www.newwaystowork.org

Description: Helps communities build systems that connect schools, community organizations and businesses, and improve the services, educational programs and support the community provides for its youth. Engages and supports local communities in the invention and renewal of connected, comprehensive youth-serving systems.

15140 ■ *15 Minute Cover Letter*
JIST Publishing
875 Montreal Way
St. Paul, MN 55102
Fr: 800-648-5478
E-mail: info@jist.com
URL: http://www.jist.com

2009. $9.95 (softcover). 192 pages. Features a collection of written cover letter samples.

15141 ■ *101 Best Resumes: Endorsed by the Professional Association of Resume Writers*
The McGraw-Hill Companies
PO Box 182604
Columbus, OH 43272
Fax: (614)759-3749
Fr: 877-883-5524
E-mail: customer.service@mcgraw-hill.com
URL: http://www.mhprofessional.com/
    product.php?isbn=0070328935

Jay A. Block and Michael Betrus. $12.95 (paper). 197 pages.

15142 ■ *101 Great Resumes*
Cengage Learning
PO Box 6904
Florence, KY 41022
Fax: 800-487-8488
Fr: 800-354-9706
E-mail: esales@cengage.com
URL: http://www.cengage.com

Ron Fry. Third edition, 2010. $10.99 (paper). 216 pages. Sample resumes cover 39 common situations and 62 career fields.

15143 ■ *201 Dynamite Job Search Letters*
Impact Publications
9104 Manassas Dr., Ste. N
Manassas Park, VA 20111-5211
Ph: (703)361-7300
Fax: (703)335-9486
Fr: 800-361-1055
E-mail: query@impactpublications.com
URL: http://www.impactpublications.com/
    201dynamitejobsearchletters.aspx

Ronald Krannich. Fifth edition, 2005. $19.95. 295 pages. Shows how to write nine different types of letters.

15144 ■ *All Work, No Pay: Finding an Internship, Building Your Resume, Making Connections, and Gaining Job Experience*
Ten Speed Press
6001 Shellmound St.
Emeryville, CA 94608
Ph: (510)285-3000
Fax: (510)285-2979
URL: http://www.randomhouse.com/crown/tenspeed

Lauren Berger. 2012. $12.99 (paper). 208 pages. Covers essential information that students and alternative career-changers need to get ahead. Contains tips on scoring the best internship, building connections and developing skills.

15145 ■ *Amazing Resumes, Second Edition*
JIST Publishing
875 Montreal Way
St. Paul, MN 55102
Fr: 800-648-5478
E-mail: educate@emcp.com
URL: http://www.jist.com

Jim Bright and Joanne Earl. 2009. $12.95 (softcover). 240 pages. Includes resumes, internet resources, insider evaluations, worksheets, lists of competencies to emphasize, power words, self-evaluation exercises, tips on reading job postings, internet resume advice, and a chapter on using narrative to achieve job goals and how to use the resume as a bridge to answering behavioral interview questions.

15146 ■ *Blue Collar Resumes*
Cengage Learning
PO Box 6904
Florence, KY 41022-6904
Fax: 800-487-8488
Fr: 800-354-9706
URL: http://www.cengage.com

Steve Provenzano. 2012. $15.99 (paper). 224 pages. Helps job seekers write effective resumes and market their skills. Provides a step-by-step guide on resume writing. Includes job search techniques, tips and strategies to win interviews and land jobs.

15147 ■ *The Business Writer's Handbook*
St. Martin's Press, LLC
175 5th Ave.
New York, NY 10010
Ph: (646)307-5151
Fax: (212)674-6132
Fr: 888-330-8477
URL: http://us.macmillan.com/
    thebusinesswritershandbookninthedition

Gerald J. Alred, Charles T. Brusaw, and Walter E. Oliu. Ninth edition, 2008. $44.95 (paper). 624 pages.

15148 ■ *Can I Wear My Nose Ring to the Interview?: A Crash Course in Finding, Landing, and Keeping Your First Real Job*
Workman Publishing Company
225 Varick St.
New York, NY 10014-4381
Ph: (212)254-5900
Fax: (212)254-8098
E-mail: info@workman.com
URL: http://www.workman.com

Ellen Gordon Reeves. 2009. $13.95 (paper). 227 pages. Gives a step-by-step guide through the job searching process. Features tips and advice on writing effective resumes and cover letters, networking and winning the interview.

15149 ■ *Career Coward's Guide to Job Searching*
JIST Publishing
875 Montreal Way
St. Paul, MN 55102
Fr: 800-648-5478
E-mail: educate@emcp.com
URL: http://www.jist.com

Katy Piotrowski. 2008. $10.95 (softcover). 224 pages. Empowers job seekers to step outside their comfort zone by breaking down the job search process into small, attainable goals.

15150 ■ *The Complete Idiot's Guide to the Perfect Resume*
Alpha Books
375 Hudson St.
New York, NY 10014
Fr: 800-631-8571
URL: http://us.penguingroup.com

Susan Ireland. 2010. $16.95 (paper). 304 pages. Contains guidelines on how to write an effective resume. Includes samples of real-life resumes and cover letters.

15151 ■ *Cover Letter Magic: Trade Secrets of Professional Resume Writers*
JIST Publishing
875 Montreal Way
St. Paul, MN 55102
Fax: 800-547-8329
Fr: 800-648-5478
E-mail: info@jist.com
URL: http://www.jist.com

Louise M. Kursmark and Wendy S. Enelow. 2010. $18.95. 448 pages. 4th edition. Contains step-by-step instructions on writing, formatting and distributing cover letters that get noticed and land interviews. Includes more than 130 sample cover letters for all types of jobseekers. Features a chapter on recession-proofing careers and lifetime career management.

15152 ■ *Cover Letters for Dummies*
1 Wiley Dr.
Somerset, NJ 08873
Ph: (732)469-4400
Fax: (732)302-2300
Fr: 800-225-5945
E-mail: custserv@wiley.com
URL: http://as.dummies.com

Joyce Lane Kennedy. Third edition, 2009. $16.99 (paper). 312 pages. Includes dozens of examples.

15153 ■ *Cover Letters That Knock 'em Dead*
Adams Media Corp.
57 Littlefield St.
Avon, MA 02322
Ph: (508)427-7100
Fax: (508)427-6790

Fr: 800-872-5627
URL: http://www.adamsmedia.com

Martin Yate. Eight edition. $12.95 (paper). 320 pages. Discusses the fundamentals of writing a superior cover letter; how to match the letter style with the resume it accompanies; which format is right for which applicant; what always goes in, what always stays out, and why. Includes a number of samples. Part of Cover Letters That Knock 'em Dead series.

15154 ■ Creating Your High School Portfolio
Jist Works
875 Montreal Way
St. Paul, MN 55102
Fr: 800-648-5478
E-mail: info@jist.com
URL: http://www.jist.com/shop/
   product.php?productid=16616&cat=0&page=1

2009. $16.95. 160 pages. This workbook shows students how to collect and store essential documents needed to apply for first jobs or college.

15155 ■ Creating Your High School Resume
Jist Works
875 Montreal Way
St. Paul, MN 55102
Fr: 800-648-5478
E-mail: info@jist.com
URL: http://www.jist.com/shop/
   product.php?productid=16507&cat=0&page=1

Kathryn Kraemer Troutman. 2009. $16.95. 144 pages. This workbook provides a step-by-step guide to preparing an effective resume for a career or college.

15156 ■ CVs For Dummies, Second Edition
John Wiley & Sons, Inc.
111 River St.
Hoboken, NJ 07030-5774
Ph: (201)748-6000
Fax: (201)748-6088
E-mail: info@wiley.com
URL: http://as.wiley.com/WileyCDA

Lois-Andrea Ferguson and Joyce Lain-Kennedy. 2009. $27.95 (paper). 266 pages. Shows how to create high quality curriculum vitae essential in today's competitive job market.

15157 ■ CV's and Job Applications
Oxford University Press, Inc.
198 Madison Ave.
New York, NY 10016-4314
Ph: (212)726-6000
Fax: (919)677-1303
Fr: 800-445-9714
E-mail: custserv.us@oup.com
URL: http://www.oup.com/us

Judith Leigh and John Seely. 2004. $16.51 Paper. Illustrated. 144 pages.

15158 ■ The Damn Good Resume Guide
Ten Speed Press
PO Box 7123
Berkeley, CA 94707
Ph: (510)559-1600
Fax: (510)559-1629
Fr: 800-841-2665
E-mail: order@tenspeed.com
URL: http://www.randomhouse.com/catalog/
   display.pperl?isbn=9781580084444

Yana Parker. Fourth edition, 2004. $11.95 (paper). 80 pages. Concentrates on producing an effective resume, with examples of functional and chronological resumes.

15159 ■ Designing the Perfect Resume
Barron's Educational Series, Inc.
250 Wireless Blvd.
Hauppauge, NY 11788-3917
Ph: (631)434-3311
Fax: (631)434-3723

Fr: 800-645-3476
E-mail: fbrown@barronseduc.com
URL: http://barronseduc.com

Pat Criscito. Third edition, 2005. $16.99 (paper). 352 pages. Focuses on resume appearance. Includes hundreds of sample resumes created using Word-Perfect software.

15160 ■ Directory of Professional Resume Writers
JIST Publishing
875 Montreal Way
St. Paul, MN 55102
Fr: 800-648-5478
E-mail: educate@emcp.com
URL: http://www.jist.com

Louise M. Kursmark. 2008. $9.97 (softcover). 304 pages. Contains list of professional resume writers in the U.S., Canada, and Australia, plus tips on choosing the best writer for the resume.

15161 ■ The Elements of Resume Style: Essential Rules and Eye-Opening Advice for Writing Resumes and Cover Letters that Work
AMACOM
1601 Broadway
New York, NY 10019
Ph: (212)586-8100
Fr: 877-566-9441
URL: http://www.amacombooks.org/
   book.cfm?isbn=9780814472804

Scott Bennett. 2005. $9.95. 128 pages. Discusses ways to write compelling and engaging resumes.

15162 ■ Expert Resumes for Baby Boomers
JIST Publishing
875 Montreal Way
St. Paul, MN 55102
Fr: 800-648-5478
E-mail: educate@emcp.com
URL: http://www.jist.com

Louise M. Kursmark and Wendy S. Enelow. 2007. $16.95 (softcover). 288 pages. Presents written sample resumes for people facing career crossroads: advancing, downsizing, retiring, returning to work after an absence, changing careers, starting their own business, and more. Includes step-by-step instructions and strategies for writing perfectly targeted and professional resumes for all situations.

15163 ■ Expert Resumes for Computer and Web Jobs
Jist Publishing
875 Montreal Way
St. Paul, MN 55102
Fr: 800-648-5478
E-mail: info@jist.com
URL: http://www.jist.com

Wendy Enelow and Louise Kursmark. Third edition, 2011. $17.95 (paper). 304 pages.

15164 ■ Expert Resumes for Engineers
JIST Publishing
875 Montreal Way
St. Paul, MN 55102
Fr: 800-648-5478
E-mail: educate@emcp.com
URL: http://www.jist.com

Louise M. Kursmark and Wendy S. Enelow. 2009. $16.95 (softcover). 272 pages. Features a collection of written resume samples for all types of engineers including civil, mechanical, industrial, electrical, electronics, computer, and more. Contains tips and strategies for writing engineering resumes and finding the best jobs.

15165 ■ Expert Resumes for Military-to-Civilian Transitions
JIST Publishing
875 Montreal Way
St. Paul, MN 55102

Fr: 800-648-5478
URL: http://www.jist.com

Wendy S. Enelow. 2009. $16.95 (softcover). 304 pages. Provides information on job search strategies, sound resume-writing advice, and tips for creating and using electronic resumes. Features a collection of professionally written resumes designed for veterans and ex-military job seekers.

15166 ■ Expert Resumes for People Returning to Work
JIST Publishing
875 Montreal Way
St. Paul, MN 55102
Fr: 800-648-5478
E-mail: educate@emcp.com
URL: http://www.jist.com

Louise M. Kursmark and Wendy S. Enelow. 2008. $16.95 (softcover). 304 pages. Contains a collection of sample resumes and resume writing advice including how to create and use an electronic resume. Contains an appendix that includes internet resources for an online job search, writing cover letters, as well as a collection of sample letters.

15167 ■ Expert Resumes for Teachers and Educators
JIST Works
875 Montreal Way
St. Paul, MN 55102
Fax: 800-328-4564
Fr: 800-328-1452
E-mail: educate@emcp.com
URL: http://jist.emcpublishingllc.com

Louise M. Kursmark and Wendy Enelow. 2011. $17.95 (softcover). 336 pages. Gives job seekers strategies and ideas needed to craft outstanding resumes and cover letters. Includes samples of cover letters and resumes, an appendix of online career and job search resources, and tips on winning interviews.

15168 ■ Federal Resume Guidebook
JIST Publishing
875 Montreal Way
St. Paul, MN 55102
Fr: 800-648-5478
E-mail: educate@emcp.com
URL: http://www.jist.com

Kathryn Kraemer Troutman. 2011. $21.95 (softcover). 448 pages. Teaches readers how to develop resumes online and how to write KSAs, ECQs, essays, and short answers that will impress employers. Features sample resumes in actual online builder format. Contains tips for writing KSAs (knowledge, skills and abilities statements) and tips on security clearance requirements.

15169 ■ Gallery of Best Cover Letters
JIST Publishing
875 Montreal Way
St. Paul, MN 55102
Fr: 800-648-5478
E-mail: educate@emcp.com
URL: http://www.jist.com

David F. Noble. 2012. $18.95 (softcover). 416 pages. Features cover letter samples and resumes for a variety of careers. Provides high school and college students, as well as adult job seekers, advice and writing strategies suited for their specific career interests.

15170 ■ Gallery of Best Resumes
Jist Works
875 Montreal Way
St. Paul, MN 55102
Fr: 800-648-5478
E-mail: info@jist.com
URL: http://www.jist.com

David F. Noble. Fourth edition, 2007. $18.95. 432 pages. Includes a wide range of styles, formats, designs, occupations, and situations.

15171 ■ Gallery of Best Resumes for People Without a Four-Year Degree
JIST Publishing
875 Montreal Way
St. Paul, MN 55102
Fr: 800-648-5478
E-mail: educate@emcp.com
URL: http://www.jist.com

David F. Noble. 2009. $18.95 (softcover). 432 pages. Contains a collection of sample resumes and cover letters representing the creations of professional resume writers targeted specifically to jobs that do not require a four-year college degree. Guides readers through the writing, design and style elements of a resume.

15172 ■ The Google Resume: How to Prepare for a Career and Land a Job at Apple, Microsoft, Google, or any Top Tech Company
John Wiley & Sons, Inc.
111 River St.
Hoboken, NJ 07030-5774
Ph: (201)748-6000
Fax: (201)748-6088
E-mail: info@wiley.com
URL: http://www.wiley.com

Gayle Laakmann McDowell. 2011. $22.95 (hardcover). 280 pages. Helps job seekers land a job in top companies such as Google, Apple and Microsoft. Includes tips and advice on resume-writing, interview preparation and other key concerns.

15173 ■ Government Job Finder
Planning Communications
7215 Oak Ave.
River Forest, IL 60305-1935
Ph: (708)366-5200
Fax: (708)366-5280
Fr: 888-366-5200
E-mail: info@planningcommunications.com
URL: http://www.planningcommunications.com

Daniel Lauber and Deborah Verlench. Fourth edition, 2008. 348 pages. $19.95. Covers 2,002 sources. Discusses how to use sources of local, state, and federal government job vacancies in a number of specialties and state-bystate, including job-matching services, job hotlines, specialty periodicals with job ads, salary surveys, and directories. Explains how local, state, and federal hiring systems work. Includes chapters on resume and cover letter preparation and interviewing.

15174 ■ Happy About My Resume: 50 Tips for Building a Better Document to Secure a Brighter Future
Happy About
20660 Stevens Creek Blvd., Ste. 210
Cupertino, CA 95014
Ph: (408)257-3000
E-mail: questions@happyabout.info
URL: http://www.happyabout.com

Barbara Safani. 2008. $16.96 (paper). 172 pages. Helps readers learn how to quickly create a resume that is professional, gets an applicant noticed, minimizes the amount of time spent in a job search, and maximizes an applicant's earning power.

15175 ■ How to Say It on Your Resume: A Top Recruiting Director's Guide to Writing the Perfect Resume for Every Job
Penguin Group (USA)
375 Hudson St.
New York, NY 10014-3658
Ph: (212)366-2000
Fax: (212)366-2933
Fr: 800-847-5515
URL: http://us.penguingroup.com

Brad Kash and Courtney Pike. 2009. $15.95 (paper). 304 pages. Features step-by-step guidelines to improve a resume's wording, content and format.

15176 ■ How to Write Better Resumes and Cover Letters
Barrons Educational Series, Inc.
250 Wireless Blvd.
Hauppauge, NY 11788
Ph: (631)434-3311
Fax: (631)434-3723
Fr: 800-645-3476
E-mail: fbrown@barronseduc.com
URL: http://barronseduc.com

Pat Criscito. 2008. $15.29 (paper). 256 pages. Features the 12-step process for producing a resume in all formats needed for a job search and how to create a cover letter. Includes model resumes.

15177 ■ The Innovative Road to Greater Success in Job Hunting and Changing Careers
PublishAmerica
PO Box 151
Frederick, MD 21705
Ph: (301)695-1707
URL: http://www.publishamerica.net

Joan M. Enering. 2011. $19.95 (softcover). 94 pages. Serves as a guide for finding a job or changing careers. Includes tips on writing resumes and cover letters, getting dressed for a job interview, and the secret of the waiting area.

15178 ■ Jobseeker's Guide
The Resume Place, Inc.
89 Mellor Ave.
Baltimore, MD 21228
Ph: (410)744-4324
Fax: (410)744-0112
Fr: 888-480-8265
E-mail: resume@resume-place.com
URL: http://www.resume-place.com

Kathryn Troutman. 2010. $14.95 (paper). 150 pages. Contains essential information for military and family members who are seeking federal employment. Includes resume and cover letter samples.

15179 ■ Knock 'em Dead Cover Letters: Features the Latest Information on: Online Postings, E-mail Techniques, and Follow-up Strategies, 8th Edition
Adams Media
57 Littlefield St.
Avon, MA 02322
Ph: (508)427-7100
E-mail: deskcopies@adamsmedia.com
URL: http://www.adamsmedia.com

Martin Yate. 2008. $9.32 (paper). 320 pages. Gives readers advice on words and phrases to use to get the first interview. Includes a step-by-step procedure for turning weak cover letters into strong ones, the strategies for online cover letters and job searching, and how to transform sloppy cover letters into powerful tools.

15180 ■ Knock 'em Dead Resumes
Adams Media Corp.
57 Littlefield St.
Avon, MA 02322
Ph: (508)427-7100
Fax: (508)427-6790
Fr: 800-872-5627
URL: http://www.adamsmediastore.com/product/knock-em-dead-resumes-9th-edition/careers

Martin Yate. Ninth edition. $9.32 (paper). 320 pages. Presents resumes that were successfully used by individuals to obtain jobs. Resumes target the most commonly-sought positions on all levels.

15181 ■ The Little Resume Book
CreateSpace
7290 B. Investment Dr.
Charleston, SC 29418
E-mail: info@createspace.com
URL: http://www.createspace.com

Stephen Douglas Baker. 2010. $11.99. 72 pages. Serves as alternative career coach in creating a

resume and preparing for first interview. Contains examples of resume with easy-to-follow templates.

15182 ■ Military to Federal Career Guide
The Resume Place, Inc.
89 Mellor Ave.
Baltimore, MD 21228
Ph: (410)744-4324
Fax: (410)744-0112
Fr: 888-480-8265
E-mail: resume@resume-place.com
URL: http://www.resume-place.com

Kathryn Troutman, Paulina Chen and Brian Moore. 2010. $14.95 (paper, CD-ROM included). 130 pages. Serves as a guide for military veterans who want to start a career in the federal government. Provides tips on how to design a federal resume that will translate a veteran's military skills and competencies into the federal skills, keywords and qualifications.

15183 ■ The Perfect Resume: Today's Ultimate Job Search Tool
Broadway Books
1745 Broadway
New York, NY 10019
Ph: (212)782-9000
Fax: (212)572-6066
Fr: 800-733-3000
URL: http://www.randomhouse.com/broadway

Tom Jackson. June 2004. $14.00 (paper). 240 pages.

15184 ■ The Quick Resume and Cover Letter Book
Jist Works
875 Montreal Way
St. Paul, MN 55102
Fr: 800-648-5478
E-mail: info@jist.com
URL: http://www.jist.com/shop/product.php?productid=16243&cat=0&page=1

Michael Farr. Fifth edition, 2011. $14.95. 416 pages. Explains how to write and use a resume in one day.

15185 ■ The Resume and Cover Letter Phrase Book: What to Write to Get the Job That's Right
Adams Media
4700 E Galbraith Rd.
Cincinnati, OH 45236
URL: http://www.adamsmedia.com

Nancy Schuman and Burton Jay Nadler. 2010. $10.95. 256 pages. Teaches applicants to win interviews and land jobs through strategic phrasing.

15186 ■ The Resume Handbook
Adams Media Corp.
57 Littlefield St.
Avon, MA 02322
Ph: (508)427-7100
Fax: (508)427-6790
Fr: 800-872-5627
URL: http://www.adamsmediastore.com/product/the-resume-handbook-5th-edition/careers

Arthur D. Rosenberg. Fifth edition. $8.76 (paper). 176 pages. Includes specific examples of excellent resumes and cover letters and examples of how weaker resumes and cover letters can be improved. Presents resumes for many types of job hunters, including recent college graduates, seasoned professionals, and women re-entering the job market. Chapters on cover letters and 'personal sales' letters and design and layout of resumes are also included.

15187 ■ Resume Magic: Trade Secrets of a Professional Resume Writer
Jist Works
875 Montreal Way
St. Paul, MN 55102
Fr: 800-648-5478
E-mail: info@jist.com
URL: http://www.jist.com

Susan Britton Whitcomb. Fourth edition, 2010.

$18.85. 608 pages. Covers every element of resume writing, with nearly 100 "before and after" examples.

15188 ■ Resume Writing Made Easy
Prentice Hall PTR
1 Lake St.
Upper Saddle River, NJ 07458
Ph: (201)236-7000
Fr: 800-922-0579
URL: http://www.pearsonhighered.com

Lola Brown. Eighth edition, 2006. $31. 192 pages.

15189 ■ Resumes for Business Management Careers
The McGraw-Hill Companies
PO Box 182604
Columbus, OH 43272
Fax: (614)759-3749
Fr: 877-883-5524
E-mail: customer.service@mcgraw-hill.com
URL: http://www.mhprofessional.com/
    product.php?isbn=0071467807

Third edition, 2006. $11.95 (paper). 144 pages. Resume guide for supervisors and line and staff managers. Provides advice on compiling a business management resume; includes a number of sample resumes and cover letters. Part of VGM Professional Resumes series.

15190 ■ Resumes for College Students and Recent Graduates
The McGraw-Hill Companies
PO Box 182604
Columbus, OH 43272
Fax: (614)759-3749
Fr: 877-883-5524
E-mail: customer.service@mcgraw-hill.com
URL: http://www.mhprofessional.com/
    product.php?isbn=007145490X

Third edition, 2004. $11.95 (paper). 153 pages. Shows how to write a resume that capitalizes on pertinent work experience, academic background, and volunteer and extracurricular activities. Includes sample resumes and cover letters.

15191 ■ Resumes, Cover-Letters, Networking, & Interviewing
Wadsworth Publishing
PO Box 6904
Florence, KY 41022
Fax: 800-487-8488
Fr: 800-354-9706
URL: http://www.cengage.com

Clifford W. Eischen and Lynn A. Eischen. 2012. $42.75 (paper). 128 pages. Professional resume using today's business technologies including the Internet and E-mail. Specifically targeted to help individuals with a two-year degree showcase their skills and experiences to get the job they want. Scanable resumes, Internet-based resumes, and etiquette for sending resumes via fax or E-mail are addressed to prepare readers to apply for jobs using today's business technologies. Dedicated chapter on the interview process coaches readers on proper interview attire, preparing for interview questions, introductions, and how to follow up after an interview. Exercises on listing qualifications, producing a first draft, gathering references, and drafting a follow-up letter, all help readers build a finished resume step by step.

15192 ■ Resumes, Cover Letters, Networking and Interviewing
Cengage Learning
PO Box 6904
Florence, KY 41022-6904
Fax: 800-487-8488
Fr: 800-354-9706
URL: http://www.cengage.com

Clifford W. Eischen and Lynn A. Eischen. 2012. $57.95 (paper). 128 pages. Takes job seekers through a step-by-step process of polishing a resume and developing strong interview techniques. Includes topics on using online resources in job hunting,

employment databases, cover letters, networking, and job applications.

15193 ■ Resumes for First-Time Job Hunters
The McGraw-Hill Companies
PO Box 182604
Columbus, OH 43272
Fax: (614)759-3749
Fr: 877-883-5524
E-mail: customer.service@mcgraw-hill.com
URL: http://www.mhprofessional.com/
    product.php?cat=106&isbn=0071388257&cat=106

Third edition, 2005. $11.95 (paper). 144 pages.

15194 ■ Resumes For Dummies, Sixth Edition
John Wiley & Sons, Inc.
111 River St.
Hoboken, NJ 07030-5774
Ph: (201)748-6000
Fax: (201)748-6088
E-mail: info@wiley.com
URL: http://as.wiley.com/WileyCDA

Joyce Lain Kennedy. 2011. $16.95 (paper). 384 pages. Presents up-to-date rules and guidelines in writing a winning resume.

15195 ■ Resumes for Health and Medical Careers
The McGraw-Hill Companies
PO Box 182604
Columbus, OH 43272
Fax: (614)759-3749
Fr: 877-883-5524
E-mail: customer.service@mcgraw-hill.com
URL: http://www.mhprofessional.com/
    product.php?isbn=0071545352

Third edition, 2008. $12.95 (paper). 144 pages.

15196 ■ Resumes for High School Graduates
The McGraw-Hill Companies
PO Box 182604
Columbus, OH 43272
Fax: (614)759-3749
Fr: 877-883-5524
E-mail: customer.service@mcgraw-hill.com
URL: http://www.mhprofessional.com/
    product.php?isbn=0071448918

Third edition, 2005. $11.95. 144 pages. Designed for the person with little or no full-time work experience. Shows how to emphasize part-work experience and highlight educational, extra-curricular and volunteer experience. Provides sample resumes and cover letters.

15197 ■ Resumes for Law Careers
The McGraw-Hill Companies
PO Box 182604
Columbus, OH 43272
Fax: (614)759-3749
Fr: 877-883-5524
E-mail: customer.service@mcgraw-hill.com
URL: http://www.mhprofessional.com/
    product.php?isbn=0071482202

Third edition, 2007. $12.95 (paper). 144 pages.

15198 ■ Resumes for Nursing Careers
The McGraw-Hill Companies
PO Box 182604
Columbus, OH 43272
Fax: (614)759-3749
Fr: 877-883-5524
E-mail: customer.service@mcgraw-hill.com
URL: http://www.mhprofessional.com/
    product.php?isbn=0071509860

2007. $11.95 (paper). 144 pages.

15199 ■ Resumes for Performing Arts Careers
The McGraw-Hill Companies
PO Box 182604
Columbus, OH 43272
Fax: (614)759-3749

Fr: 877-883-5524
E-mail: customer.service@mcgraw-hill.com
URL: http://www.mhprofessional.com/
    product.php?isbn=0071442464

2004. $10.95 (paper). 160 pages.

15200 ■ Resumes for Re-Entering the Job Market
The McGraw-Hill Companies
PO Box 182604
Columbus, OH 43272
Fax: (614)759-3749
Fr: 877-883-5524
E-mail: customer.service@mcgraw-hill.com
URL: http://www.mhprofessional.com/
    product.php?isbn=007164203X

Second edition, 2008. $12.95 (paper). 144 pages. Part of VGM Professional Resumes series.

15201 ■ Resumes for Scientific and Technical Careers
The McGraw-Hill Companies
PO Box 182604
Columbus, OH 43272
Fax: (614)759-3749
Fr: 877-883-5524
E-mail: customer.service@mcgraw-hill.com
URL: http://www.mhprofessional.com/
    product.php?isbn=0071482199

Third edition, 2007. $12.95 (paper). 144 pages. Provides resume advice for individuals interested in working in scientific and technical careers. Includes sample resumes and cover letters.

15202 ■ Resumes for Social Service Careers
The McGraw-Hill Companies
PO Box 182604
Columbus, OH 43272
Fax: (614)759-3749
Fr: 877-883-5524
E-mail: customer.service@mcgraw-hill.com
URL: http://www.mhprofessional.com/
    product.php?isbn=0071467815

2006. $11.95 (paper). 144 pages.

15203 ■ Resumes That Resume Careers
CreateSpace
7290 B. Investment Dr.
Charleston, SC 29418
E-mail: info@createspace.com
URL: http://www.createspace.com

Donald M. Burrows. 2010. $14.95 (paper). 168 pages. Teaches job applicants how to create a functional resume that makes them stand out from other candidates.

15204 ■ Step-by-Step Cover Letters
JIST Publishing
875 Montreal Way
St. Paul, MN 55102
Fr: 800-648-5478
URL: http://www.jist.com

Evelyn U. Salvador. 2010. $19.95 (softcover). 304 pages. Provides step-by-step procedures in making effective cover letters for resumes. Includes a CD-ROM of cover letter samples and templates, letter-building worksheets and additional tools.

15205 ■ Top Secret Executive Resumes: Create the Perfect Resume for the Best Top-Level Positions
Course Technology PTR
20 Channel Center St.
Boston, MA 02210
Fr: 800-354-9706
E-mail: ct.news@cengage.com
URL: http://www.courseptr.com

Steve Provenzano. 2011. $16.49. 240 pages. Guides jobseekers in creating a high-impact resume for executive careers. Includes real-life resume samples and tips on cover letter writing, design and format.

15206 ■ _Unbeatable Resumes_
AMACOM Publishing
1601 Broadway
New York, NY 10019-7420
Fax: (212)903-8083
Fr: 800-250-5308
URL: http://www.amacombooks.org

Tony Beshara. 2011. $16.95 (paper). Shows job seekers of all types how to present themselves through a well-written resume.

AUDIO/VISUAL RESOURCES

15207 ■ _Expert Job Search Strategies for the Ex-offender: Resume Realities_
JIST Publishing
875 Montreal Way
St. Paul, MN 55102
Fr: 800-648-5478
E-mail: educate@emcp.com
URL: http://www.jist.com

2007. $149.00. 15 minutes. Offers tips on what to include and what not to include when creating resume.

15208 ■ _Expert Job Search Strategies: Resume Realities_
JIST Publishing
875 Montreal Way
St. Paul, MN 55102
Fr: 800-648-5478
E-mail: educate@emcp.com
URL: http://www.jist.com

2007. $149. 15 minutes. Covers information on what to include and what not to include when creating a resume.

15209 ■ _From Parole to Payroll_
Cambridge Educational
PO Box 2053
Princeton, NJ 08543-2053
Ph: 800-257-5126
Fax: (609)671-0266
Fr: 800-468-4227
E-mail: custserv@films.com
URL: http://cambridge.films.com

VHS and DVD. 2008. $311.80. Contains solid, real-world content designed to help job seekers find satisfying work, and features informative interviews, helpful tips, and colorful graphics.

15210 ■ _Getting and Using Your Resume, Cover Letter, Portfolio, and JIST Card_
JIST Publishing
875 Montreal Way
St. Paul, MN 55102
Fr: 800-648-5478
URL: http://www.jist.com

2011. $139.00. Covers the purpose and importance of resumes, cover letters, portfolios and other job search materials.

15211 ■ _The Job Seeker's Toolkit_
JIST Publishing
875 Montreal Way
St. Paul, MN 55102
Fr: 800-648-5478
E-mail: educate@emcp.com
URL: http://www.jist.com

2009. $129. 25 minutes. Covers information on writing resumes, the type of resume that suits a job/individual, the parts of a resume, the do's and don'ts of job seeking, cover letters, job applications, and portfolios.

15212 ■ _Resumes and Job Applications_
Cambridge Educational
PO Box 2053
Princeton, NJ 08543-2053
Ph: 800-257-5126
Fax: (609)671-0266

Fr: 800-468-4227
E-mail: custserv@films.com
URL: http://cambridge.films.com

$99.95. 2008. 20 minutes. Part of the "From Parole to Payroll" Series.

ONLINE AND DATABASE SERVICES

15213 ■ 1ExecutiveResume.com
E-mail: info@1executiveresume.com
URL: http://www.1executiveresume.com

Description: Serves executives and senior level professionals. Offers complimentary resume evaluation, executive resume writing, executive cover letter writing, and job search tools. Also provides executive coaching services.

15214 ■ 1st-Writer.com
E-mail: sue1stwriter@gmail.com
URL: http://www.1st-writer.com

Description: Provides links to professional resume writing services and career resources for job hunters.

15215 ■ CareerXpress.com
Interweb Connections, Inc.
Dept. 732
PO Box 34069
Seattle, WA 98124
URL: http://www.careerxpress.com

Description: Resume writing and distribution service. Fee: Pricing depending on desired range of search; begins at $69.

15216 ■ Cover-Letters.com
URL: http://www.cover-letters.com

Description: Provides cover letters for consultants, career changers, and job hunters.

15217 ■ Execume.com
E-mail: inquiry@execume.com
URL: http://www.execume.com

Description: Offers resume writing resources and services including books, CDs, and online resume building tools.

15218 ■ GraduateResumes.com
URL: http://graduateresumes.com

Description: Provides resume writing assistance for new graduates, entry-level jobseekers, and students. Features career advice articles and interview questions for new graduates.

15219 ■ GreatSampleResume.com
URL: http://www.greatsampleresume.com

Description: Serves as an online resource for professional sample resumes. Provides tips on how to customize resumes. Includes job descriptions of various occupations.

15220 ■ The Job Explorer
URL: http://www.thejobexplorer.com

Description: Provides detailed descriptions of various jobs. Includes tips on writing resumes, cover letters and handling job interviews.

15221 ■ MyCareerGuide.com
E-mail: advertising@mycareerguide.com
URL: http://www.mycareerguide.com

Description: Offers career tips and job search articles to assist users in finding a rewarding and profitable career. Provides links to other job search sites.

15222 ■ MyResumeAgent.com
URL: http://www.myresumeagent.com

Description: Allows job seekers to spread their credentials out to a large group of recruiters who can help connect them with the right job for their skill set.

15223 ■ Professional-Resumes.com
URL: http://www.professional-resumes.com

Description: Provides resume writing services for job seekers. Helps people land their new job faster with their insider knowledge of the career industry.

15224 ■ ProvenResumes.com
URL: http://www.provenresumes.com

Description: Contains resume and cover letter writing tips and samples. Helps users correctly identify and market their skills, analyze job ads, write powerful content, and replace weak titles.

15225 ■ ResumeL.com
URL: http://www.resumel.com

Description: Provides information on resume and cover letter writing. Features samples of resumes for different industries.

15226 ■ ResumeLogic.com
URL: http://www.resumelogic.com

Description: Assists engineers from all disciplines in building effective resumes. Utilizes a resume writing system that provides free advice and free resume writing help for engineers and those seeking engineering jobs. Provides engineers with job hunting resources.

15227 ■ SeeMeResumes.com
6767 W Tropicana Ave.
Las Vegas, NV 89103
Ph: (702)248-1032
URL: http://www.seemeresumes.com

Description: Resume coaching and distribution service. Confidential e-mail inboxes available. Fee: Pricing based on desired intensity and range of search; starts at $39.

SOFTWARE

15228 ■ ResumeMaker
Individual Software Inc.
4255 Hopyard Rd., Ste. 2
Pleasanton, CA 94588
Ph: (925)734-6767
Fax: (925)734-8337
E-mail: business@resumemaker.com
URL: http://www.resumemaker.com

CD-ROM. $39.95 for professionals and executives. $29.95 for students and entry-level professionals. Contains resume-writing solutions that provide resumes and additional tools for finding one's dream job.

15229 ■ Resumes Quick & Easy
Individual Software, Inc.
4255 Hopyard Rd., Ste. 2
Pleasanton, CA 94588
Ph: (925)734-6767
Fax: (925)734-8337
Fr: 800-822-3522
E-mail: orders@individualsoftware.com
URL: http://www.individualsoftware.com

CD-ROM. $19.95. Helps the user create resumes, write cover letters, find a salary range, manage contacts, and fax or email their resume.

OTHER SOURCES

15230 ■ Careers2000
10602 Timberwood Cir., Ste. 3
Louisville, KY 40223
Ph: (502)214-4000
Fax: (502)214-4003
Fr: 800-898-0969
URL: http://www.careers2000.net

Description: Offers resume writing done by professional and experienced resume writers. Accepts job orders through phone calls.

15231 ■ Professional Association of Resume Writers & Career Coaches
1388 Brightwaters Blvd., NE
St. Petersburg, FL 33704
Ph: (727)821-2274
Fax: (727)894-1277

Fr: 800-822-7279
E-mail: parwhq@aol.com
URL: http://www.parw.com

Description: Consists of independent business owners, as well as non-profit career centers such as colleges and universities, military bases, workforce development offices, and state Departments of Labor. Exists as a group of career professionals to exchange information, enhance their skills, or demonstrate their commitment to providing professional services to the general public. Upholds dedication to excellence in meeting client career goals.

*This Index is an alphabetical listing of all entries contained in Volumes One, Two, and Three. Index references are to **entry numbers** rather than to page numbers. Publication and film titles are rendered in italics.*

American Association of Teachers of French 2413, 6710, 11805

American Association of Teachers of German 2414, 6711, 11806

American Association of Teachers of Spanish and Portuguese 2415, 6712, 11807

American Association for Teaching and Curriculum 6503

American Association of Textile Chemists and Colorists 2031

American Association of University Professors 2416

American Association of Veterinary Laboratory Diagnosticians 12829

American Association of Wildlife Veterinarians 900, 12830

American Association for Women in Community Colleges 466, 2417, 4182

American Association of Women Dentists 3679

American Association of Women Dentists Chronicle 3579, 14993

American Association for Women Radiologists 8676, 10887

American Association of Zoo Veterinarians 12831

American Astronomical Society 10216

American Auditory Society 12188

American Bakers Association 1295

American Banker 3270, 4853, 7577

American Bankers Association 1317, 3293, 4999, 7596

The American Bar 6928

American Bar Association 7066

American Bar Association—Directory 6929, 7169

American Bee Journal 868

The American Biology Teacher 1381, 2295, 6624, 11714

American Biotechnology Laboratory 1382, 1507, 1964, 11682

American Board of Criminalistics 5147, 6861

American Board of Forensic Toxicology (ABFT) 5148

American Board of Funeral Service Education 5329

American Board of Genetic Counseling 5628

American Board of Genetic Counseling—Membership Directory 5617

American Board of Medical Genetics 5629

American Board of Opticianry 4007

American Board of Oriental Reproductive Medicine 381

American Board of Podiatric Orthopedics and Primary Podiatric Medicine 10283

American Board of Podiatric Surgery 10284

American Board of Professional Liability Attorneys 7067

American Board of Professional Psychology—Directory of Diplomates 10633

American Board of Registration of EEG and EP Technologists 4235

American Board of Trial Advocates 7068

American Border Leicester Association 901

American Camp Association 11002

American Casino Guide 5333

American Catholic Historical Association 6125

American Catholic Lawyers Association 7069

American Catholic Philosophical Association 2418

American Ceramic Society 8350

American Chamber of Commerce Executives 5593

American Chemical Society 1947, 2032, 11705

American Chemical Society Career Sources 1934, 2019, 13722

American Chemical Society Southeastern Regional Meeting and Conference 1942

American Chiropractic Association 2104

American City and County 2122, 2915, 3059, 5025, 6437, 6781, 6811, 10976, 11883, 12409, 12725

American Civil Liberties Union 6311

American Classical League 2419, 11808

American Clinical Neurophysiology Society Annual Meeting 4234, 4258

American College of Apothecaries Newsletter 9283, 9409

American College of Cardiology Annual Scientific Session 4259

American College of Chest Physicians 10100

American College of Chiropractic Orthopedists 2105

American College of Clinical Pharmacy 9395

American College Counseling Association 3186

American College of Counselors 3187

American College of Dentists 3680

American College of Emergency Physicians 10101

American College of Emergency Physicians Scientific Assembly 4467

American College of Environmental Lawyers 7070

American College of Epidemiology 4794

American College of Forensic Examiners International 5149

American College Health Association 6034, 10102

American College of Health Care Administrators 6035

American College of Healthcare Executives 6036

American College of Medical Genetics 5630

American College of Medical Quality 6037, 10103

American College of Nurse-Midwives 11255

American College of Nurse Practitioners 11256

American College of Occupational and Environmental Medicine 10104

American College of Osteopathic Internists 10105

American College of Osteopathic Obstetricians and Gynecologists Annual Convention 10072

American College of Osteopathic Surgeons 10106

American College Personnel Association 3188, 4183

American College of Physician Executives 10107

American College of Preventive Medicine 10108

American College of Prosthodontists 3423, 3498, 3557, 3681

American College of Radiology 10109

American College of Sports Medicine 5072, 10110

American College of Sports Medicine Annual Meeting 10073

American College of Surgeons Annual Clinical Congress 10074

American College of Trial Lawyers 7071

American College of Veterinary Pathologists Annual Meeting 12812

American College of Veterinary Pathologists—Membership Directory 12786

American Concrete Institute 1061, 2192, 3047

American Congress on Surveying and Mapping 12424

American Conservatory Theater Foundation 282

American Correctional Association 3071

American Correctional Health Services Association 6038

American Council on Education, Fellows Program 4184

American Council on Exercise 5073, 11003

American Council of Life Insurers 353, 6546, 12711

American Council on Rural Special Education 12132

American Council on the Teaching of Foreign Languages Convention 11793

American Counseling Association 3189

American Counseling Association Conference and Exposition 854, 3182, 8091

American Credit Union Mortgage Association 3294

American Crystallographic Association 2033, 10217

American Culinary Federation 1296, 1853

American Dance Guild 3327

American Dental Assistants Association 3424

American Dental Association 3425, 3499, 3558, 3682

American Dental Education Association 3426, 3500, 3559, 3683

American Dental Hygienists' Association 3501

American Dental Hygienists' Association Access 3367, 3436, 3511, 3580, 5898, 6139

American Design Drafting Association 3778, 4031

American Dietetic Association 3907

American Disc Jockey Association 3989

American Economic Association 4067

American Electrology Association Annual Convention 3092, 7718

American Electronics Association—Member Directory 4270, 4332

American Employment Law Council 7072

American Engineering Association 560, 618, 2193, 4550, 4684, 5288, 6383, 8632, 12552

American Experiment Quarterly 10289

American Family Physician 7399, 9714, 9819, 11054

American Family Therapy Academy 3190

American Farmers for the Advancement and Conservation of Technology 619, 671

American Federation of Musicians of the United States and Canada 8568

American Federation of Police and Concerned Citizens 6862

American Federation of School Administrators 4185

American Federation of Teachers 467, 6713, 10406, 11809, 12133

American Financial Services Association 1318, 3295, 5000

American Foreign Law Association 7073

American Forests 5226

American Gaming Association 5343

American Gastroenterological Association 10111

American Genetic Association 5631

American Geographical Society 5660

American Geological Institute 5697

American Geophysical Union 5698, 8127

American Geriatrics Society 6196

American Glass Guild 5737

American Glass Guild Annual Conference 5733

American Group Psychotherapy Association—Membership Directory 3151, 9969, 10634, 11129, 11900

American Guild of Musical Artists 8569

American Guild of Organists 8570

American Hardware Manufacturers Association—Rep/Factory Contact Service Directory 7766

American Harp Society National Conference 8554

American Health Care Association 6039, 6197, 7549, 8803, 8877, 9665, 11040, 11257, 12189

American Health Information Management Association 8289

American Health Lawyers Association 7074

American Health Quality Association 10112

American for the Healthcare Environmental 6040

American Healthcare Radiology Administrators Annual Meeting and Exposition 10881

American Hearing Aid Associates 12190

American Heart Association Scientific Sessions 10075

American Heart Journal 4237, 9820

American Highway Users Alliance 12599

American Historical Association 6126

American Historical Association Annual Meeting 6116

American Hockey Coaches Association 12242

American Holistic Nurses Association 7550, 11258

American Hospital Association 6041, 7551, 8804, 9396, 10113, 10285, 11259

American Hotel and Lodging Association 6249

American Human Resources Associates Ltd. (AHRA) 1314, 4913, 10923

American Hydrogen Association 5289

American Immigration Lawyers Association 7075

American Immigration Lawyers Association Conference 6306

American Incite 5410

American Indian National Business Directory 14885

American Indian Science and Engineering Society 561, 1590, 1948, 2194, 2714, 2906, 4380, 4551, 4685, 6384, 8198, 8351, 8429, 8633, 9270, 12073, 12571, 14928

American Industrial Hygiene Association—Directory 6444

American Industrial Hygiene Association Journal 6438

American Institute of Aeronautics and Astronautics 562

American Institute of Aeronautics and Astronautics Career Planning and Placement Services 538, 13723

American Institute of Architects 1062

American Institute of Architects-AIArchitect 996

American Institute of Architects National Convention 1055

American Institute of Biological Sciences 672, 1478, 11706

American Institute of Biological Sciences Classifieds 1457, 13724

American Institute of Certified Planners 12752

American Institute of Certified Public Accountants 173

American Institute of Chemical Engineers 1949

American Institute of Chemical Engineers Journal 1864, 1965

American Institute of Chemists 1950, 2034

American Institute for Conservation of Historic and Artistic Works 1124, 6127

American Institute of Constructors Annual Forum 3030

American Institute of Constructors and the Constructor Commission Newsletter 2967

American Institute for CPCU 6547, 12712

American Institute of Engineers 5290, 12553

American Institute of Floral Designers 5120

American Institute of Floral Designers National Symposium 5119

American Institute of Graphic Arts 5804, 10430, 12666, 13047

American Institute of Physics 10218

American Institute of Professional Geologists 5699

American Institute of Ultrasound in Medicine 10888

American Institute of Wine and Food 12965

American Intellectual Property Law Association 7076

American Jail Association Training Conference & Jail Expo 3069

American Journal of Agricultural and Biological Science 1383

American Journal of Alternative Agriculture 625

American Journal of Analytical Chemistry 1865, 1966

American Journal of Animal and Veterinary Sciences 12761

American Journal of Archaeology 965

American Journal of Biochemistry and Molecular Biology 1326

The American Journal of Cardiology 4238, 9821

American Journal of Clinical Nutrition 3847, 9822

The American Journal of Drug and Alcohol Abuse 833

American Journal of Drug Discovery and Development 1327

American Journal of Emergency Medicine 4426, 8211, 9715, 9823, 12327

American Journal of Epidemiology 4758, 9824

American Journal of Family Therapy 8074, 10590

American Journal of Geriatric Psychiatry 8688, 10591

American Journal of Health-System Pharmacy 9284, 9410

American Society of Pharmacognosy **9401**
American Society of Picture Professionals **9584**
American Society of Plant Biologists **1484, 2040**
American Society of Plant Biologists Job Bank **1458, 13728**
American Society of Plumbing Engineers **10251**
American Society of Plumbing Engineers Convention **10247**
American Society of Podiatric Medical Assistants **8264**
American Society of Primatologists **948**
American Society of Professional Estimators **3050, 3121**
American Society for Radiation Oncology **10892**
American Society of Radiologic Technologists **8678, 10893**
American Society for Reproductive Medicine **10130**
American Society of Safety Engineers **6455**
American Society of Sanitary Engineering **10252**
American Society of Spine Radiology Annual Symposium **10883**
American Society of Test Engineers **4381**
American Society of Transportation and Logistics **7638**
American Society of Travel Agents **12650**
American Society of Travel Agents—Membership Directory **12635**
American Society of Veterinary Ophthalmology—Directory **12787**
American Society of Women Accountants **174**
American Society of Women Accountants Conference **152**
American Society of Women Accountants—Membership Directory **29**
American Sociological Association **11964**
American Sociological Association Annual Meeting **11957**
American Sommelier Association **12967**
American Speech-Language-Hearing Association Annual Convention **12183**
American Sportscasters Association **10811, 11327**
American Staffing Association **4496, 9186**
American Statistical Association **12285**
American String Teachers Association **8572**
American Student Dental Association **3687**
American Studies Association **949**
American Studies Association Newsletter **6089, 11945**
American Supplier Institute **6385, 8960**
The American Surveyor **12410**
American Swimming Coaches Association **12244**
American Technical Education Association National Conference on Technical Education **2398**
American Teleservices Association—Membership Directory and Resource Guide **12519**
American Theological Library Association Newsletter **7241**
American Therapeutic Recreation Association **11042**
American Therapeutic Recreation Association Annual Conference **11038**
American Therapeutic Recreation Association Newsletter **11021**
American Thoracic Society **10131**
American Thoracic Society International Conference **10079**
American Traffic Safety Services Association **12601**
American Translators Association—Membership Directory **12611**
American Urological Association **10132**
American Veterinary Medical Association **902, 12832**
American Veterinary Medical Association Annual Convention **12813**
American Veterinary Medical Association—Directory and Resource Manual **12788**
American Vineyard Foundation **12968**
American Viola Society **8573**
American Volleyball Coaches Association Convention **12241**
American Watchmakers-Clockmakers Institute **6616**
American Water Spaniel Club **903**
American Water Works Association **1485, 2041, 2197**
American Wholesale Marketers Association **7797, 8038**
American Wholesalers and Distributors Directory **7767**
American Wine Society **12969**
American Wine Society Journal **12911**
American Woman's Society of Certified Public Accountants **175**
American Woman's Society of Certified Public Accountants—Roster **30**
America's Corporate Finance Directory **4884**
America's Health Insurance Plans Center for Policy and Research **5872**
America's Job Exchange **13502**
Americas Lodging Investment Summit **6243**
America's Most Organized **10459**
America's Top 100 Computer and Technical Jobs **2504, 2597, 2671, 2754, 2810, 2876**

Amerind Foundation **950, 986**
AMHCA Advocate **834**
Amherst Writers and Artists Newsletter **13175**
AMI Bulletin **5350**
AMIA Newsletter **1082**
Amplitude Research, Inc. **12395**
AMS Annual Meeting **8381**
Amtec Human Capital **513, 760, 1442, 1560, 2012, 4640, 12031, 13259**
Analytic Recruiting, Inc. **7823, 8954, 12281**
AnalyzeMyCareer.com **13599**
Andean Explorers Foundation & Ocean Sailing Club—Membership Roster **974**
Andersen Steinberg Group **3924**
Anderson & Associates **5411, 5970, 11414**
Andover Research, Ltd. **319**
Andre David & Associates Inc. **5412**
Andrew Associates Executive Search Inc. **4540, 5413**
Anesthesia & Analgesia **9836**
Anesthesiology **9837, 12329**
The Angus Group Ltd. **4641, 4914, 5414**
Animal Keepers' Forum **871, 12763**
AnimalJobs.com **896, 12801**
Annals of Emergency Medicine **9838**
Annals of Human Genetics **5606**
Annals of Medicine **2297, 4081, 4427, 4759, 6625, 8212, 9716, 9839, 10362, 11346, 11715, 12086, 12330, 12463**
Annals of Neurology **9840**
The Annals of Pharmacotherapy **9285, 9411**
Annals of Plastic Surgery **9841**
Annals of Surgery **9842, 12331**
Annotation **1083, 6090**
Annual Accounting Show **153**
Annual Employee Benefits Conference **9177**
Annual Ethics & Compliance Conference **6452**
Annual Home Decorating and Remodeling Show **6588**
Annual Hotel, Motel, and Restaurant Supply Show of the Southeast **1790, 6244, 11444**
Annual Immigration Law & Policy Conference **6307**
Annual Meeting of the American Academy of Ophthalmology **8983**
The Annual Meeting for Commercial Real Estate **10569**
Annual Meeting and TransComp Exhibition **7634**
Annual NAIW Convention - National Association of Insurance Women International **6538**
Annual National Association of Women Law Enforcement Executives Conference **6852**
Annual Regional Anesthesia Meeting and Workshops **10080**
Annual Review of Genetics **1387, 1508, 5607**
Annual Review of Law and Social Science **6893, 7136**
Annual Review of Microbiology **1388, 1509, 11683**
Annual Review of Psychology **8692, 10594**
Annual RNS Conference **11229**
Annual Scientific Sessions **3654**
Annual State Health Policy Conference **5866**
Annual World EAP Conference **9178**
ANR National Directory of Community Newspapers **11306, 13208**
Answers4Dancers.com **3324, 13729**
Anthropology in Action **912**
Anthropology of Consciousness **913**
The Anthropology Graduate's Guide: From Student to a Career **936**
Anthropology News **914**
Anthropology of Work Review **915**
AnthroSource **916**
Antique Week **1222**
AOAC International Annual Meeting and Exposition **2028**
AOCS Annual Meeting & Expo **1944**
AOPA Aviation Summit - Aircraft Owners and Pilots Association **826**
AOPA Pilot **783**
AOPA's Airport Directory **733, 755, 796**
AORN Journal **11058**
AOSA Foresight **8993**
AOTA Conference & Expo **8875**
APA Search Inc. **5415, 6417, 11492, 11591**
APHON Annual Conference and Exhibit **7528, 11230**
APIC Annual Meeting and Educational Conference **2273**
APICS: The Association for Operations Management **7639**
Aplus-SummerJobs.com **15120**
APMA News **10260**
APMI International **8352**
Apparel **7724**
Apple and Associates **55, 1920, 2013, 4344, 5416, 7899, 9146, 10492, 11592**
Apple One Employment Services **415, 12673**
AppleOne.com **13503, 13730**
Appliance Design—Buyers Guide **4271**
Appliance DESIGN Magazine **3698**

Appliance Service News **4261**
Applied Mechanics Transactions **8136**
Applied Radiation and Isotopes **8645, 10826**
Applied Radiology **9843, 10827**
Applied Survey Data Analysis **12366**
Applied Survey Methods: A Statistical Perspective **12278, 12367**
Appraisal Institute **10965**
Appraisal Institute—Directory of Designated Members **10953**
APRA (Association of Professional Researchers for Advancement) **8961**
APS Observer **10595**
Aquent.com **3714, 13083**
Arboriculture Consultant **6743**
Archaeological Conservancy **987**
Archaeological Institute of America **988**
ArchaeologyFieldwork.com **979, 13731**
Archetype **1739**
Archinect.com **1044, 13732**
Architect Jobs **1045**
Architect Jobs.com **1046**
Architect Magazine **997**
Architectural Products **998**
Architectural Record **999, 4013, 6744, 12411, 12726**
Architecture Student's Handbook of Professional Practice **1031**
ArchitectureCrossing.com **1047, 13733**
ArchitectureWeek **1000**
Archival Outlook **1084**
Archives of Dermatology **9844**
Archives of General Psychiatry **9845, 10596**
Archives of Neurology **9846**
Archives of Surgery **9847, 12332**
Archivist Jobs **1117**
ArchVoices **1063**
Argus & Associates **11519**
ARI Admin **8938**
Arizona Business Gazette **14471**
Arizona Chamber of Commerce **14514**
ArizonaMentor.org **13600**
Arkansas Business **14472**
Arkansas Library Association Annual Conference **7306**
Arkansas State Chamber of Commerce **14515**
Arkansas Veterinary Medical Association's Winter Meeting **12814**
Arlene Clapp Ltd. **4915, 10549**
Arlington Resources, Inc. **9147**
ARMA International - The Association of Information Management Professionals **8291**
Armed Forces Journal International **14848**
Army Aviation Association of America **14868**
Army Aviation Magazine **14849**
Army and Navy Union U.S.A. **14869**
Art in America **12997**
The Art and Craft of User Research Interviewing **12368**
Art Directors Club **2423, 5805, 9585, 13049, 13299**
Art Libraries Society of North America **1126, 7334, 13050**
Art Libraries Society of North America Conference **1121, 7307, 13045**
Art and Living **12998**
Art Therapy **1133**
Art Therapy Activities: A Practical Guide for Teachers, Therapists and Parents **1137**
Art Therapy Connection **1145, 3196**
ARTA E-News **12627**
ArtBistro.com **3761, 13041**
Arthur Diamond Associates Inc. **5417**
Artisan Creative **3747, 5776**
Artisan for Hire, Inc. **3748, 5777**
The Artist's Magazine **12999**
Artizen, Inc. **3925**
ArtJob Online **5789, 13042, 13734**
ARTnews Magazine **13000**
Arts & Humanities Jobs **14828**
ArtSEARCH **205, 1134, 3307, 8504**
Arvada Chamber of Commerce **14516**
ASA Bulletin **872**
ASA-CSSA-SSSA Career Placement Center **593, 645, 4624**
ASBMB Today **1328**
ASBSD-Bulletin **4082**
ASCE News **2123**
Ascend **176**
ASCnet Quarterly **301, 6505**
ASCPT Annual Meeting **10081**
ASDA News **3582**
ASHRAE Journal **6058**
Ashton Lane Group **56, 12314**
The Asia Pacific Journal of Anthropology **917**
Asian America MultiTechnology Association **7798**

National High School Athletic Coaches Association **12258**
National Highway Traffic Safety Administration **12606**
National Human Genome Research Institute **1376**
National Human Services Assembly **5887**
National Immigration Project **6318**
National Indian Council on Aging, Inc. **14957**
National Industrial Transportation League **7643**
National Institute for Automotive Service Excellence **1272**
National Institute of Ceramic Engineers **8362**
National Institute for Certification in Engineering Technologies **4558**
National Institute of Governmental Purchasing **10742**
National Insurance Recruiters Association **349, 6535, 14005**
National Investment Banking Association **5019**
National Jeweler **6603, 11475, 13159**
The National Job Bank **13491**
National JobBank **13445**
National Journalism Center **11339**
National Labor Relations Board **14217**
National Latino Cosmetology Association **3104**
National Law Enforcement Associates **6882**
The National Law Journal **6921, 7163**
National Lawyers Association **7123**
National Lawyers Guild **7124**
National League for Nursing **6201, 7574, 8812, 11286**
National League of Postmasters of the United States **10354**
National LGBT Bar Association **7125**
National LGBT Bar Association Annual Career Fair & Conference **7059**
National Locksmith **11845**
National Lutheran Outdoors Ministry Association **8492**
National Managed Care Leadership Directory **5850**
National Management Association **5602, 8061, 10743, 11457, 11681**
National Marine Representatives Association **7805**
National Medical Association **10166**
National Medical Association Annual Convention and Scientific Assembly **10082**
National Middle School Association Annual Conference & Exhibit **11801**
National Minority and Women-Owned Business Directory **14893**
National Money Transmitters Association **5020**
National Mortgage News **4876, 7579**
National Naval Officers Association **14879**
National Newspaper Association **13342**
National Oceanic Society **4752, 5250**
National Optometric Association **9031**
National Organization of Bar Counsel **7126**
National Organization of Black Law Enforcement Executives **6883**
National Organization of Gay and Lesbian Scientists and Technical Professionals **14809**
National Organization for Human Services **6277, 11942**
National Organization of Minority Architects **1075**
National Organization of Minority Architects Conference **1058**
National Organization for the Professional Advancement of Black Chemists and Chemical Engineers **1958, 2053**
National Paralegal Association **7239**
National Paralegal Reporter **7164**
National Partnership News **14438**
National Pest Management Association International **9222**
National Pharmaceutical Association **9405, 9459**
National Pharmacy Technician Association **9460**
National Police Canine Association **6884**
National Postal Forum **10355**
National Postal Mail Handlers Union **10356**
National Postsecondary Agricultural Student Organization **686**
National Press Club **13343**
National Press Photographers Association **9593**
National Property Management Association **10584**
National Public Employer Labor Relations Association **9197**
National Puerto Rican Forum **14937**
National Recruiting Service **8340**
National Register **3161**
National Register - USA **7792, 11500, 11879**
National Registry of Certified Chemists **2054**
National Registry of Emergency Medical Technicians **4474**
National Registry of Environmental Professionals **14204**
National Rehabilitation Association **3214, 8884, 9674, 10167, 11046, 12197**
National Rehabilitation Counseling Association **3215**
National Religious Broadcasters **1713, 10822, 11340**

National Restaurant Association **1802, 1859, 11458**
National Restaurant Association Educational Foundation **11459**
National Restaurant Association Restaurant and Hotel-Motel Show **1292, 1796, 1852**
National Restaurant Search **11430**
National Resume Writers' Association **13344**
National Retail Federation **11512, 13173**
National Robotics Engineering Center **11542**
National Roofing Contractors Association **11564**
National Roofing Contractors Association—Membership Directory **11554**
National Rural Health Association **3433, 3507, 3693, 6053, 6202, 7575, 8813, 9813, 10168, 11287**
National Rural Letter Carriers' Association **10357**
National Safety Council Congress and Expo **6453**
National Sales & Marketing Consultants Inc. **11501, 11641**
National School Public Relations Association **8062, 10722**
National School Public Relations Association—Directory **4141, 10696**
National Severe Storms Laboratory **8385**
National Sheriffs' Association Annual Conference **6857**
National Society of Accountants **200**
National Society of Accountants for Cooperatives **201**
National Society of Accountants for Cooperatives Tax & Accounting Conference for Cooperatives **165**
National Society of Black Physicists **10227**
National Society of Certified Healthcare Business Consultants **6054, 7705**
National Society of Consulting Soil Scientists **687**
National Society of Genetic Counselors **5642**
National Society of Genetic Counselors E-Blast **5625, 14006**
National Society of Genetic Counselors Job Connection Service **5626, 14007**
National Society of Hispanic MBAs **5603, 14938**
National Society of Newspaper Columnists Conference **13291**
National Society of Professional Engineers **571, 1596, 1959, 4393, 4694, 5297, 6394, 8207, 8363, 8434, 8639, 9276, 12080, 12559**
National Society of Public Accountants Annual Convention **166**
National Society of Tax Professionals **12457**
National Sportscasters and Sportswriters Association **13345**
National Staff Development and Training Association **11943**
National Star Route Mail Contractors Association **10358**
National Strength and Conditioning Association **9675, 12259**
National Student Nurses' Association **11288**
National Student Nurses' Association Convention **7539, 11243**
National Tax Association **12458**
National Traditional Country Music Association **8586**
National Underwriter Property and Casualty/Risk and Benefits Management **306, 2211, 6509, 12688**
National Urban Fellows **12758**
National Utility Contractors Association Convention **4281**
National Verbatim Reporters Association **12305**
National Weather Association **8386**
National Weather Service Offices and Stations **8376**
National Wellness Conference **13144**
National Western Stock Show **667**
National Writers Association **13346**
National Writers Union **13347, 14819**
National Youth Employment Coalition **14967**
NationJob Network **14008**
Nation's Capital Dental Meeting **3664**
Nationwide Actuarial Search **332**
Nationwide Insurance Independent Contractors Association **6558**
NativeAmericanJobs.com **14923**
NATPE Annual Conference **10809**
Natural Fitness Trainers Association **5080**
Natural History Network **6133**
Natural Resources **4614, 4710, 5188**
Nature Biotechnology **1418, 1990, 11692**
Nature International Weekly Journal of Science **640, 1419, 1991, 2249, 5189, 5675, 8370, 10194, 11693, 14170**
Naturejobs.com **1372, 1469, 1585**
Nature's Voice Our Choice **5251, 14205**
Navin Group **11642**
Navy Times **14854**
The NAWIC Image **2934, 15001**
NCC **3145**
NCPA Convention and Trade Exposition **9386**
NCPA Newsletter **9297, 9418**
NCS Group **3974**

NDIA Ground Robotics Capabilities Conference and Exhibition **11532**
Neal Management Inc. **4959**
Nebraska Chamber of Commerce and Industry **14617**
NeedTechs.com **1264**
Negotiating Your Salary: How to Make $1,000 a Minute **14668**
Negotiation Fieldbook **14669**
Neil Frank & Company **5546, 7952**
Neil Michael Group **1353**
NEJM CareerCenter **10059**
Nelson Information's Directory of Institutional Real Estate **10916**
Neonatal Network **7440, 11104**
Neonatology on the Web **10060**
Neotropical Grassland Conservancy **5252, 14206**
Nephrology Nursing Journal **7441, 11105**
Net Temps **14009**
Net.Finance **8020**
NetJobs.com **14010**
NetShare.com **5589, 14011**
Netter's Sports Medicine **1185**
Network of Conservation Educators and Practitioners **4753, 5253**
NetworkEngineer.com **3360, 9117, 12063**
Networking For Professionals **14702**
Networking Like a Pro: Turning Contacts into Connections **14690**
Networking for People Who Hate Networking: A Field Guide for Introverts, the Overwhelmed, and the Underconnected **14691**
The Networking Survival Guide: Get the Success You Want by Tapping into People You Know **14692**
Networking Works!: The WetFeet Insider Guide to Networking **14693**
Neuro-Developmental Treatment Association **8885, 8915, 10169, 12198**
The Neurohospitalist **9751, 9932**
Neuroimaging Clinics of North America **5934, 8653, 10837**
Neuroscience and Medicine **2250, 9752, 9933**
Neuroscience Quarterly **9934**
Never Eat Alone **14694**
New Architecture Jobs **1054**
The New Business of Acting: How to Build a Career in a Changing Landscape **259**
New Challenges Facing Academic Librarians Today: Electronic Journals, Archival Digitization, Document Delivery, Etc. **7284**
New England Archivists Newsletter **1101**
New England Chapter of the American Academy of Orthotists and Prosthetists **9051**
The New England Journal of Medicine **9935, 10264, 11106**
New England Library Association Annual Conference **7321**
New England Real Estate Journal **10537, 10910, 10951**
New England Theatre Conference **293**
New England Theatre Conference—Resource Directory **242**
New Executive Jobs **14012**
The New Graduate Experience: Post-MLS Residency Programs and Early Career Librarianship **7285**
New Guide for Occupational Exploration, Fourth Edition **13446**
New Hampshire's Statewide Chamber of Commerce **14618**
New Jersey Accounting, Business & Technology Show & Conference **167**
New Jersey Chamber of Commerce **14619**
New Jersey Employment Law Letter **14439**
New Jersey Family Lawyer and the Labor and Employment Law Quarterly **14440**
The New Jersey JobBank **13447, 14467**
New Jersey Law Journal **6922, 7165**
New Jersey State Funeral Directors Association Convention **5327**
New Journal of Glass and Ceramics **8317**
New Law Enforcement Jobs **6845**
New Logistics Jobs **7632**
New Non Profit Jobs **14728**
New Programmer's Survival Manual **2675**
New Public Relations Jobs **10711**
New Real Estate Jobs **10562, 10929, 10960**
The New Republic **11302, 13193**
New Restaurant and Food Jobs **1286, 1789, 1845, 11440**
New Sales and Marketing Jobs **7996, 11505, 11668, 11882**
The New Social Worker **3146, 11894**
New Urban News **12737**
New Ways to Work **13673, 15139**
New World Staffing **5547**

Rancho Cucamonga Chamber of Commerce **14634**
Randolph Associates, Inc. **3756, 4651, 6585, 13040**
Randstad Engineering **2499**
Randstad Finance and Accounting **93**
The Rangefinder **9537**
Rapid Excavation & Tunneling Conference & Exhibit **8426**
Raymond Alexander Associates **94, 4968, 12443**
RCSB Protein Data Bank **1377**
RDH **3386, 3454, 3611**
RDLink.com **3843, 3901**
Re-Greening the Environment: Careers in Clean-up, Remediation and Restoration (Green-Collar Careers) **4721**
Reaction Search International Inc. **13573**
Readex Research **12401**
README FIRST for a User's Guide to Qualitative Methods **12382**
ReadWaering Associates **6528**
Real Estate Blues: A Guide to Jump Start Your Real Estate Career **10545, 10920**
Real Estate Brokerage: A Guide to Success **10921**
Real Estate Executive Search, Inc. **2950, 3116, 4969, 10559, 10927, 10958**
Real Estate Issues **10539, 10912, 10952**
Real Estate Job Store.com **10563**
Real Estate Manager Jobs **10564**
Real Food **1776, 1813, 3864**
Real-Jobs **10565**
Real-Resumes for Administrative Support, Office and Secretarial Jobs **8936**
Real-Resumes for Firefighting Jobs **5039**
Real Resumes for Jobs in Non-Profit Organizations **14718**
Real-Resumes for Legal and Paralegal Jobs **6980, 7195**
Real-Resumes for Sports Industry Jobs **12224**
The Real Work Begins **13492, 13665**
RealEstateAndLandCrossing.com **10566, 10930, 10961**
RealEstateJobsite.com **10567**
Realtors Land Institute **10585, 10941, 10975**
The Recorder **6923, 7166**
Recovery Today Online **853**
Recreational Sports Directory **10988, 12207**
Recreational Therapist Jobs **11035**
RecreationalTherapistJobs.com **11036**
The Recruiter Directory **15079**
Recruiter's Guide **13458**
Recruiters Online Network **13546, 14066**
Recruiting Partners **2172, 2691, 2757, 3353, 5561, 7021, 7959, 8181, 9107, 10497, 11649, 12046, 13269**
Recruiting Services Group Inc. **6429**
RecruitingJobs.com **9175**
RecruitMilitary.com **14881**
Recycling Today **14172**
Red Roof Directory **6210**
Redwood Region Logging Conference **5220**
Reference Guide For Pharmacy Technician Exam **9494**
The Reference Librarian **7259**
Reflective Interviewing: A Guide to Theory and Practice **12383**
Refrigeration Service Engineers Society **6087**
Refrigeration Service Engineers Society Educational Conference **6079**
RefugeeWorks Employment Quarterly **6291**
Regional Theater Directory **243, 3316, 8530**
Register of Professional Archaeologists **993**
Registered Rep. **12307**
RegisteredDieticiansJobs.com **3844, 3902**
RehabCareer.com **8867, 9657, 12172**
Rehabilitation Nursing **6176, 7452, 8741, 11120**
Rehabilitation Techniques in Sports Medicine **1194**
RehabJobs Online **8868, 8910, 9658, 9705, 11379, 12173, 14067**
RehabWorld.com **3179, 8869, 8911, 9659, 9706, 10661, 11922, 12174, 14068**
Reinventing the CFO: How Financial Managers Can Reinvent Their Roles and Add Greater Value **4900**
Reinvention: How to Make the Rest of Your Life the Best of Your Life **13595**
Religious Conference Management Association **4831**
Remarkable Service: A Guide to Winning and Keeping Customers for Servers, Managers, and Restaurant Owners **11412**
Remedial and Special Education (RASE) **12118**
Remodeling **2937, 2991, 6571, 6755**
The Rental Property Manager's Tool Box: A Complete Guide Including Pre-Written Forms, Agreements, Letters, Legal Notices with Companion CD-ROM **10546**
Replacement Contractor **1749, 2992**
Report on IBM **2493**
Reporting Clear?: A Pilot's Interview Guide to Background Checks & Presentation of Personal History **804**

Request Technology **3931**
Requirements for Certification of Teachers, Counselors, Librarians, Administrators for Elementary and Secondary Schools **3164, 4145, 6684, 7276, 7370, 11772**
Research in Accounting Regulation **26**
Research Chefs Association **1861, 11461**
Research Methods in Practice: Strategies for Description and Causation **12384**
Research in Nursing & Health **7453, 8742, 11121**
Research in Veterinary Science **12779**
ResearchInfo.com **7829**
ResearchingCrossing.com **7830, 8958**
Reserve Police Officers Association **6888**
Resident & Staff Physician **9954**
Residential Architect **1020, 2938, 2993**
Residential Concrete **1646, 2939, 2994**
Residential Construction Workers' Association **3057**
Residential Contractor **1021, 1750, 2995**
Residential Design & Build **1647, 2996, 11551**
Residential Interior Design: A Guide to Planning Spaces **6581**
Resort and Commercial Recreation Association **11018**
Resource: Engineering and Technology for Sustainable World **589**
Resource Recycling **14173**
Resources Objectives Inc. **12047**
Responsible Industry for a Sound Environment **9224**
Restaurant Business **1777, 1814, 11397**
Restaurant Hospitality **1778, 1815, 11398**
Restaurant Startup & Growth **1816, 11399**
Restaurant Wine **12914**
RestaurantManager.net **11441, 14069**
RestaurantOperator.com **1847, 11442**
The Resume and Cover Letter Phrase Book: What to Write to Get the Job That's Right **15185**
The Resume Handbook **15186**
Resume Magic: Trade Secrets of a Professional Resume Writer **15187**
Resume Writing Made Easy **15188**
ResumeL.com **15225**
ResumeLogic.com **15226**
ResumeMaker **15228**
ResumeRobot.com **13547**
Resumes for Business Management Careers **15189**
Resumes for College Students and Recent Graduates **15190**
Resumes, Cover-Letters, Networking, & Interviewing **14389, 14390, 14695, 15191, 15192**
Resumes for First-Time Job Hunters **15193**
Resumes For Dummies, Sixth Edition **15194**
Resumes for Health and Medical Careers **2093, 2260, 3401, 3471, 3537, 3622, 3884, 4230, 4252, 4459, 5963, 6186, 8246, 8279, 8666, 8768, 8978, 9013, 9328, 9435, 9633, 9778, 10001, 10274, 11028, 11164, 11370, 12155, 12359, 15195**
Resumes for High School Graduates **14960, 15196**
Resumes and Job Applications **14818, 15212**
Resumes for Law Careers **6981, 15197**
Resumes for Nursing Careers **7485, 11165, 15198**
Resumes for Performing Arts Careers **263, 3322, 8546, 15199**
Resumes Quick & Easy **15229**
Resumes for Re-Entering the Job Market **14946, 15200**
Resumes for Scientific and Technical Careers **511, 654, 1441, 1559, 1919, 2009, 2162, 4343, 4539, 4637, 5210, 5699, 6350, 8168, 8330, 8413, 8614, 9252, 10210, 12030, 15201**
Resumes for Social Service Careers **11914, 15202**
Resumes That Resume Careers **15203**
Retail Advertising and Marketing Association **8070**
Retail Bakers of America **1303**
Retail Design Institute **6599**
Retail Industry Leaders Association **7806, 11513**
Retail Marketing Conference **8023**
Retail Recruiters **4001, 8979, 9014, 11503**
Retailing Today **11477, 13161**
RetailSalesManager.net **11506, 14070**
RETINA **9004, 9955**
RetiredBrains.com **14947**
RetiredStars.com **14948**
RetireeWorkforce.com **14949**
RetirementCrossing **14950**
Revenue **2494, 2589, 2662, 2749, 2803, 2868, 3808, 7856, 9098, 12010**
Reverb **8590, 14207**
Reverse Logistics Association **7644**
Reverse Logistics Magazine **7608**
The Review of Asset Pricing Studies **4879**
Review of General Psychology **8743, 10630**
The Review of Network Economics **4046, 4880**
Review of Optometry **3998, 8972, 9005**
Reviews in Biomedical Engineering **1547**
RF Design **4322**

RFID Journal **14308**
RGT Associates Inc. **6430**
Rice Professional Search **5562**
Ricklin-Echikson Associates Inc. **14635**
Right Brain Resource, LLC **13079**
The Right Job for You **13493**
The Riley Guide **13548**
RiseSmart, Inc. **15051**
Rising Star Internships **15131**
Rising Tide North America **4698, 5257**
Risk and Insurance Management Society **5021**
Risk and Insurance Management Society Annual Conference and Exhibition **6543**
Risk Management Association **3305, 5022, 7602**
RitaSue Siegel Resources, Inc. **1041, 3757, 6586**
Rivers Without Borders **4699, 5258**
R.L. Stevens & Associates Inc. **13574**
RN **11122**
RN Network **11188**
RO-LAN Associates Inc. **13575, 14981**
Roads & Bridges Magazine **2146, 12741**
Roadway Safety Foundation **12607**
Roberson & Co. **95, 4652, 4970, 6006, 7960**
Robert A. Borissoff, Security Consultant **11853**
Robert Drexler Associates Inc. **526, 607**
Robert Half Finance & Accounting **96**
Robert Half Legal **7022, 7215**
Robert Half Management Resources **97**
Robert Half Technology **3932**
Robert Howe and Associates **3019, 6007, 6233**
Robert Shields and Associates **3933**
Robert W. Dingman Company Inc. **5563, 6234**
Robins Consulting **7621**
RoboBusiness Conference and Exposition **11533**
Robot Report **11527, 14071**
Robotic Industries Association **11543**
Robotica **698, 11515**
Robotics Industry Directory **11520**
Robotics Institute **11544**
Robotics: Science and Systems Conference **11534**
Robotics Trends **11516**
Robotics World **699, 11517**
Rockford Area Chamber of Commerce **14636**
The Rocky Mountain Archivist **1104**
Rocky Mountain Recruiters, Inc. **98, 4971, 10734**
Rogue River Guides Association **9075**
The Role of the Physical Therapist Assistant: Regulations and Responsibilities **9695**
The Role of Work in People's Lives: Applied Career Counseling & Vocational Psychology **10657**
Rollins Search Group, Inc. **336**
Romance Writers of America **13352**
Romance Writers Report **13198**
Ronald Dukes Associates LLC **6431, 7694**
RooferJobs.org **11557**
Ropella Group **5564**
Ross Reports Television and Film **218, 3311**
Roster of Women Economists **4053**
The Rothschild Image **6283**
Rotor & Wing **753, 793**
Routledge International Handbook of Green Criminology **4722**
RPA Blueprint **12742**
RSA Conference **11857**
RSMR Global Resources **5565**
RSNA News **10842**
RSR Partners **12444**
RT Image **10843**
RTI International **11710**
RTNDA Communicator—Directory Issues **1688, 10793, 11315**
RTstudents.com **10877, 14072**
Rubber World **1900**
Rural Sociological Society **11972**
Russ Hadick & Associates Inc. **6432**
Russell Reynolds Associates, Inc. **5566, 7695**
Ruth Jackson Orthopaedic Society **10172**
RV Business **7756**
Rx Career Center **9380, 9449, 14073**
RxJobPostings.com **9381, 9450**
Ryze Business Networking **10465, 14074**

S

SAA Bulletin **972**
Saddle Horse Report **885**
SAE International Journal of Aerospace **498**
Safer Pest Control Project **9225**
Safety Consultant **8821**
The SAGE Handbook of Interview Research **12385**
The SAGE Handbook of Public Relations **10707**
The SAGE Handbook of Social Work **11915**
Sai Strategies **15052**

X

Y

Z